KEY TO BROADLE... W9-BTM-467

TREES, SHRUBS AND FLOWERS TO KNOW
IN WASHINGTON

BIOTIC OR LIFE ZONE MAP

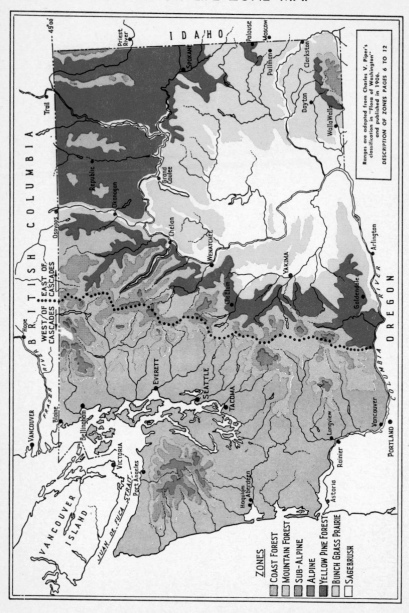

Ranges are adapted from Charles V. Piper's classification in "Flora of Washington" and published in 1906.

DESCRIPTION OF ZONES PAGES 6 TO 12

ZONES
- COAST FOREST
- MOUNTAIN FOREST
- SUB-ALPINE
- ALPINE
- YELLOW PINE FOREST
- BUNCH GRASS PRAIRIE
- SAGEBRUSH

TREES, SHRUBS AND FLOWERS

TO KNOW

IN WASHINGTON

C. P. LYONS

ILLUSTRATIONS AND COVER PHOTO BY THE AUTHOR

J. M. DENT & SONS (CANADA) LIMITED
TORONTO

ISBN 0-460-95302-8

Published by
J. M. DENT & SONS (CANADA) LIMITED

Printed in Canada
by
THE ALGER PRESS LIMITED
Oshawa, Canada

TABLE OF CONTENTS

ABOUT THIS ILLUSTRATED GUIDE

PURPOSE:

To most people a string of words such as "radical leaves; short-petioled obovate-flabelliform, crenately toothed; cauline sessile . . ." might well be a druggist's prescription or words to an ancient Greek war dance. But to the trained botanist they describe concisely and accurately part of the anatomy of one particular little buttercup. While not belittling the value of a special jargon to the scientist this book attempts a different treatment—one suitable for the non-specialist who wants guidance in terms of everyday language and observation opportunities.

You should realize that there is plenty of scope to record your own observations and thereby add to the start made here. As your interest grows you may well investigate more technical writings covering family relationships and the almost unbelievable intricacies of floral structure, adaption to environment, pollenization and seed dispersal. It is hoped this small book will provide the incentive.

SPECIAL FEATURES:

Illustrations are given for nearly every described tree, shrub, and flower. These not only show the conspicuous detail but depict the form and size of an average specimen. The complex arrangement of minute flower parts has not been attempted but rather the impression the eye receives of the outstanding aspect of flower, leaf, fruit, or cone.

The frontispiece is a map of the State with the different biotic or life zones shown. Each zone has its peculiarities of climate which reflect in the type of flora to be found. Lists of the more common plants for each zone are given. From this grouping persons travelling throughout Washington may be aware of the different zones they pass through and what is likely to be found.

Illustrated keys for the trees have been given which allow an easy and rapid breakdown to individual species. The shrubs have been grouped in various size classes and regrouped further to bring together those with a similarity of form or habitat. Flowers have been divided on the basis of broad color groups. An illustrated page makes it easy to recognize eight of the more common ferns in Washington. Edible plants are always interesting and knowledge of them may be vital in case of emergency. The more common ones have been listed in a special table.

The Flowering Timetables will be of special value to visitors unfamiliar with the native plants. A quick glance will show which shrubs and flowers will be in bloom at any particular time of the year. The chart also can prove of help by suggesting possibilities to the observer. Anyone climbing a mountain or crossing a high divide will find the Altitudinal Chart a handy guide to what may be expected at different elevation ranges.

BOOK ARRANGEMENT:

A departure is made from botanical tradition in arrangement whereby an arbutus tree, salal bush and clump of heather conceivably might follow one another because of their similarity in minute flower parts. Broad divisions have been made into trees, shrubs, flowers, and ferns. These are further arranged to bring together plants that frequent the same habitat or closely resemble one another. For example unarmed creepers form one group, plants growing in wet bogs another, and so on.

NAMES:

Botanical names have been determined from those considered to have the widest favour among such authorities as Abrams, Piper, Peck, Brockman, and St. John. It is felt that anyone interested in possible conflict arising through names used in this publication can clarify the point by checking any of the above references which list the alternatives.

Common names generally have been chosen on the same basis but with wider reference to less extensive works than previously listed. Common alternatives have been given as sub-titles.

Scientific names are known throughout the world while common names are often a matter of local usage. The Latin name usually is in two parts like a person's. The following chart shows how a comparison might be made:

ANGLO-SAXONS (A clan of peoples)	ERICACEAE (A clan of plants)
JONES, SMITH, CLARK (Families in the clan)	VACCINIUM, RHODODENDRON, GAULTHERIA (Families in the clan)
JONES, WILLIAM (A certain individual)	VACCINIUM OVALIFOLIUM (A certain blueberry)

The last part of the Latin name is either a descriptive term or honors someone who discovered or described the plant. Often you will see such words as ovalifolium (oval—foliage or leaves) and tomentose (covered with matted hairs) which, if their Latin derivation is known, give leading clues. *Arbutus menziesii* and *Larix lyallii* show the significance of arbutus first being found by Archibald Menzies, surgeon and botanist with Captain Vancouver during his explorations from 1790-1795. Dr. David Lyall was also a surgeon and botanist who worked with the International Boundary Survey while the British Columbia-Washington Boundary was being marked.

ACKNOWLEDGMENT:

A person who, without a specialized training in botany, attempts to produce a reference book is ever conscious of his inadequacies when compared with the highly qualified experts in the field.

To them one must go for advice and it is their degree of encouragement that sparks the urge to go on or, alternatively, results in the loss of heart for the project.

Without exception this so necessary encouragement was forthcoming from everyone contacted. Such co-operation was very deeply appreciated especially when the recipient was a resident of another country.

Mr. J. Herbert Stone, Regional Forester, U.S. Forest Service at Portland, Oregon, gave valuable advice and made library reference books available. Mr. Alex Jaenicke, also of the Regional Office helped with forest cover maps and a number of other thoughtful courtesies. From Dr. C. Frank Brockman came encouragement for attempting such a project. Help in planning field trips and identifying specimens was received from Mr. Gunnar Fagerlund, Park Naturalist at Olympic National Park.

Various members of the staff at Washington State College in Pullman gave freely of their time in identifying field specimens—a service of inestimable value to a puzzled amateur. Among these have been Dr. Marion Owenby, Professor of Botany and Xerpha M. Gaines, Senior Laboratory Technician in the Seed Laboratory, Agronomy Department.

Mrs. C. R. Fox, Assistant Librarian for the British Columbian Provincial Library has very kindly made valuable reference books available for study. The staff of the British Columbia Forest Service Library have also been extremely obliging in the matter of book loans. In any such book as this, constant revision, checking and re-arrangement become necessary. These and many other tasks have been undertaken by my wife. Without this extensive help and encouragement the book would have become a burdensome task instead of a project of sustained interest.

C. P. LYONS,
1354 Monterey Ave.,
Victoria, B. C.

HOW TO USE THIS BOOK

I. IS IT A TREE, SHRUB OR FLOWER?

TREES have strong trunks covered with bark. They are usually over 20' high with trunks more than 2" in diameter. There may be a single trunk or a number of them.

SHRUBS have tough woody stems with a bark cover. Generally they are under 20' in height and 2" in diameter and have several stems.

FLOWERS have soft stems which die each year. Sometimes the root lives on producing a new flower each summer (perennials). Some flowers grow from seed and only live a year (annuals).

CONFUSING FORMS OF SHRUBS AND TREES AND HOW THEY ARE GROUPED IN THIS BOOK

AS TREES

Alders (mountain and Sitka)
Cherries
Dogwood
Junipers
Maples (vine and Douglas)
Western yew
Willows (Pacific and peachleaf)

AS SHRUBS

Elder (blue-berry)
Willows (all except two)
Mountain ashes
Scrub birch

II. MAKE SURE YOU HAVE A TYPICAL SAMPLE SPECIMEN!

Young shoots often have unnaturally large and misshapen leaves. Look carefully for flowers and fruit. Check a number of plants if necessary.

III. STUDY THE APPROPRIATE KEY!

See inside front and back cover for keys to the trees, and pages 57-58 for help with the shrubs. The Elevation Range Chart on page 14 and the Biotic Zone Lists on pages 7-13 give the common flora of each region which helps in narrowing the field and suggesting possibilities.

IV. COMPARE LEAF, FLOWER AND FRUIT DETAILS WITH DRAWINGS AND NOTES!

All the native trees are illustrated and all the native shrubs except the less common and confusing species of willow, currant, gooseberry and wild rose. These usually have features in common with illustrated varieties which allow for a general grouping. Only the more common flowers and eye-catching plants and ferns are included.

V. COLOR THE DRAWINGS!

Use colored pencils, crayons or water colors to tone the drawings the correct color of living specimens. A touch of color will work wonders.

THE FLORA OF WASHINGTON

There is always the tendency to think that something more attractive and interesting lies just beyond our reach. For example, how colorful the Eastern hardwoods are pictured, the exotic waving palms of California or the bristling cacti of New Mexico. But perhaps if we made a quick inventory of Washington we would appreciate what an outstanding variety of flora there is within a few miles of us. No less than seven out of the ten forest regions of all the United States are found here. Few States can claim more than three types.

Central and Eastern Washington, although almost surrounded by verdant mountains, has a parching desert climate. Here on the sun-baked slopes and benches grow the twisted antelope bush, the drab sagebrush and mats of spiny cactus. What a striking contrast with the sombre Coast forest with its forest giants, lush green ferns and thick ground cover of bracken and salal.

The floral changes experienced in a few miles of distance are amazing. Mountains rise from the shadowy forests of giants at sea level, through the twisted and stunted sub-alpine trees and shrubs, beyond the brilliant flower meadows of alpine terrain and continue bleak and bold until finally capped by ice or snow. Here in this land of solitude and silence, at elevations of from 7,500 to 10,000 feet, the conditions are similar to that of the arctic wastes. Tiny flowers and mosses pinch themselves into sheltered niches and smile briefly and brightly during the fleeting summer they know.

Over 3,000 different plants, which term includes trees and shrubs, have been collected in Washington. New ones are discovered each year and the list should grow for many years.

A full appreciation of the trees, shrubs and flowers is often dulled because we are in such close association with them. Perhaps like old and valued friends they are taken too much for granted or possibly because they are strangers, the true worth of them isn't realized.

Our famous scenery, beautiful lakes and streams, watersheds, and commercial timber stands are only of value as long as the trees and plants are properly evaluated and managed. Learn first to recognize the flora as individuals. Then notice the special conditions each requires. See how the hardhack masses in wet road ditches or around ponds, the skunk cabbage in black muddy soil. Certain other plants will be discovered every time the hardhack or skunk cabbage is found. As more and more plants are identified there comes the realization that every one is part of an intricate living community; a community in very delicate balance, a friend if understood or a potential enemy in the form of floods, erosion or scenic scars if mishandled.

You will find these forest friends almost as close as your next door neighbor. Make their acquaintance and you can't help meeting more and more relations, each with some specially attractive feature to add pleasure to your every outing.

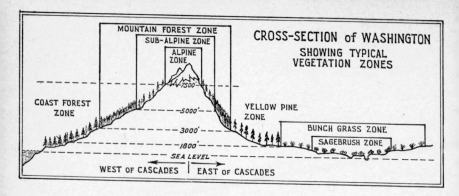

CROSS-SECTION of WASHINGTON
SHOWING TYPICAL
VEGETATION ZONES

OUTSTANDING FLORAL AREAS

The following regions and dates are suggestions to persons wishing to see some of the most interesting and colorful floral areas in Washington.

1. From Seattle on State Highway No. 2 through the lush Coast and Mountain Forest Zones to the summit of the Cascades. Thence descending to Cle-Elum in the scenic Yellow Pine Zone. A further 20 miles takes one through the Bunchgrass Zone into the Sagebrush Zone at Ellensburg. A strikingly beautiful area is found about 20 miles east of Ellensburg on State Highway No. 10. The gaunt hills and rocky slopes are alive with bright color. Here among a great variety of bloom will be found the rather rare cone-shaped Simpson's cactus with its handsome yellow or purple flowers.

   The first half of May will find the largest number of plants in bloom except for those near the summit of the Cascades.

2. From Tonasket, in Okanogan County, by State Highway No. 4 to Republic, thence eastward or southeasterly on dirt roads to Franklin D. Roosevelt Lake. This route traverses a varied topography little disturbed by man's activities. It gives an excellent sampling of the intriguing flora of northeast Washington. The month of July is preferable.

3. The Blue Mountains in the extreme southeast corner of the State have an appeal all their own. Go east and south from Dayton on a dirt road which climbs rapidly to a high ridge. The road is passable for modern cars for a distance of 25 miles. A spectacular display of flowers is found in shady forest and open ridge during the last half of July.

4. Mt. Rainier and its bejewelled alpine meadows are a "must". See them in August.

5. The gorge of the Columbia is a favored area of botanists. Not only does it provide an exceptionally large variety of flowers but many species are found only in this locality. The scenery is superb, rugged and wild. Start at Vancouver and travel eastward on State Highway No. 8. If you go as far as Maryhill you will have traversed four of the seven life zones of the State. Early May is the best time of the year.

6. The spectacular alpine meadows of Hurricane Ridge in the Olympic Mountains can be reached by car from a point near Port Angeles. August finds the flowers at their best. While in the Olympics be sure to visit the Hoh Valley and the unique rain forest with its giant trees, among them the Sitka Spruce. June to August is recommended.

BIOTIC OR LIFE ZONES

Washington can be divided into a number of biotic or life zones each resulting from its particular topography and climatic conditions. (See frontispiece for Life Zone Map.) So variable are these forces that they produce dramatic contrasts difficult to duplicate elsewhere in the entire United States. Here lie some of the highest and steepest mountains to be found, their tops encased in sprawling icefields hundreds of feet thick. Within view of them vast barren plateaus stretch away for hundreds of miles in a remarkable tableland. The westerly and southerly flank of the Olympic Mountains is saturated with an annual rainfall of 140" while regions in the Central Interior of the State parch with a meagre 12". No wonder then at a lush rain forest in one place and a parching desert in another.

The Coastal Range, dominated by five great volcanic peaks, intercepts moisture-laden westerly winds. The resultant rainfall leads to a luxuriant flora, even as the comparatively dry zone beyond the mountains is characterized by a meagre scattering of trees and shrubs.

Progressive increases in elevation usually intensify the amount of rain and snow resulting in longer winters and moderate summer temperatures. Such changes are reflected very markedly in the kinds of trees, shrubs, and flowers, that thrive under these special conditions.

Within each zone the flora has a characteristic association pattern. Certain species of trees grow together and with them particular shrubs and flowers. Various birds, animals, and insects thrive in this special condition of climate and forest because the things they depend on for feed and cover are found there. This dependency process of one life community existing because of another can be continued to the most minute forms of life.

One point that must be stressed about the flora of Washington is the tendency for certain plants to occur very abundantly in localized areas rather than widespread throughout a biotic zone. For example there are three kinds of "cactus" in the most arid regions designated as the "Sagebrush Zone". Each has a widely different and also a limited range so it is quite possible for the casual observer to examine large tracts of the Sagebrush Zone and find none of them or conversely be astounded at the seeming abundance of any one. Again there are trees such as the broadleaf maple, vine maple, and garry oak which are very characteristic of the Coast Forest Zone yet intrude into various parched valleys of Central Washington.

An attempt has been made in the Zone listings to include any plant that is reasonably sure to be noticed while those with slight or occasional overlapping have been omitted for simplification.

A brief description is given of seven biotic zones as they occur from west to east across the State. They will be readily recognizable to most people although specialists in ecology may make finer divisions.

COAST FOREST ZONE: This embraces the undulating lowlands from the ocean to the Cascade Mountains. It continues part way up the lower mountain slopes to where the dense forest of Douglas fir, red cedar, western hemlock, broadleaf maple, and red alder gives way to mountain hemlock, yellow cedar, and alpine fir. The upper elevation limit may range from 2,800' - 5,000'. Salal and a heavy growth of ferns are other zonal characteristics. Winters verge on freezing temperatures while summers are moderate. Rainfall averages around 100" a year at the westerly edge with an appreciable decrease inland.

A picturesque variation of the above are various localized areas such as the Gulf Islands in the Strait of Juan de Fuca, headlands along the Coast, and gravelly ridges south of Olympia, where the gnarled garry oak and flaunting arbutus are the dominant trees.

TREES	SHRUBS	FLOWERS
Douglas fir	Blackberry, trailing	Alumroot
Western hemlock	Black twinberry	Anemone, little mountain
Western red cedar	Broom	Anemone, three-leaved
Grand fir	Cranberry	Aster, Douglas

TREES

Pacific silver fir
Western white pine
Western yew
Lodgepole (shore) pine
Sitka spruce
Yellow cedar
Red alder
Broadleaf maple
Black cottonwood
Northwestern white birch
Western white birch
Bitter cherry
Dogwood
Vine maple
Cascara
Pacific willow
Pacific crabapple
Black hawthorn
Garry oak
Oregon ash

SHRUBS

Currant, red flower
Currant, stink
Devil's club
Elder, blue-berry
Elder, red-berry
False box
Goats' beard
Gooseberry, gummy
Gooseberry, swamp
Gooseberry, wild
Hardhack
Hazel
Honeysuckle, orange
Huckleberry, evergreen
Huckleberry, red
Indian plum
Kinnikinnick
Labrador tea
Mahonia, tall
Manzanita, hairy
Mock orange
Mountain ash, Sitka
Ninebark
Ocean spray
Oregon grape
Poison oak
Raspberry, black
Red-osier dogwood
Rhododendron, red
Salal
Salmonberry
Saskatoon berry
Scrub birch
Sweet gale
Swamp laurel
Squashberry
Thimbleberry
Twin-flower
Waxberry
Wild rose spp.

FLOWERS

Avens, large-leaved
Baneberry
Bleeding heart
Blue-eyed Mary
Bluebell
Blue sailors
Brodiaea, harvest
Buckbean
Bunchberry
Butter and eggs
Camas
Camas, death
Cat-tail
Cat's ear
Chocolate lily
Coltsfoot
Columbine
Coral root
Cotton grass
Cow parsnip
Delphinium
Easter lily
Fairy bells, Oregon
False bugbane
False lady's slipper
False Solomon's seal
Field chamomile
Field chickweed
Filaree
Goldenrod
Gumweed
Indian paintbrush
Indian pipe
Ladies' tresses
Lungwort, western
Lupine spp.
Miner's lettuce spp.
Mint, Canada
Montia
Musk flower

FLOWERS—Continued

Nettle, hedge
Nettle, stinging
Nightshade, bittersweet
Nightshade, black
Onion, Hooker's
Ookow
Oxalis, Oregon
Oxeye daisy
Peacock
Pearly everlasting
Pipsissewa
Purple pea
Pussytoes, white and rosy
Rattlesnake plantain
Satin flower

Saxifrage
Skullcap
Sea blush
Self-heal
Silver-green
Silverweed
Skunk cabbage
Spring gold
Star flower
Star-flowered Solomon's seal
Stonecrop
Sundew, spp.
Sunflower, woolly
Synthyris
Thrift

Trillium
Twayblade
Twisted stalk
Vanilla leaf
Violet, blue
Violet, yellow
Water parsnip
Water plantain
Wild cucumber
Wild ginger
Wild lily-of-the-valley
Wild tiger lily
Yarrow
Yellow monkey flower
Yerba buena
Youth-on-age

MOUNTAIN FOREST ZONE: This is called the Canadian Zone in most technical writings. It comprises the thick evergreen forest that clothes the mountain slopes in an almost unbroken mantle. At the upper elevation limit of approximately 5,000' it is bordered by the scattered growth and intrusion of meadows while its lower boundary adjoins the Coast Forest Zone. Winter temperatures range below freezing and snowfalls of 10' are not uncommon. Moderate summer temperatures are alleviated by dense forest shade, the coolness of mountain creeks, and a considerable drop in temperature each night.

The bulk of this zone flanks the Cascade Range and re-occurs on lesser mountain systems.

TREES	SHRUBS	FLOWERS
Douglas fir	Alderleaf buckthorn	Alumroot, oval-leaf
Pacific silver fir	Blackberry, sub-alpine	Arnica, heart-leaf
Western red cedar	Blueberry, red alpine	Baneberry
Yellow cedar	Clematis, blue	Bear-grass
Mountain hemlock	Crowberry	Bleeding heart
Western hemlock	Currant, stink	Brooklime
Western white pine	Currant, sticky	Bunchberry
Grand fir	Deer brush	Columbine
Noble fir	Dogwood, red-osier	Coral root
Western larch	Elder, black-berry	Cow parsnip
Lodgepole pine	False azalea	Dentaria, mountain
Engelmann spruce	False box	Eriogonum
Western yew	Gooseberry, swamp	Fairy-bells, Oregon
Aspen	Honeysuckle, orange	False bugbane
Black cottonwood	Goat's beard	False lady's slipper
Northwestern white birch	Kinnikinnick	False Solomon's seal
Bitter cherry	Labrador tea	Foam flower
Sitka alder	Labrador tea, mountain	Hellebore, Indian
Douglas maple	Mountain ash, Sitka	Hellebore, white false
	Ocean spray	Indian paintbrush
	Rhododendron, white	Lady's slipper, mountain
	Saskatoon berry	Larkspur
	Scrub birch	Lupine
	Soopolallie	Monkshood
	Squashberry	Musk flower
	Sweet gale	Onion, Hooker's
	Teaberry, western	Mountain valerian
	Thimbleberry	Peacock
	Trailing rubus	Pearly everlasting
	Twinberry, black	Penstemon, yellow
	Twinberry, red	Pipsissewa
	Twin-flower	Polemonium

FLOWERS—Continued

Pussytoes, white	Silver-green	Trillium, western
Pyrola	Skunk cabbage	Twayblade
Queen's cup	Star flower	Twisted stalk
Ragwort, giant	Star-flowered Solomon's seal	White bog orchid
Ragwort, western golden	Stenanthium, western	Wild ginger
Rattlesnake plantain	Stonecrop	Yarrow
Scarlet gilia	Snow lily	

SUB-ALPINE ZONE: This is the highest zone with trees and ranges between elevations of 5,000' and 7,000'. Here are found the appealing mountain slopes where glades and meadows break the monotony of heavy forests, where trees clump together in a fantasy of pyramidal architecture. At the upper levels they are often reduced to bushy mats in their tenacious struggle to survive the buffeting winds and extremes of temperature.

As may be expected the winters are long and severe with snow depths ranging to 20'. Heavy spring rains with swirling mists are common leaving only a short summer season with its sunny days and chilly nights. Snow usually arrives by mid-November.

This zone flanks the high ridges and peaks of the Cascade and Olympic Ranges and also occurs to a limited extent in the Blue Mountains of southeast Washington. In technical parlance this zone is often referred to as the Hudsonian.

TREES	SHRUBS	FLOWERS
Engelmann spruce	Blackberry, sub-alpine	Agoseris
Alpine fir	Blueberry, red alpine	Anemone, alpine
Lodgepole pine	Cinquefoil, shrubby	Anemone, western
Douglas fir	Copper bush	Arnica, broad-leaf
Western white pine	Crowberry	Beard tongue, Menzies
Alpine larch	Dwarf bramble	Bear-grass
Dwarf juniper	Elder, black-berry	Bunchberry
Alder, Sitka	False box	Butterwort, common
	Gooseberry, swamp	Cinquefoil, fan-leaf
	Heather, red	Columbine spp.
	Heather, white moss	Cotton grass
	Heather, yellow	Dwarf bramble
	Kinnikinnick	Elephant head
	Mountain ash, Sitka	Eriogonum, sulphur
	Mountain ash, western	Eriogonum, cushion
	Rhododendron, white	False asphodel
	Squashberry	False forget-me-not
	Teaberry, mountain	False Solomon's seal
	Teaberry, western	Fireweed, alpine
	Trailing rubus	Foam flower
	Twinberry, black	Gentian
	Twinberry, red	Globe flower
	Twin-flower	Grass of Parnassus

	FLOWERS—Continued	
Green lily	Mountain bluebells	Ragwort, western golden
Harebell, alpine	Mountain daisy	Rockcress, Drummond's
Indian hellebore	Mountain forget-me-not	Spirea, meadow
Indian paintbrush	Mountain sorrel	Stenanthium, western
Ladies' tresses	Mountain valerian	Stonecrop
Leptarrhena	Onion, nodding	Veronica
Lily, avalanche	Onion, Hookers	Waterleaf, Fendler
Lily, snow	Peacock	White bog orchid
Lupine	Penstemon, Cascade	White cat's breeches
Marsh marigold, white	Phlox, spreading	Willow herb, yellow
Monkey flower, red	Polemonium	Wood betony
Monkey flower, yellow	Pyrola	
Moss campion	Queen's cup	

ALPINE ZONE: All terrain lying above the timberline is included here. It is the picturesque country of flower meadows, rocky ridges, snowfields and glaciers. The major part of the classification occurs along the summit of the Cascade and Olympic Mountains. The lower elevation limit may vary from 5,000' - 7,500' while the upper is governed only by the height of the mountains.

Winters are severe with snowfalls up to 30'. This may blanket the ground until early summer and arrive again in October. Although summer days may be comparatively warm there is a sudden decrease in temperature once the sun goes down.

TREES	SHRUBS	FLOWERS
Above timberline, but possibly stunted alpine fir, and dwarf juniper.	Dwarf willow	Alpine coltsfoot
	Cascade willow	Anemone, alpine
	Alpine willow	Anemone, western
	White moss heather	Aplopappus
	Red heather	Beard tongue, Menzies
	Cinquefoil, shrubby	Bistort, American
	Mountain teaberry	Broad-leaf arnica

TREES	SHRUBS	FLOWERS
	Labrador tea	Butterwort, common
	Yellow heather	Cinquefoil, fan-leaf

FLOWERS—Continued

TREES	SHRUBS	FLOWERS
Columbine	Harebell, alpine	Moss campion
Dryas, white	Indian hellebore	Mountain daisy
Elephant head	Indian paintbrush	Mountain forget-me-not
Eriogonum, cushion	Ladies' tresses	Mountain sorrel
Eriogonum sulphur	Larkspur, pale	Mountain valerian
False asphodel	Leptarrhena	Phacelia, mountain
False forget-me-not	Lily, avalanche	Sandwort, mountain
Fireweed, alpine	Lily, snow	Saxifrage, rusty
Fleabane, golden	Lupine spp.	Saxifrage, spotted
Gentian spp.	Marsh marigold, white	Saxifrage, Tolmie
Giant ragwort	Meadow spirea	Veronica
Globe flower	Monkey flower, alpine	Wallflower
Grass of Parnassus	Monkey flower, red	Whitlow grass
Green lily	Monkey flower, yellow	Wood betony

YELLOW PINE FOREST ZONE: This zone is readily distinguished by the presence of yellow pine either as widely scattered individuals at lower elevations around 1,800′ where there is a merging with the Bunchgrass Prairie Zone or in relatively heavy stands in combination with Douglas fir up to an elevation of 3,200′. The bulk of this grassy area lies to the north of the Columbia and Spokane Rivers in north-eastern Washington. Dry climatic conditions in the lee of the Cascade Range also have resulted in a zonal strip of varying width extending southward through Chelan, Kittitas, and Klickitat Counties to the Columbia River.

The climate is relatively arid with hot summer days and freezing winter temperatures. Annual rainfall ranges between 6″ and 20″.

TREES	SHRUBS	FLOWERS
Ponderosa (yellow) pine	Alderleaf buckthorn	Aster, large purple
Lodgepole pine	Ceanothus, redstem	Arnica, heart-leaf
Douglas fir	Clematis, blue	Avens, large-leaved
Engelmann spruce	Clematis, white	Balsamroot, Hooker
Aspen	Currant, sticky	Bistort, American
Bitter cherry	Dogwood, red-osier	Bluebell
Black cottonwood	Elder, blue-berry	Blue-eyed Mary
Black hawthorn	Gooseberry, mountain	Butterweed
Cascara	Hazel	Camas
Douglas maple	Honeysuckle, orange	Cat-tail
Western choke-cherry	Indian hemp	Columbine
Water (black) birch	Kinnikinnick	Delphinium
	Mahonia, creeping	Fairy bells, Oregon
	Mahonia, tall	False Solomon's seal
	Mallow ninebark	Field chamomile
	Mock orange	Field chickweed
	Ninebark	Fleabane, large purple
	Ocean spray	Fringe cups
	Poison ivy	Geranium, sticky
	Raspberry, black	Grass widow
	Raspberry, red	Hawkweed, white
	Saskatoon berry	Lady's slipper
	Scrub-birch	Long-plumed purple avens
	Snowbrush	Lupine
	Spirea, flat-top	Mariposa lily
	Sumac	Meadow rue
	Thimbleberry	Miner's lettuce
	Twinberry, black	Mint, Canada

TREES	SHRUBS	FLOWERS
	Twinberry, red	Mocassin flower
	Wild rose	Monardella, mountain
	Willow spp.	Monkshood

	FLOWERS—Continued	
Montia	Pussytoes, rosy	Violet, yellow
Nettle, stinging	Scouring rush	Waterleaf, ballhead
Nightshade, bittersweet	Skullcap	Weterleaf, Fendler
Onion, nodding	Self heal	Water-hemlock
Peacock	Star-flowered Solomon's seal	Water-parsnip
Penstemon, white	Sunflowers, spring	Water-plantain
Peony, Brown's	Thistle, common	Wild tiger lily
Phacelia	Tower mustard	Yarrow
Phlox, Douglas	Trillium, western	Yellow bell
Purple pea	Violet, blue	

BUNCHGRASS PRAIRIE ZONE: Various floral belts may be traced between the valley level of the arid sagebrush deserts and the start of the Yellow Pine Forest Zone on the lower mountain slopes and benches. However they are grouped as one here. The tufted bunchgrass is the characteristic ground cover in an area where few trees or shrubs are seen other than those bordering waterways.

In general this zone flanks the desert terrain of Douglas, Adams, Yakima, Franklin, and Walla Walla Counties with the Columbia and Spokane Rivers forming a northern boundary.

The elevation range is from 1,500'-2,400' and slightly more arid conditions prevail than in the Yellow Pine Forest Zone. Summers are extremely hot and below freezing temperatures are experienced most of the winter. Snow to a depth of 1' or 2' blankets the ground for several months.

TREES	SHRUBS	FLOWERS
Ponderosa pine	Antelope bush	Aplopappus
Douglas fir	Ceanothus, red-stem	Aster, golden
Rocky mountain juniper	Clematis, white	Aster, large purple
Engelmann spruce	Currant, golden	Balsamroot, hairy
Aspen	Currant, squaw	Balsamroot, Hooker
Black cottonwood	Dogwood, red-osier	Bedstraw, northern
Cascara	Elder, blue-berry	Bistort, American
Water (black) birch	Gooseberry, mountain	Blue-eyed grass
Western choke-cherry	Huckleberry, dwarf	Blue-eyed Mary
	Indian hemp	Bluebell
	Mahonia, creeping	Blue sailors
	Mahonia, tall	Brodiaea, large-flowered
	Mallow ninebark	Brown-eyed Susan
	Mock orange	Burdock, common
	Poison ivy	Butterweed
	Rabbitbush	Camas
	Raspberry, black	Camas, death
	Raspberry, red	Carrot-leaf
	Sagebrush	Catchfly, night-flowering
	Saskatoon berry	Clarkia
	Spirea, flat-top	Collomia
	Sumac	Columbo
	Waxberry	Delphinium
	Wild rose	Eriogonum, heart-leaved
	Willow spp.	Evening primrose

	FLOWERS—Continued	
Fiddleneck	Fringe cups	Goldenrod
Fleabane, daisy	Geranium, sticky	Gold star
Fleabane, dwarf mountain	Globe mallow, stream-bank	Grass widow

FLOWERS—Continued

Great mullein
Hawkweed, hairy
Iris, western
Johnny-jump-up
Lemonweed
Lily, mariposa
Long-plumed purple avens
Lungwort
Mariposa lily
Milkweed
Monardella, mountain
Montia

Oyster plant
Parsley, narrow-leaved
Peacock
Penstemon, white
Penstemon, yellow
Pepper pod
Phacelia
Phlox
Pond lily, yellow
Pussytoes, rosy
Sagewort, cudweed
Sagewort, dragon
Skullcap

Sugar bowls
Sunflower, smooth dwarf
Sunflower, spring
Sunflower, woolly
Tansy
Teasel
Thistle, common
Trillium, long-stemmed
Violet, sagebrush
Waterleaf, ballhead
White cat's breeches
Yarrow
Yellow bell

SAGEBRUSH ZONE: The driest desert country in the State is included here. It occupies the valley bottoms and plateaus of the Columbia Basin up to an approximate elevation of 1,800'.

Vegetation is shrubby as characterized by drab sagebrush which marks the edges of the zone quite accurately. Broken clumps of low trees and shrubs follow creek bottoms and draws.

The summer heat is intense, often reaching 100°. Winters see freezing temperatures from November to March. Annual rainfall is less than 10".

TREES

Only occurring along watercourses, swamps, etc.

Ponderosa pine
Douglas fir
Rocky mountain juniper
Black cottonwood
Water (black) birch
Western choke-cherry
White alder
Peachleaf willow

SHRUBS

Antelope bush
Bitterbrush
Clematis, white
Currant, golden
Currant, squaw
Dogwood, red-osier
Elder, blue-berry
Greasewood
Hop sage
Indian hemp
Mahonia, tall
Mahonia, creeping
Mock orange
Poison ivy
Rabbitbush
Raspberry, black
Sagebrush
Saskatoon berry
Silverberry
Sumac
Tetradymia
Waxberry
Wild rose
Willow spp.

FLOWERS

Aplopappus
Aster, golden
Balsamroot, Hooker
Bedstraw, northern
Bitterroot
Blue-eyed grass
Blue-eyed Mary
Brodiaea, bicolored
Brooklime
Brown-eyed Susan
Butterweed
Cactus
Cactus, Simpson's
Clarkia
Collomia
Columbo
Dagger-pod
Delphinium
Eriogonum
Evening primrose
Fiddleneck
Fleabane, cushion
Fleabane, daisy
Gilia, scarlet

FLOWERS—Continued

Globe mallow, stream-bank
Globe mallow, white-leaved
Grass widow
Great mullein
Horsemint nettleleaf
Horseweed
Iris, western
Johnny-jump-up
Lemonweed
Lily, mariposa

Lungwort
Lupine
Milkweed
Monardella, mountain
Nightshade, black
Parsley, narrow-leaved
Peacock
Penstemon, white
Penstemon, yellow
Pepper pod

Phacelia
Phlox
Primrose, pallid evening
Sagewort, cudweed
Sagewort, dragon
Sunflower, smooth dwarf
Sunflower, woolly
Wallflower
Waterleaf, ballhead
Winterfat
Yellow bell

ELEVATION RANGES
OF
COMMON TREES, SHRUBS AND FLOWERS

TREES	SHRUBS	FLOWERS	
ABOVE TIMBERLINE. STUNTED ALPINE FIR, WHITE-BARK PINE AND DWARF JUNIPER.	WHITE MOSS HEATHER, YELLOW AND RED HEATHER, CASCADE AND DWARF WILLOW, SHRUBBY CINQUEFOIL, MOUNTAIN TEABERRY.	MOUNTAIN DAISY, ARNICA, GENTIAN, INDIAN HELLEBORE, RED AND YELLOW MONKEY FLOWER, COLUMBINE, MTN. VALERIAN, AVALANCHE AND SNOW LILY.	7000' + ↑ ↓ 4500'
MOUNTAIN HEMLOCK, ALPINE AND AMABILIS FIR, YELLOW CEDAR, WHITE-BARK AND WHITE PINE, DWARF JUNIPER, SITKA ALDER.	FALSE AZALEA, COPPER BUSH, WHITE RHODODENDRON, CROWBERRY, MTN. ASH, BLACK MTN. HUCKLEBERRY, TRAILING RUBUS, MTN. SPIREA.	STENANTHIUM, QUEEN'S CUP, FALSE SOLOMON'S SEAL, TWISTED STALK, MEADOW SPIREA, BEAR-GRASS, BUNCHBERRY, FALSE LADY'S SLIPPER.	4500' ↑ ↓ 2800'
DOUGLAS FIR, HEMLOCK, RED CEDAR, PACIFIC SILVER FIR, GRAND FIR, SITKA SPRUCE, RED ALDER, BROADLEAF AND VINE MAPLE, DOGWOOD, CASCARA, BLACK COTTONWOOD, PACIFIC WILLOW, PACIFIC CRAB-APPLE, BLACK HAWTHORN.	FALSE BOX, SALAL, GOAT'S BEARD, DEVIL'S CLUB, BLACK TWINBERRY, SALMONBERRY, THIMBLEBERRY, MOCK ORANGE, OCEAN SPRAY, RED-BERRY ELDER, HARDHACK, RED HUCKLEBERRY, TWIN-FLOWER, ORANGE HONEY-SUCKLE, RED RHODODENDRON.	OXALIS, VANILLA LEAF, WILD LILY-OF-THE-VALLEY, STAR FLOWER, PURPLE PEA, RATTLESNAKE PLANTAIN, TRILLIUM, BLEEDING HEART, FAIRY BELLS, PIPSISSEWA, BLUE-EYED MARY, PEACOCK, MINER'S LETTUCE, VIOLETS, SKUNK CABBAGE, YERBA BUENA.	2800' ↑ ↓ 0'
ABOVE TIMBERLINE.	WHITE MOSS HEATHER, RED AND YELLOW HEATHER, DWARF WILLOWS, MOUNTAIN TEABERRY, DWARF HUCKLEBERRY, BLACK-BERRY ELDER, WILLOW SPECIES.	BROAD-LEAF ARNICA, COLUMBINE, WHITE DRYAS, CUSHION ERIOGONUM, ELEPHANT HEAD, SNOW LILY, GENTIAN, INDIAN HELLEBORE, INDIAN PAINTBRUSH.	8000' ↑ ↓ 6000'
WHITE PINE, ENGELMANN SPRUCE, LODGEPOLE PINE, DOUGLAS FIR, PACIFIC SILVER FIR, ALPINE FIR, LARCH, ASPEN, MOUNTAIN AND SITKA ALDER.	BLACK AND RED TWINBERRY, RED ALPINE BLUEBERRY, BLACK MTN. HUCKLEBERRY, KINNIKINNICK, LABRADOR TEA, SITKA MTN. ASH, SOOPOLALLIE, FLAT-TOP SPIREA, TWIN-FLOWER, SWAMP GOOSEBERRY.	BROAD-LEAF ARNICA, BUNCHBERRY, COLUMBINE, FALSE LADY'S SLIPPER, FALSE SOLOMON'S SEAL, INDIAN PAINTBRUSH, LUPINE, MEADOW RUE, MOUNTAIN DAISY, MOUNTAIN VALERIAN, PIPSISSEWA, LARKSPUR.	6000' ↑ ↓ 2900'
PONDEROSA PINE, DOUGLAS FIR, BLACK COTTONWOOD, DOUGLAS MAPLE, WATER BIRCH, MOUNTAIN ALDER, CHOKECHERRY, HAWTHORN.	ANTELOPE BUSH, SAGEBRUSH, RABBIT-BUSH, SASK. BERRY, SUMAC, TALL MAHONIA, BLUE-BERRY ELDER, POISON IVY, SQUAW CURRANT, SOOPOLALLIE, WHITE CLEMATIS, HAZEL.	BITTERROOT, YELLOW BELLS, PEACOCK, DELPHINIUM, PHLOX, PHACELIA, SCARLET GILIA, SPRING SUNFLOWERS, FRINGE CUPS, MARIPOSA LILY, CAMAS.	2900' ↑ ↓ 1100'
ABOVE TIMBERLINE. DWARF JUNIPER, STUNTED ALPINE FIR AND WHITE-BARK PINE.	HUCKLEBERRY, DWARF HUCKLEBERRY, WHITE MOSS HEATHER, RED HEATHER, DWARF AND ALPINE WILLOWS, CROWBERRY.	GRASS OF PARNASSUS, GENTIAN, LADY'S TRESSES, MOSS CAMPION, MOUNTAIN DAISY, LUPINE, MTN. VALERIAN, WESTERN ANEMONE, WOOD BETONY, ELEPHANT HEAD, PAINTBRUSH, BEARGRASS, MARSH MARIGOLD, AVALANCHE LILY.	9000' + + ↑ ↓ 5500'
ENGELMANN SPRUCE, ALPINE FIR, NOBLE FIR, MOUNTAIN HEMLOCK, PACIFIC SILVER FIR, YELLOW CEDAR.	BLACK-BERRY ELDER, FALSE AZALEA, BLACK MTN. HUCKLEBERRY, WESTERN MTN. ASH, WHITE RHODODENDRON.	WHITE FALSE HELLEBORE, WILD TIGER LILY, GRASS OF PARNASSUS, BROAD-LEAF ARNICA, WESTERN ANEMONE.	5500' ↑ ↓ 4500'
DOUGLAS FIR, WESTERN HEMLOCK, RED CEDAR, WHITE PINE, GRAND FIR, LODGEPOLE PINE, YEW, ASPEN, BLACK COTTONWOOD, N. W. WHITE BIRCH, BITTER CHERRY, MOUNTAIN ALDER, DOUGLE MAPLE, VINE MAPLE, BROADLEAF MAPLE.	BLACK TWINBERRY, DEVIL'S CLUB, RED-BERRY ELDER, FALSE BOX, HARDHACK, GOAT'S BEARD, KINNIKINNICK, SAL-MONBERRY, THIMBLEBERRY, ORANGE HONEYSUCKLE, RED-STEM CEANOTHUS, TWIN-FLOWER, SNOWBRUSH, RED HUCKLEBERRY, TRAILING RUBUS, DWARF BRAMBLE.	HEART-LEAF ARNICA, BLEEDING HEART, BUNCHBERRY, LUPINE, COLUMBINE, COW PARSNIP, FOAM FLOWER, SNOW LILY, QUEEN'S CUP, PIPSISSEWA, CATCHFLY, INDIAN PAINTBRUSH, MEADOW RUE, BANE-BERRY, WILD GINGER, ALUMROOT, SAXIFRAGE.	4500' ↑ ↓ 2000'
BITTER CHERRY, CURL-LEAF MOUNTAIN MAHOGANY, WHITE-BARK PINE.	SNOWBRUSH, RED-STEM CEANOTHUS, RED ALPINE BLUEBERRY, FALSE BOX.	WHITE FALSE-HELLEBORE, MOUN-TAIN VALERIAN, MOUNTAIN DAISY, WHITE-LEAVED PHACELIA, LONG-PLUMED PURPLE AVENS, SULPHUR ERIOGONUM, YARROW, DEATH CAMAS, MENZIES AND SHRUBBY PENSTEMON.	7,500' ↑ ↓ 5500'
PONDEROSA PINE, DOUGLAS FIR, GRAND FIR, DOUGLAS MAPLE, WESTERN CHOKE CHERRY, ENGELMANN SPRUCE, SITKA ALDER, LARCH.	BLUE ELDER, OCEAN SPRAY, KINNIKINNICK, ORANGE HONEY-SUCKLE, SITKA MTN. ASH, MALLOW NINEBARK, THIMBLEBERRY, WAX CURRANT, ALDERLEAF BUCKTHORN, BLACK MOUNTAIN HUCKLEBERRY, SASKATOON BERRY.	HEART-LEAF ARNICA, STAR-FLOW-ERED SOLOMON SEAL, PENSTEMON, PAINT-BRUSH, SELF-HEAL, WOOD BETONY, PIPSISSEWA, PYROLA, FALSE BUGBANE, COLUMBINE, STONECROP, COLLOMIA, SCARLET GILIA, NETTLELEAF HORSEMINT, CLARKIA, SUGAR BELL, HOOKER SUNFLOWER.	5500' ↑ ↓ 3000'
WESTERN CHOKECHERRY, HACKBERRY.	BLUE ELDERBERRY, RABBITBUSH, SAGEBRUSH, WHITE CLEMATIS, POISON IVY, GOLDEN CURRANT, HOP SAGE.	TEASEL, ST. JOHNSWORT, OYSTER PLANT, COMMON SUNFLOWER, BUTTERWEED, MILKWEED, GREAT MULLEIN, GRASS WIDOW, CAT-TAILS.	3000' ↑ ↓ 1600'

(14)

ELEVATION RANGES
of
COMMON TREES, SHRUBS & FLOWERS

7000'
6000'
5000'
TIMBERLINE
4000'
3000'
2000'
1000'
0' (PORT ANGELES)
OLYMPICS

7000'
6000' TIMBERLINE
5000'
4000'
3000'
2000'
1100' (CHELAN)
DRY INTERIOR REGION

9000'
8000'
7000'
6000' TIMBERLINE
5000'
4000'
3000'
2000' (MT. RAINIER)
CASCADE MOUNTAINS

8000'
7000'
6000'
HIGH RIDGES
5000'
4000'
3000'
1600' (DAYTON)
BLUE MOUNTAINS

(15)

WESTERN WHITE PINE
(*Pinus monticola*)

White Pine - Silver Pine

RANGE: Generally at middle elevations as characterized by the Mountain Forest Zone. Olympics, Cascades, mountains of northeastern Washington. Sporadic in Coastal and Subalpine Zones. Usually well scattered among other forest trees.

FORM: When growing under fair conditions it has a remarkable straight trunk iike a sturdy flag-pole. Trees 1' - 3' in diameter and to 120' high are most common. Regular whorls of horizontal limbs are characteristic and these form a narrow crown on the top two-thirds of the tree. Here and there an overly long limb protrudes making a recognizable design from afar.

BARK: Silvery grey on trees up to 6" in diameter. Then becoming dark and deeply fissured to form a regular pattern of small, thick plates that is quite distinctive from any other native tree.

LEAVES: Bundles of 5 needles to a sheath. Needles 2" - 5" long and bluish-green in color. Other 5-needle pines have needles about 2" long.

FRUIT: An unusual cone 5" - 9" long, slightly curved and with the tips of the scales a darker brown. The cones are so large that the clusters can be seen plainly on the topmost limbs during summer and fall months.

WOOD: A light, fine-grained wood, easily worked and a high proportion free from defects. Prized for special construction purposes, also match blocks. An ideal wood for carving.

DID YOU KNOW that there is usually a thick carpet of brown needles under this pine. In heavy timber its presence is often noticed this way.

QUICK CHECK: From afar, a few protruding limbs and clusters of large cones in upper crown. 5-needle pine with needles 2"-9" long. Curved cones 5" - 9" long.

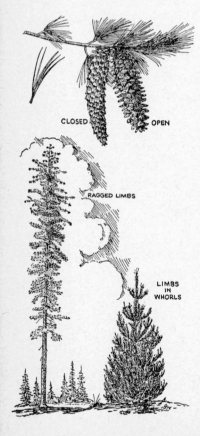

CLOSED   OPEN

RAGGED LIMBS

LIMBS IN WHORLS

WHITEBARK PINE
(Pinus albicaulis)

RANGE: A timberline tree growing in rocky exposed situations—the only pine in Washington found at elevations of 5,000' and over. High places in the Cascade Mountains. Mt. Baker, Mt. Rainier, Mt. Adams.

FORM: A crooked, lop-sided tree seldom over 30' high and 20" diameter. Long, limber branches drooping to ground on old trees. Sometimes shrub-like from severe exposure.

BARK: Thin, smooth and light-colored on young trees but becoming grey and brown with reddish tones and loosely scaly on old trees.

LEAVES: 5 needles to a sheaf. Needles are stout, slightly curved and from 1½" - 3" long. They tend to cluster thickly at twig ends and thus give a view of whitish-barked limbs throughout the tree.

WHITEBARK

FRUIT: A heavy purplish cone to 3" long. Often very pitchy.

WOOD: A soft, light wood only used in cases of necessity.

DID YOU KNOW that the limbs of this tree are quite rubbery giving them the resilience to withstand severe ice and snow loads. The cones drop to the ground unopened and the seed is released as the cone falls apart.

QUICK CHECK: High mountain habitat, 5 needles and thick cones.

(17)

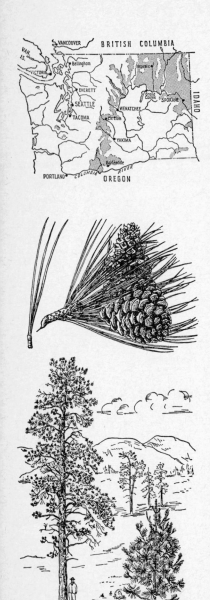

PONDEROSA PINE
(Pinus ponderosa)

Western Yellow Pine

RANGE: The common tree in the lowest forested part of central and eastern Washington. Usually between elevations of 1,500'-3,500'. Often extends into Bunchgrass Zone as scattered individuals. Very local and meagre occurrence in dry gravelly places west of the Cascades. Lake Crescent, Shelton, Sequim, and Hillhurst.

FORM: A distinctive tree of straight trunk topped by a loose mass of heavy branches with tufts of brushy foliage. The large twisted branches stick out here and there without plan but nevertheless produce a tousled narrow cone outline. Few trees over 3' thick are to be seen but fine specimens around 2' through and 80'-90' high are quite common. Young trees have a distinct whorl to their branches and a characteristic voluptuousness to their glossy green foliage.

BARK: The flaky terra-cotta red bark of this stately pine stands out in bold color on distant hillsides making tree recognition possible from afar. Young trees have a very dark bark but as they age, reddish furrows begin to show. Trunks over 12" thick produce thin flaking scales much like pieces of a jig-saw puzzle.

LEAF: The yellow pine has the longest needles of any evergreen in the State. The brushy tufts are made up of needles about 6"-9" long with 3 needles to the sheaf. Sometimes 4 or 5 to the bundle are found here and there on young trees.

FRUIT: A roundish, shiny, light-brown cone that ripens on the tree and falls during September and later months. It is usually 3"-4" long and 2"-3" thick. The seed is plump and heavy but the stout wing whirls it through the air.

WOOD: A light yellow color with contrasting dark brown knots when freshly cut. Soft and light. Used for interior finishing (knotty pine), boxes.

DID YOU KNOW that Indian braves used the bark scales to make small hot fires which gave off no smoke and cooled rapidly leaving enemies no clue as to their time of movements. Pine cones too, are excellent for a quick hot fire.

QUICK CHECK: From afar, orange-red bark. Watch for possible confusion with larch if in its range. Three long needles to a sheaf is positive proof.

LODGEPOLE PINE
(Pinus contorta latifolia)

Jack Pine - Black Pine

NOTE: the most commonly used name for this tree is jack pine. However this name is correctly used for *Pinus banksiana,* a close relative east of the Rockies.

RANGE: A tree of widespread range likely to occur almost anywhere in the Mountain Forest Zone and up to sub-alpine elevations. Also in boggy regions along the sea coast and in dry gravelly places south of Puget Sound. Extends here and there into Yellow Pine Forest.

FORM: Under normal conditions a tall, slender tree to 18" in diameter and 100' high. The crown is narrow and rounded with the thin limbs often occurring only on the top third of the tree. Young trees are narrowly conical with regular whorls of bushy, up-pointing limbs.

BARK: Mottled, dark grey with some trees showing light brown areas. Light covering of small, loose scales.

LEAVES: 2 needles to a bundle. 1½" - 2½" long and often with yellowish-green tinge.

FRUIT: A hard oval cone, spiny, and up to 2" long. Usually clustered and often hanging unopened on tree for several years.

WOOD: A straight grained, light wood, pale in color. Until recently regarded as a weed species in the west but gradually assuming importance because of abundance and accessibility. Used largely for railway ties, mine props and fuel.

DID YOU KNOW that most burned-over forests east of the Cascades grow up in a very dense stand of lodgepole pine. This is because the cones withstand fires and later open to release their seed.

QUICK CHECK: A two-needle pine, the only one in Washington.

LARCH (WESTERN AND *ALPINE)
(Larix occidentalis and Larix lyallii)

Larch - Tamarack

ALPINE LARCH *(Larix lyalli):* A scarce timber-line tree of the high Cascade Mountains. More common in the northern half of the States and extending about 12 miles into B.C.

RANGE: Generally east of the Cascades and occurring most frequently in the Mountain Forest Zone of northeastern Washington. Also in the Blue Mountains. Altitudinal range approx. 2,000' - 4,500'.

FORM: A straight, tapering trunk possibly 3' thick and 160' high. Most trees 1' - 2' in diameter. In the narrow, open crown every one of the short horizontal limbs can be seen. Limbs near the top of the tree have a distinctive up-curve to their tips and the lower ends a downward twist.

BARK: Changing from thin, scaly, light brown bark on trees up to 10" in diameter to a deeply furrowed, orange-red and loosely scaly bark on old trees. Resembles ponderosa pine from a distance.

LEAVES: Needle-like, in clusters of 1 - 2 dozen arising from knobs on the twigs. About 1" long and yellow-green. Turning light golden yellow in fall and dropping to the ground.

FRUIT: A light cone 1" - 1½" long with protruding bracts. Old cones often failing to drop from some limbs.

WOOD: Heavy, reddish wood, very durable in contact with ground. Used for ties, pit props and general construction. Important commercial species.

DID YOU KNOW that in the fall larches can be seen on distant mountains by their yellow-gold color? Grouse often eat the fallen needles.

QUICK CHECK: Loose, open crown displaying all limbs with ends twisting up or down. Needles in bunches.

WESTERN LARCH

ALPINE LARCH

WESTERN LARCH

ALPINE LARCH

ENGELMANN SPRUCE
(Picea engelmanni)

Mountain Spruce

RANGE: Starts high on the westerly slopes of the Cascades but is most common on the easterly side from 4,000' to near timberline. Also seen in wet places in low valley bottoms in Bunchgrass and Yellow Pine Zones. In Blue Mountains but doubtful if in Olympics.

FORM: When in thick stands, narrowly conical with straight clean trunk. Topmost branches twist upwards, middle ones point out and lower drop strongly. Branchlets hang like tassels from main boughs particularly in trees in the open or at lower elevations. Ordinarily a tree 1' - 3' in diameter and 100' -140' high.

BARK: Trunk covered by loose greyish scales between which show a brownish or rusty red tinge.

LEAVES: 4-sided, dull-pointed needles about 1" long and blue-green in color. Tendency to curve towards topside of twig. Pungent smell when crushed.

RAGGED CONE

FRUIT: A light brown cone 1" - 2½" long. Scales thin, finely ridged on back and tip slightly ragged. Purplish when immature.

WOOD: Soft, straight-grained and creamy white in color. Very important tree to Interior forest industry. Cut extensively for general construction and pulp.

DID YOU KNOW a quick way to tell spruce needles is to roll them between the fingers? The 4 edges allow them to roll easily whereas a flat needle won't turn.

QUICK CHECK: A spruce by stalked needles. Cones with flexible ridged scales and finely-waved margin. Untidy look.

SITKA SPRUCE
(Picea sitchensis)

Tideland Spruce - Coast Spruce

RANGE: Occupies a narrow strip along the sea coast. Seldom more than 50 miles inland or at elevations of over 2,000'. Although frequent along the Coast its occurrence around Puget Sound is very sporadic.

FORM: Varies considerably depending on whether a forest tree or one growing in the open. In humid Coast forests it produces a long, clean trunk 3' - 6' thick and reaching 150' in height. The top is a thin crown of short branches. In the open, limbs are strongly out-thrust and carry a triangular fringe of drooping branchlets. Limbs extend almost to the ground. This latter form is easily distinguishable from a considerable distance.

BARK: Covered with thin, loose, crisp scales of rusty-brown hue.

LEAVES: Flattish rather than 4-angled and bristle out in all directions from twig. Very sharp to the touch.

FRUIT: An easily recognized cone by reason of its disorderly array of thin, irregular, wavy-edged scales. Most cones about 2" long.

WOOD: Fairly light and soft and varying from creamish to pale buff in color. Forest trees have a large proportion of clear, straight-grained wood making it excellent for fine construction. Also very important as a pulp tree.

DID YOU KNOW that Sitka spruce was chosen during the last war as the most desirable wood for aircraft construction?

QUICK CHECK: Coast habitat, needles bristling out all around twig and light, disorderly cone.

HEMLOCK (WESTERN AND *MOUNTAIN)
(*Tsuga heterophylla* and *Tsuga mertensiana*)

Alaska Pine

WESTERN HEMLOCK
MOUNTAIN HEMLOCK

*MOUNTAIN HEMLOCK (*Tsuga mertensiana*) is a common tree of the Olympic and Cascade Mountains found at the higher elevations of 5,000' to timberline. The dark green needles grow in disorderly array around the twigs giving a thick tufted appearance to the foliage. Branches tend to have an upward sweep at their tips. The stout leader has the characteristic "hemlock" droop. Cones are 1" - 2" long, twice the length of those of western hemlock.

RANGE: A common tree of Coastal forests and extending upwards to elevations of 4,000'. Also occurs on moist east slopes of Cascades from 2,000' - 4,500' elevation and in northeastern Washington.

FORM: A large tree thriving in dense shade. From 2' - 4' in diameter and 120' - 160' high. Limbs long and irregularly spaced on trunk. The top-most twig (leader) droops in graceful fashion. Foliage on young trees is drooping, feathery, and very attractive.

BARK: About 1" thick with flat scaly ridges and deep furrows on mature trees. Dark rich brown in color. Young trees have thin, fine-scaled bark of lighter color.

LEAF: About ½" long, flat and blunt. More or less two-ranked. Two fine white lines on under surface. Each leaf with short stalk and twist at base of needle.

FRUIT: A light cone not over 1" long which ripens in fall and drops during winter.

WOOD: A tree that 20 years ago was considered of low value now ranks high in importance as a pulpwood species. Finds wide use in lumber industry and bark is high in tannin content.

DID YOU KNOW that hemlock is a prized ornamental in Great Britain? It can grow and reproduce in dense shade. Young trees often start on top of stumps or fallen logs. It usually grows with Douglas fir, red cedar, and Sitka spruce.

QUICK CHECK: The drooping tree tip identifies hemlock from afar. Leaves and cones are good points, too.

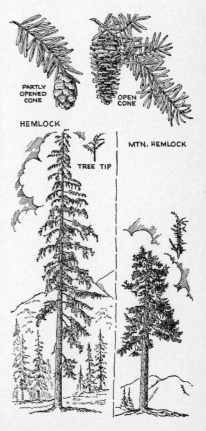

PARTLY OPENED CONE

OPEN CONE

HEMLOCK

MTN. HEMLOCK

TREE TIP

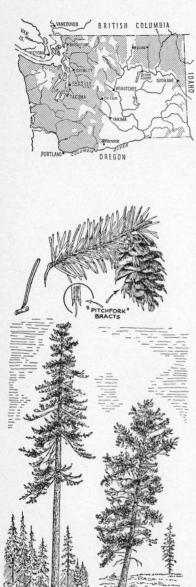

COAST FIR

INTERIOR FIR

"PITCHFORK" BRACTS

DOUGLAS FIR
(*Pseudotsuga menziesii*)
(*Pseudotsuga taxifolia*)

Fir - Douglas Spruce - Oregon Pine

The Coast Douglas Fir is recognized by some authorities as a different variety from the Interior or Dry Belt Tree. The differing features are so slight that only the one tree is considered here.

RANGE: The most widespread conifer in the State likely to be found wherever there are evergreens and stands below sub-alpine elevations. Reaches its best growth in Coastal forests. Altitudinal limit approx. 4,500'.

FORM: Trees over 200' high and 6' in diameter are seldom seen now. Most mature trees on Pacific Coast, 3'-4' in diameter, 200' high, and in Interior seldom over 30" in diameter. Young trees form broad sloping pyramid. Lower branches straight or drooping and higher curve upward. Old trees lose this form and develop heavy crooked limbs and have a flattened or irregular top. In shade, lower limbs drop off leaving a long clear trunk.

BARK: Smooth grey-brown with resin blisters on young trees up to 6" in diameter. Then as tree increases in age bark becomes thick and deeply fissured into reddish-brown ridges. Sometimes reaches over 1' thick. This prevents damage from fires but makes an excellent fuel.

LEAF: Flat, sharp-pointed needles about 1" in length. Not prickly to the touch like spruce.

FRUIT: A cone ripening in the fall and dropping to the ground. Cones hang downward and are 2" - 3" long. The bracts between the cone scales are triple-pronged and protrude so as to be easily visible and thus make an unmistakable indentifying feature.

WOOD: Generally reddish but sometimes yellowish in color with prominent annual rings. Splits cleanly and is very strong. Important for heavy construction and interior and exterior finishing.

DID YOU KNOW that Douglas fir is the tree seen most often by people in Washington? It grows in dense stands on the Coast or associated with hemlock, cedar and amabilis fir. East of the Cascades it is found with ponderosa pine at the lower elevation and lodgepole pine, white pine and larch at higher levels. Discovered by David Douglas, famed Scottish botanist, in 1829. Favorite Christmas tree—mostly cut in Interior because of thicker form. Largest tree in Washington and only exceeded in the west by redwoods on Pacific Coast.

QUICK CHECK: "Pitchfork" bracts on cone.

ALPINE FIR
(Abies lasiocarpa)

Mountain Fir

RANGE: A tree of sub-alpine and near elevations. Occurs on all the higher mountain systems of Washington. Usually between elevations of 4,500' and 7,000'. Chinook Pass, Snoqualmie Pass, Stevens Pass.

FORM: Distinguished by its symmetrical, narrow, spire-like form. The branches are in whorls and very short and stiff toward the top. Most slope downward. Trees may reach 4' in diameter and 150' high but usually are 10" - 16" in diameter and 50' - 75' high. At timberline it becomes stunted and sprawls with limbs to the ground.

BARK: On young trees thin, smooth, and grey with conspicuous resin blisters. On old trees, 12" or more in diameter, irregular, shallow furrows and reddish scales but still smooth on upper section.

LEAF: Flat, blunt needles about 1" long twisting upward from underside of twigs to bush densely around twig. Sharp-pointed on cone limbs. Blue-green in color with pungent smell. Silvery tinge to new growth. Twig ends orange brown and older growth hairy.

CONE BRANCH

LOWER BRANCH

CONES IN TREE TIP

FRUIT: A group of heavy, hard, wooden cones 2" - 4" long, purple in color and standing erect near the top of the tree. Often blotched with sticky pitch.

WOOD: A light-colored soft wood of little commercial importance.

DID YOU KNOW that most sub-alpine and timberline pictures in Washington show the alpine fir as the picturesque symmetrical trees in the scene? The short stiff branches usually slope downward and are constructed to withstand heavy loads of ice and snow that may completely encase them in mid-winter.

QUICK CHECK: Flat needles, circular scars on twigs. Spire form. Locality and altitude ranges.

PACIFIC SILVER FIR
(*Abies amabilis*)

Balsam Fir - Amabilis Fir - White Fir - Lovely Fir

RANGE: A fairly common tree of the Olympic and Cascade Mountain systems. Wide tolerance in altitude giving a range from near the sea coast to elevations of 6,000'.

FORM: A straight tree up to 100' and 2½' in diameter, spire-pointed, rounded cone on older trees, thickly foliated and very symmetrical. Branches except those on top third, curving down and away from trunk and often extending to the ground. A remarkably beautiful tree in form and color. At high elevations it resembles alpine fir in general shape.

BARK: Smooth ash-grey unbroken bark splotched with chalky-white patches. Old trees usually seamed and much like mountain hemlock bark.

LEAF: Flat needle leaf about 1¼" long, grooved on upper side and has two white lines on under surface. Needles blunt-pointed and most with small notch on end. Notice how they point forward along the top of the twigs and those near the underside twist up to produce a flattish effect when a bough is seen from beneath. These characteristics should limit any confusion with grand fir which has two-ranked needles. Twigs tend to be hairy.

FRUIT: An erect cone 4" - 5" long, dark purple in color. Falls apart in early fall leaving spike core standing on bough for several months.

WOOD: Soft, light, and yellowish brown. Generally cut for pulp.

DID YOU KNOW that the silvery color is given by two white lines on the lower side of the needles? Trees likely to be associated with it at lower levels are Douglas fir, hemlock and white pine. At higher elevations mountain hemlock and alpine fir are common companions. Many woodsmen prefer the springy boughs of amabilis fir to any other tree for making a "bough" bed.

QUICK CHECK: Circular leaf scars on twigs identify true firs. Needles point forward along top sides of twigs. Young trees and those in good growing sites have smooth bark with white patches.

POSSIBLE VARIATION IN LOWER BRANCHES

TOP NEEDLES POINTING AHEAD

WHITE BLOTCHES ON BARK

GRAND FIR
(Abies grandis)

Lowland Fir - Western Balsam

RANGE: Grows best in moist situations such as valley bottoms but will extend upwards to 5,000' elevation. Coastal forests and slopes of Olympics, Cascades and Blue Mountains. Also mountain systems of northeastern Washington.

FORM: A tall straight tree averaging 2' - 3' in diameter and up to 125' high. A broad pyramidal shape when young with distinct horizontal pattern to branch ends. Older trees with rounded top and conical form when open grown but free of lower branches and irregular of crown in shade. All branches except tip have graceful downward swing.

BARK: Young trees up to 8" in diameter have thin smooth bark with numerous resin blisters. White mottlings may lead to confusion with the bark of amabilis fir or young Douglas fir. Older trees have hard irregular furrows and ridges.

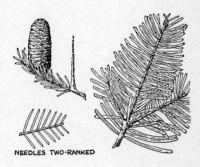

NEEDLES TWO-RANKED

LEAF: Flat needle leaves 1¼" - 2" long. They are blunt or slightly notched and grow in a flat rank from either side of the twig. The upper surface is dark green and has a central groove while the underside is silvery from two whitish stripes.

FRUIT: An erect cone 2" - 4" long and about 1" thick. They are very noticeable on the tips of trees in late August. As the cones ripen and the scales and seeds start to fall an untidy brown mass marks the tree top. Most of the cones have broken up by October.

WOOD: A soft light wood with a faint brownish color. Grand fir is usually cut as part of a logging operation and sees utilization for pulp or lumber for cheap wood products.

TOP OF OLD TREE

DID YOU KNOW that woodsmen place great faith in the healing properties of the gum from the resin blisters? It makes a handy glue too. Grand fir is usually found in valley bottoms growing as part of the Douglas fir - hemlock - red cedar forest.

QUICK CHECK: From afar the heavy conical crown tip is quite reliable. If close make sure it is a true fir either by leaf scars on the twigs or from the erect cones. Two-ranked needles make it grand fir.

(27)

NOBLE FIR
(*Abies procera*)

RANGE: A tree of comparatively high mountain slopes generally between 2,500' and 5,000' elevation. Occurs on both sides of the Cascade Mountains. Common in Mt. Rainier region. Reported in Olympic Mountains but if so is extremely limited in range. Doesn't extend into British Columbia. Mountain Forest Zone.

FORM: In common with alpine, balsam, and grand fir, noble fir has beautiful symmetry of form. The straight trunk with its slight taper is complimented by a thin conical outline formed by stiff out-pointing branches. Lower branches often droop. The crown is characteristically narrow and rounded but quite open in marked contrast to the overly dense top of most grand firs. Mature trees range from 2' - 5' in diameter and may reach 200' in height.

BARK: Relatively smooth with resin blisters on trees less than 14" in diameter, then starting to seam into ridges which break crossways to form long, shingly plates which are easily flaked off. Grey in color when young with a tinge of brown when older. New exposed bark a dark rusty shade.

LEAF: A 4-sided needle from 1" - 1½" long. Needles on lower limbs more flattened and sometimes notched at tip. They twist upward from the branches and are more densely clustered near the top of the tree. Blue-green in color they are given a silvery tinge by rows of tiny white markings. A groove along the upper surface is a notable feature.

FRUIT: An erect hard cone 4" - 6" long shingled with sharp-pointed bracts. Light brown in color when mature in early fall. They fall apart in October.

WOOD: A light brown wood with reddish tinges. Hard yet light in weight with a medium fine grain, it finds a place in airplane manufacture, interior finish and general construction purposes.

DID YOU KNOW that noble fir is an exceptionally long-lived tree possibly reaching close to 1,000 years in some favored specimens?

QUICK CHECK: Range limited to middle mountain slopes of Cascades. Leaf-scars on twigs and channeled needles. Shingled, spiny cone.

WESTERN RED CEDAR
(Thuja plicata)

RANGE: Achieves best growth and greatest abundance west of the Cascades at elevations below 3,500'. Elsewhere it is usually confined to creek bottoms and similar wet places but extends to near 5,000' in elevation.

FORM: A giant tree on the Coast often over 150' high and 6' in diameter. The trunk tapers from a fluted base to a long spike-like top which is often dead. On mature trees the branches are long and irregular and usually point downward very distinctly. The frond-like branchlets impart a feathery or lacy appearance to the form. Young trees have a conical outline from regular spreading branches. A yellowish green color marks this tree from other dark green conifers.

BARK: Thin and stringy and can be pulled off in long strips. No other native tree except yellow cedar has bark resembling this. Indians valued it highly for making baskets, clothes and mats.

LEAF: Scaly, blunt leaves pressed in pairs tightly to the twig. Branchlets hang like fronds or sprays from main boughs.

FRUIT: A small cone ½" long which hangs on over winter.

WOOD: A reddish fragrant wood splitting with remarkable ease into thin boards. It is very light and free from pitch or resin. Used at one time by Indians for massive war canoes and lodges. Now valuable for shingles, siding and posts because of its resistance to decay. Fallen trees remain sound after 100 years.

DID YOU KNOW that the largest red cedars in the world grow on the Olympic Peninsula? Indians hollowed canoes 60' long from a single trunk.

QUICK CHECK: Stringy dark bark and fluted trunk at base. Twigs are smooth and, when stroked against the grain, are not prickly to the touch like yellow cedar.

(29)

PRICKLY SCALES

YELLOW CEDAR
(Chamaecyparis nootkatensis)

Alaska Cypress

RANGE: Ranges from near sea level on west slopes of Olympics to customary 3,000'-7,000' elevation limits in Cascades. Most plentiful in northern part of Cascades. Southern limit near Mt. Adams.

FORM: A shaggy tree usually less than 80' high. The trunk is often slightly twisted and tapers quickly toward the top. Well formed trees up to 2' in diameter are common but growth appears slow and breakage heavy with increased age. The limbs sweep out and down with fern-like fronds hanging from them. The tip of the tree is slender and droops very much like hemlock. Young trees are shrubby and warped but gradually straighten as they grow taller.

BARK: On trees over 8" in diameter, the bark appears a distinctive dirty white from a distance. It is stringy and brittle and hangs in loose rough pieces. Unlike red cedar it won't pull off in long strips but breaks in stiff sections. Young trees have a fairly smooth, reddish bark.

LEAF: Scaly overlapping leaves very similar to red cedar but prickly to the touch when stroked "against the grain."

FRUIT A knobby rounded berry, greenish white in color until ripening in late September or October to a reddish brown cone which falls during the winter.

WOOD: Soft, light yellow in color with a very noticeable sharp fragrance when freshly cut. It resists rot and insects and, being easily worked, is a favorite of boat builders. It is one of the most popular woods in Washington for arrow making and carving.

DID YOU KNOW that some gnarled monarchs 5' and 6' in diameter may be the oldest trees in the State with ages of over 1,000 years?

QUICK CHECK: Prickly cedar-like foliage and stringy white bark. Limited range and elevation.

DWARF JUNIPER
(Juniperus communis)

Dwarf juniper is included as a tree in botanical descriptions because it reaches tree proportions in one or two places in its widely distributed range embracing the northern half of the world.

RANGE: High timberline and alpine regions of Olympics and Cascades. Stevens Pass, Mt. Rainier, Mt. Adams.

FORM: A sprawling shrub holding close to the rock at higher elevations but in valley bottoms often a bushy, upright mat several feet high and 4' - 10' across.

BARK: A thin, reddish-grey bark rough with scales.

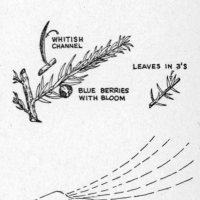

LEAVES: Narrow, sharp-pointed needles with shallow, whitish channel on underside. Close examination shows that the needles are arranged in whorls of three.

FRUIT: Dark blue, knobby berries covered with whitish bloom.

WOOD: Shrubs are too small to produce wood of any value.

DID YOU KNOW that dwarf juniper is the most widely distributed tree or shrub in the northern half of the world?

QUICK CHECK: "Juniper" shrub with all needles, short, channelled and mostly in groups of three.

(31)

ROCKY MOUNTAIN JUNIPER
(Juniperus scopulorum)

Rocky Mountain Red Cedar - Western Juniper

WESTERN JUNIPER *(J. occidentalis)* is very similar to the above but has resinous leaves marked with a glandular pit on the back. It occurs in several very limited localities in the southeast corner of the State. Ryegrass Coulee on Snake River, Franklin County; Yakima Canyon, Kittitas County, Columbia R. Canyon below Sentinel Bluffs. Mouth of John Day River.

RANGE: Quite rare in Washington although very common in British Columbia. High northern ridges of Olympics, northern Gulf Islands, scattered individuals or small groups in eastern Washington in Bunchgrass and Sagebrush Zones.

FORM: Generally a bushy, shrublike tree with one or several short, stout, trunks to 8" thickness. Commonly 6'-15' high. Varies from neat symmetrical shape to extremely ragged. Sometimes even crawling in habit.

BARK: Thin, stringy bark with reddish-brown tinges.

KNOBBY BLUE BERRIES

LEAVES: Often two distinct kinds on same tree. Young shoots with sharp, needle-like leaves about $1/2$" long. Older branches with smooth, scaly leaves like western red cedar. Foliage variable in color and exceedingly attractive in many cases.

FRUIT: Lumpy blue berries requiring two years to ripen. They contain one or two large, grooved seeds.

WOOD: A reddish heart wood with a wide ring of white sapwood. Light and soft. Used occasionally for small ornamental work. In the East, a near species is much sought for pencil wood.

DID YOU KNOW that the berries of juniper are used in the flavoring of gin?

QUICK CHECK: "Juniper" look, scaly leaves on older branches, bluish berries.

WESTERN YEW
(Taxus brevifolia)

Pacific Yew

RANGE: A tree of river banks, deep canyons and seeking the shade of other trees. Grows from sea-level to near 5,000' in Cascades and mountains of northeast Washington. Although very wide-spread as scattered individuals its optimum range is west of the Cascades. West slopes of Stevens, Snoqualmie and Chinook Passes.

FORM: A small bushy, untidy tree averaging 15'-30' high. The seamed twisting trunk seldom is over 12" in diameter. Because the yew prefers deep shade and grows under larger trees it develops an ungainly limb pattern with long branches of uneven length. Sometimes the limbs grow almost to the ground. Spiny shoots from the trunk add to the ragged appearance. In extreme shade a sprawling shrub may be formed.

BARK: The rich red tints of the rough scaly bark usually draw attention to this hide-away tree. Often the thin bark is fluted and seamed as if the tree had suffered agonies in its slow growth.

LEAF: Flat, sharp-pointed needles with a short stem. Most needles are between ½" and ¾" long but some twigs have shorter ones. Dull green in color on top they show stripes of two-tone light green below. Although new shoots have a brushy needle effect, older limbs have a rough, two-ranked appearance much like hemlock.

RED BERRIES

FRUIT: Single greenish berries turning reddish in September. The horny seed uses this eye-catching dress to attract birds and so be carried to new fields.

WOOD: Perhaps the most attractively colored native wood because of the yellow sapwood contrasting with the rich red heartwood. Extremely hard and durable but of neglible commercial importance because of its small size and rarity.

DID YOU KNOW that the tough and springy yew supplied the fighting bows for most of the ancient armies and today is still prized by archers?

QUICK CHECK: Scaly red trunk. Sharp-pointed needles with two-tone color beneath.

TREMBLING ASPEN
(*Populus tremuloides*)

Quaking Aspen

RANGE: Found in most of the State except for the Olympic Peninsula (rare), and the Sagebrush, Sub-alpine and Alpine Zones. Very sporadic in occurrence with altitudinal range from 1,000' to 6,000'.

FORM: In the drier regions it gathers in low spreading groves 20' - 30' high where there is evidence of moisture. In wetter regions graceful trees to 80' high are common. These have straight trunks to 16" in diameter and carry on their top halves a loose, rounded crown of brittle branches. The characteristic groves of aspen result from spreading roots which send up shoots.

BARK: Mostly smooth and white with black "horseshoe" markings here and there. Chalk-like substance can be rubbed off. Older trees with fissured and blackened bark near base. Young cottonwood trees with which it might be confused have smooth, green-white bark without black patches.

LEAVES: An abruptly tipped, rounded or heart-shaped leaf to 3" long. Leaf stems flattened at right angles to leaf blade. Foliage is an attractive fresh green color.

FRUIT: Appears with the first leaves as catkins of small, greenish capsules. Generally unnoticed.

WOOD: A weak, soft wood almost white in color. Brittle and fast rotting. Although used for pulp and crating in the East and favored in some states for excelsior and match stock it is seldom used locally except for firewood.

DID YOU KNOW that the leaves tremble with the slightest breeze because of the flattened leaf stems. The chalky substance on the bark is supposed to be heaviest on the south side of the tree. Thus aspen can act as a direction finder.

QUICK CHECK: Whitish bark marked with black splotches. Flat leaf stem.

FLAT LEAF STEM

NORTHERN BLACK COTTONWOOD
(Populus trichocarpa)

RANGE: Very extensive range but usually confined to river banks, gravel bars or low-lying land. Most common east of the Cascades even occurring along water-courses in Sagebrush Zone. Elevations range from sea level to 4,500'.

FORM: The great change in form between young and old trees confuses many people into thinking there are two distinct species. Young trees up to 40' or 50' high assume a symmetrical conical form with stout, up-pointing branches. With increased age, the limbs become very thick, irregular, and crooked, and point outward or twist downward. The top tends to flatten from breakage of the higher limbs.

BARK: On young trees up to 6" in diameter the bark is smooth and green. Don't be confused with aspen which has white bark marked with black blotchings. Bark-furrowing increases with age until mature trees show a series of hard, dark grey ridges several inches thick.

LEAVES: In general, widely triangular and from 2½" - 5" long. Yellowish-green in color but much lighter beneath. Some leaves on young trees or sprouts may be to 8" long and have a more narrow tapering leaf. Teeth on new leaves are quite regular but ragged and wavy on old leaves.

FRUIT: In spring, a long string of rough greenish beads. These ripen and split open in a cottony mass which blows far and wide.

WOOD: A soft light wood of drab color used largely for veneer and the making of boxes. Its suitability for these varied purposes including pulpwood and the wide distribution make it a very important broadleaf tree. Rots quickly when in contact with the ground.

DID YOU KNOW that the thick sticky buds have a fragrant odor in springtime? The sticky substance can be used as an ointment on small cuts or as a makeshift glue. The hard, unripe seeds have been adapted for pea-shooter ammunition.

QUICK CHECK: Yellowish-green foliage among other trees. Smooth, whitish-green bark on young trees; thick, furrowed bark on older trees. River and bottomland habitat.

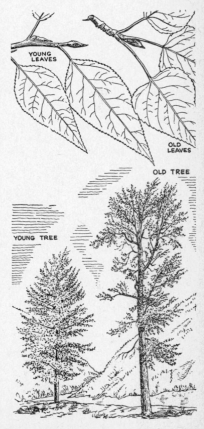

(35)

PACIFIC WILLOW
(*Salix lasiandra*)

Western Black Willow - Black Willow

PEACHLEAF WILLOW (*S. amygdaloides*) is a tree ranging along streams in the Sagebrush Zone. Its main characteristics are thin drooping branchlets and "peachlike" leaves. It can be confused easily with Pacific willow. Snake River Canyon, Yakima and Whitman Counties.

RANGE: A tree of stream banks and lowlands generally confined to the Coastal Forest Zone. Occasional occurrence east of the Cascades. Lake Chelan, Almota.

FORM: A crooked trunk branching into a number of upright limbs which produce a ragged, rounded outline to the crown. Seldom more than 30' high and 16" in diameter. The thin leaves and long slender twigs impart a graceful appearance.

BARK: Blackish in color and channelled into irregular, rough plates from many furrows and cross seams. The rather thick branchlets are smooth and orange to brown in color, while new twigs are light green.

"EARS" ON YOUNG LEAVES

TWIST TO LEAF END

LEAVES: Quite distinctive because of a long thin point with a sideways twist. From 2" - 5" long and very finely toothed. A shiny, dark green above but with a whitish pallor beneath. Leaf stems are thickish and less than ½" long.

FRUIT: Thick catkins about 2" long and appearing with the leaves. A bright yellow color is characteristic at maturity followed by a fuzzy white cotton often showing on the trees until July.

WOOD: Pale brown and brittle. Very soft and not used for any specific purpose.

DID YOU KNOW that the liking for water often results in long rows of these trees outlining the margins of sloughs and streams. Sections of limbs stuck in wet ground will root easily and quickly. Most willows have two small "ears" or wings at the base of their leaf stems when the leaves are young.

QUICK CHECK: A black-barked, ragged tree growing near water. Shiny, dark green leaves with a long thin point usually twisted to the side.

THE WHITE BIRCHES
(*Betula papyrifera* varieties)

These birches are most confusing as to name, identification and range. For many years *Betula occidentalis*, variously called Western White Birch or Western Birch, was regarded as the white-barked birch extending from the Coast to the Rockies. The botanical name *occidentalis* is now used for water birch while the white birches in Washington have been divided into 2 varieties. The writer's experience suggests that few persons will be able to separate the first two varieties listed below with any certainty or describe features that aren't so subject to variation as to render them unworkable. Most experts attempt identification by catkin scales and seeds. Because of the sporadic occurrence of outlying groups of trees, the range is impossible to outline with definite boundaries.

WESTERN WHITE BIRCH (*B. papyrifera commutata*): Often a tall tree reaching 100' or more in height and 16" in diameter. Leaves to 3" long, many wedge-shaped at base. Most doubly-serrate. Peeling, white to orange bark.

RANGE: The range map gives an outline of the most common regions of occurrence. Seldom is any extensive area found. Gulf Islands eastward at low to medium elevations.

NORTHWESTERN WHITE BIRCH (*B. papyrifera subcordata*): Relatively small birch tree to 60' high. Leaves to 3" long, squarish or slightly heart-shaped to base. A suggestion of double teeth on some leaves. Bark in thin layers, creamish-white to light orange on old trees. Often reddish-brown on young trees.

RANGE: The same general range as the above but favoring slightly higher elevations.

WESTERN LOW BIRCH (*B. pumila glandulifera*): A brushy shrub of bogs with leaves mostly 1" long. Bark—chestnut brown. Peck gives its range from sphagnum bogs in the Williamette Valley to northern Cascades. Occurs in one place on Vancouver Island.

SCRUB BIRCH (*B. glandulosa*) is described under the shrub section of this book.

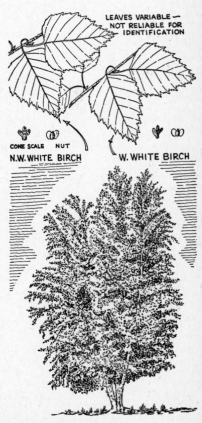

LEAVES VARIABLE— NOT RELIABLE FOR IDENTIFICATION

CONE SCALE NUT
N.W. WHITE BIRCH   W. WHITE BIRCH

WATER BIRCH
(Betula occidentalis)
(Betula fontalis)
(Betula microphylla)

Black Birch - Red Birch - Mountain Birch

RANGE: East of the Cascades, mostly in Bunchgrass and Yellow Pine Zones. Oroville, Tonasket, Ferry County, Dayton in Columbia County.

FORM: Most commonly a wide spreading, graceful shrub to 20' high with stems arising from one main clump. In rich soils beside creeks or in meadows it occasionally becomes a tree to 50' high and 12" in diameter. Branches very slender and willowy.

BARK: Rich reddish-brown with prominent light-colored markings. Not peeling except on larger trees where there is some curling. Greenish young twigs very warty. Mature twigs shiny red.

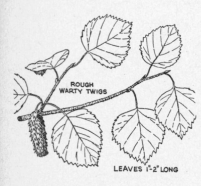

ROUGH WARTY TWIGS

LEAVES 1"-2" LONG

LEAVES: A roundish leaf with an abrupt, sharp point. Mostly 1" - 2" long. Light green undersurface often finely dotted.

FRUIT: Catkins showing up prominently by summer. Thickish, about 1" long.

WOOD: Fine-grained, soft and light, splitting easily. Larger trees used for firewood and farm use.

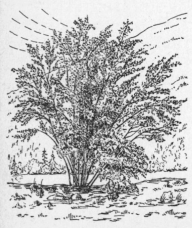

DID YOU KNOW that all birch bark is very durable? The wood of fallen trees will rot away leaving a shell of bark. The attractive, richly colored bark was once used by the Indians in their basket weaving to give a decorative pattern.

QUICK CHECK: Wet places along creeks and meadows in drier regions. Copper-brown bark and new twigs heavily warty.

(38)

RED ALDER
(*Alnus rubra*)

Oregon Alder

There are four alders in Washington, red, Sitka, mountain and white. Alders produce naked buds in the summer, each on a short stalk. Tassel-like catkins several inches long appear in early spring. Small woody cones form in the fall and hang until the following spring. Leaves have straight veins running to the margin.

RANGE: Very common west of the Cascades but probably appearing infrequently at low elevations on east slopes. Streams, valley bottoms and slopes with rich soils.

FORM: This varies a good deal with age and density of stand. Young trees to 30' high and growing in the open are broadly conical from irregularly spaced, long, straight limbs pointing out and upward. With increased age the lower limbs disappear leaving a long clear trunk with a narrow conical crown. The common size for older trees is from 8" - 14" in diameter and up to 80' high. Much larger trees do occur.

BARK: Slightly roughened bark, dirty grey in color. Older trees with clear trunks are blotched with white markings. Their base is sometimes seamed and thickly scaly.

LEAVES: Most leaves 3" - 5" long, dull green above and sometimes rusty-tinged below. The dull teeth form rounded lobes quite unlike the other two native alders. The extreme outer leaf edge curls under on most leaves.

FRUIT: A cluster of brownish cones each slightly more than ½" long and remaining on the tree until late spring. The nut is bordered by very narrow wings. Very attractive catkins, several inches long, appear in early spring before the leaves and show up vividly as they change in color from yellow to brown.

WOOD: Light, fine grained and easily worked without splintering. Does not check or warp and is valuable in furniture construction. Serves as a base for expensive veneers but finishes well itself. The dry wood makes excellent fuel and burns leaving very little ash.

DID YOU KNOW that freshly peeled alder bark turns bright orange on the undersurface? The Indians used this inner bark to make a dye.

QUICK CHECK: Round-lobed leaves with edges rolled under.

DULL ROUNDED TEETH

EDGES ROLLED UNDER

(39)

WHITE ALDER
(*Alnus rhombifolia*)

RANGE: Because of its rather confusing resemblance to both red and mountain alder, the westerly and northerly range of white alder is not too well known. It doesn't extend into British Columbia nor west of the Cascades as a rule. The general range is along streambanks in the Sagebrush Zone, particularly in southeast Washington.

FORM: Resembling red and mountain alder in having a broad open crown produced by strong branches. Large trees around 20" in diameter reach 60' in height but the usual growth is less than a foot in diameter and about 30' high. Often the trunks are clear of limbs for half of their length.

BARK: Light grey and smooth on young trees up to 6" in diameter. Then turning greyish-brown in color and breaking into rectangular scales which continue well up on the trunk.

LEAVES: Light yellow-green in color on top surface and from 2" - 3½" long. Leaf stems and underside of leaves carry very fine downy hairs. Prominent yellow mid-rib. Margins irregularly toothed with gland-tipped teeth.

FRUIT: A cluster of brown cones, each from 1/3" - ¾" long. Seeds shed in late fall or winter months. These are very small and surrounded by a narrow hard wing of extreme thinness. Thick clumps of catkins show in January and February.

WOOD: Sapwood dull white and heartwood light brown. Soft, brittle and comparatively light. Limited use because of meagre supply but suitable for furniture and woodenware. Good fuelwood.

DID YOU KNOW that birch and alders are close relatives each bearing seed as a small winged nut held in a cone? In birch the cones fall apart to release the seed. In alders the seeds fall from a hard cone.

QUICK CHECK: Limited range is good guide. Catkins in winter, scaly bark on older trees and irregular toothing of leaves.

MOUNTAIN ALDER
(*Alnus tenuifolia*)

Thinleaf Alder

RANGE: East of the Cascades and mostly in the Bunchgrass Zone. Occurs from valley bottom to high mountain elevations. Often growing with Sitka alder at higher elevations. Seeks wet ground, creek edges, and usually found in pure clumps and borders where there is good exposure. This is the most common alder of the Interior.

FORM: At higher elevations, much like Sitka alder, sprawling and shrublike. In valleys it is a small tree to 40' high and 12" in diameter. The branches are fairly straight and point upward to form a loose conical crown.

BARK: Thin, smooth, dirty green-grey with lighter horizontal markings especially prominent on younger trees. Older trees tend to flake and scale near their base. In the wetter parts of its range it is often partially covered by a scaly, whitish-green lichen.

LEAVES: Distinctly double-toothed with definite sharp teeth unlike red alder which has shallow, rounded teeth. Leaves, 2" - 4" long, are dark green with a yellow central vein.

FRUIT: A cluster of 3 - 9 hard, brown cones about ½" long. These hang on the trees until the following summer and are very prominent in the spring. The nut is bordered by very narrow wings.

WOOD: A soft light wood similar to Sitka alder but, because of the tree size, sees some use as fuel. Rots quickly in contact with the earth.

DID YOU KNOW that the leaves of alder trees do not turn brown in the fall but remain green until they drop? A decoction of alder bark was used by Indians in the treatment of rheumatic fever. Quite recently the bark has been found to contain salicin, a standard medicinal prescription for this disease.

QUICK CHECK: Check for alder by small, woody cones, naked buds, or straight-veined leaves. Distinct, double-toothed leaves identify it. Red alder leaves are rolled inward on their margins and its general range is west of the Cascades.

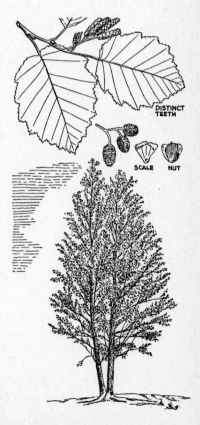

DISTINCT TEETH

SCALE   NUT

SITKA ALDER
(*Alnus sinuata*)

Green Alder - Mountain Alder

RANGE: Throughout Washington on mountain slopes of 3,000' and upward. Occasionally extends to low levels. Almost always in damp places such as along streams or bordering swampy meadows. Will stand partial shade. The range map includes regions where this tree may be found at low levels.

FORM: Usually a sprawling shrub to 10' high with crooked, upward curving limbs. Sometimes it grows as a small twisted tree to 30' high. Branches stick outward to form a loose, ragged outline.

BARK: Smooth, greyish-green in color and marked with light-colored, warty lenticels. In the wetter parts of its range it is often mottled by a scaly, greenish-white lichen.

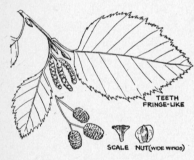

TEETH FRINGE-LIKE

SCALE NUT (WIDE WINGS)

LEAVES: Readily distinguished from the other alders by the fine sharp teeth which give a fringe-like appearance to the margin. Leaves are from 2" - 4" long, ovalish in shape and glossy green in color.

FRUIT: A cluster of 3 - 6 hard, brownish cones about $1/2$" long. The small nuts which can be shaken from the cones have wide wings on either side.

WOOD: A soft wood with little strength and not used for anything unless of necessity.

DID YOU KNOW that the crooked sprawling limbs are protection against the deep snows of winter? They bend to the ground when weighted and rise back as they are released.

QUICK CHECK: An alder by reason of cones, naked buds or leaves with straight veins running to margin. Fringe-like margins make it Sitka alder.

GARRY OAK
(Quercus garryana)

White Oak - Oregon Oak

RANGE: The only oak in Washington and rather limited in range. On Gulf Islands and extending southward in patches along Puget Sound on open, rocky locations. East of Cascades in several localities; Klickitat River, Tampico and Tieton River in Yakima County. Vicinity Cle Elum. A tree of low elevations and often mixed with arbutus.

FORM: A most picturesque tree when mature because of its huge, gnarled limbs and massive, shaggy crown. The heavy trunk may be up to 3′ thick and shortly branches into stout limbs. Its form is unmistakable with that of any other native tree.

BARK: Soon fissuring to produce narrow, horny ridges with occasional stout scales. Light grey in color.

LEAVES: Typical lobed oak leaf, 3″ - 6″ long, thick, and dark green.

FRUIT: A smooth, brown acorn ½″ - 1″ long dropping in the fall with a knurled or roughened cup often attached to its base. Although the acorns are purported to be sweet and edible they see little or no use for this purpose.

WOOD: Typical hard, strong and heavy as in other oaks. Wood checks and warps with drying which, together with the short trunks, gives garry oak little commercial value. It makes excellent fuel when thoroughly dry. Rots quickly in contact with the ground.

DID YOU KNOW that the shiny acorns are used in making novelty items and costume jewelry?

QUICK CHECK: A massive, shaggy tree with oak leaves and acorns.

(43)

PACIFIC CRAB-APPLE
(Malus diversifolia)
(Pyrus diversifolia)

Oregon Crab-Apple

RANGE: Coastal Forest Zone including Gulf Islands. Seeks low, damp places such as stream and swamp edges where it often forms an impenetrable thicket. Common on low ocean frontage.

FORM: A small, scraggly tree to 30' high and 12" in diameter or often shrublike with a number of straight, smooth stems an inch or two thick. Very bushy when growing in the open. It doesn't carry true thorns but numerous, stout and sharp spurs an inch or two long give a realistic imitation.

BARK: Very fissured, scaly and patchy on old trunks and branches.

LEAVES: Much like those of apple trees except for tendency to produce irregular lobes and a variety of shapes. Thick, sharply toothed and with prominent veins. Mostly 2" - 3½" long.

SHARP SPURS

LEAVES VERY VARIABLE IN SHAPE

FRUIT: Clusters of white, fragrant, "apple blossoms" appear from April 15 to May 15. Followed by bunches of little, oblong apples about ½" long. These are first greenish in color but turn yellowish or blushed with red. They are edible but rather acid in flavor.

WOOD: Very compact and fine-grained. Sometimes used in small ornamental turnery because of toughness and brownish hue of wood.

DID YOU KNOW that beautiful autumn colors are produced from yellow and russet colored leaves?

QUICK CHECK: Wet land habitat, some lobed "apple" leaves, fragrant flowers, or clusters of small apples.

BLACK HAWTHORN
(*Crataegus douglasii*)

Black Haw

COLUMBIAN HAWTHORN (*C. columbiana*) is found also in Washington. It has slender thorns from 1" - 2" long and dark scarlet berries. The range is in the Yellow Pine Zone but its occurrence is very limited and by no means as frequent as black hawthorn. Vicinity Gifford Ferry.

ENGLISH HAWTHORN (*C. Oxyacantha*) is an escape in certain localities. Its spiny limbs carry deeply lobed leaves and colorful bunches of scarlet berries that persist over winter.

RANGE: Wettish places like edges of streams and meadows. Common along roadsides and fields. Wide range from low to middle mountain elevations. Mostly Coastal Forest and Yellow Pine Zones. Tonasket, Republic, Stevens County, Whitman County, Spokane.

FORM: Either a small, bushy tree to 20' high or a tangle of lower shrublike growth making an impenetrable thicket. Twigs have alternating crooks. Spines are from 1/2" - 1 1/4" long and needle-sharp.

BARK: Dirty grey in color, very rough and scaly. Often mottled with patches of lichen. Young shoots smooth and shiny. Very similar to Pacific crab-apple.

LEAVES: Thickish, oval leaves to 3" long with 5-9 small lobes at top end.

FRUIT: Showy clusters of smelly white blossoms during April to May, followed by bunches of small, black-purple "apples"—ripe by late July. Though quite edible, rough seeds make them unpopular for eating. The apples wither quickly once ripe.

WOOD: Tough, close-grained but seldom utilized.

DID YOU KNOW that Paul Bunyan always used a big hawthorn tree as a back-scratcher?

QUICK CHECK: A bushy tree with sharp spines 1/2" - 1 1/4" long. Zig-zag twigs.

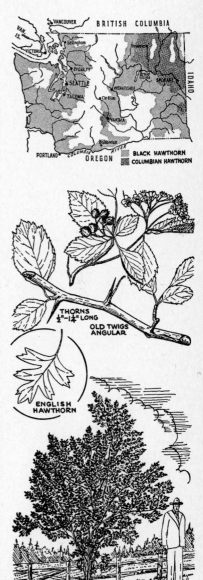

THORNS 1/2" - 1 1/4" LONG
OLD TWIGS ANGULAR

ENGLISH HAWTHORN

BLACK HAWTHORN
COLUMBIAN HAWTHORN

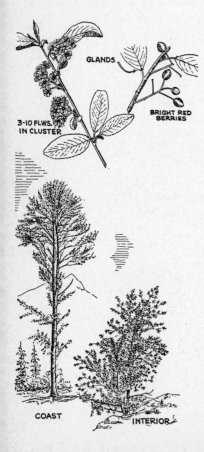

COAST INTERIOR

BITTER CHERRY
(Prunus emarginata)

The tree form of this cherry sometimes is distinguished as a variety, *Prunus emarginata mollis*. It is found west of the Cascades. Leaves are slightly hairy on the under-surface and reach 4" in length. This book treats them as one species. Be on the watch around towns and farms for hybrid forms resulting from cross pollenization with domestic trees.

RANGE: Coastal Zone to 3,000'. East of Cascades most common in Yellow Pine Zone. Kamiak, Butte, Blue Mountains, Yakima, White Pass.

FORM: Presents a wide variation depending on type of soil and climatic factors. At the Coast it is a slender tree up to 10" in diameter and 60' high. The branches are straight and point upwards. On drier sites and at higher elevations a low crooked shrub up to 10' high with leaves less than 1" long may be expected. Leaves grow along the branches rather than on side twigs, thus the tree framework is quite accurately outlined.

BARK: Dirty, lightly roughened and grayish-brown in color. Marked with grayish lenticels up to 2" long.

LEAVES: On shrubby trees, they vary from 1/2" - 3" long but in tall trees they may be 4" long. Blunt leaf points on older leaves, sharp on new growth; fine, rounded teeth and two small knobs or glands on the stem are other features.

FRUIT: The fragrant white flowers may be seen during April and May. They form rounded clusters toward limb ends and are replaced by pea-size bright red berries of extremely bitter taste. Each berry is on a short stem about 1/2" long. These stems branch from a stouter central stem from 1/2" - 1" in length.

WOOD: A brittle, quick-rotting wood sometimes cut for fuel.

DID YOU KNOW that the cherry bark can be peeled from the tree and polished to a rich red? Indians used strips of this bark in their basket weaving to give color to their work.

QUICK CHECK: From a distance the small narrow leaves outline the limb framework. Glands on dull-pointed leaf make it the bitter cherry. Rounded clusters of white flowers (5 - 10) or bright red berries on stems about 1/2" long.

WESTERN CHOKE CHERRY
(*Prunus virginiana demissa*)

This is the cherry listed in many writings as *Prunus demissa*. A variety of this, black choke cherry, *Prunus virginiana melanocarpa* is now recognized by some authorities. It is described as having fruit almost black, and stems without sparse occurrence on Gulf Islands. Common in drier regions across the State. Although often glands. For simplification the above are treated as one similar to past practice in most botanical writings.

RANGE: East of the Coast Range except for found on exposed locations it prefers damp ground of fair richness. White clematis and poison ivy are likely to be growing in the vicinity. Sagebrush, Bunchgrass, and Yellow Pine Zones.

FORM: Varying from heavy crooked shrubs less than 10' high to small trees 20' in height. Often forming a sprawling irregular mass from several bushes grouped together. A noticeable feature is the abundance of dark green leaves.

BARK: Greyish brown in color and roughened from numerous small fissures.

LEAVES: Dark green and wider above the middle. Sharp-pointed and finely saw-toothed. Leaf stems above ½" - ¾" long. Two small knobs or glands are located on the upper part of the stem but supposedly not on those of black choke cherry.

WHITE FLOWERS   GLANDS

DARK PURPLE BERRIES

FRUIT: The flowers preceding the fruit are very noticeable in May. They are white, about ½" across and form in dense, cylindrical clusters near the ends of the limbs. Berries are a dark purple and between ¼" and ½" in diameter. Although very puckery to taste they make fine jams and jellies.

WOOD: Brittle, fine-grained and of no importance.

DID YOU KNOW that the bruised bark gives off a pungent smell. It has a very bitter taste as has the bark of all cherries.

QUICK CHECK: From a distance the crooked form and heavy, dark green foliage. In spring, long clusters of white flowers; in fall, masses of dark purplish berries. Glands on the leaf stems.

(47)

BROADLEAF MAPLE
(Acer macrophyllum)

Bigleaf Maple - Oregon Maple

RANGE: Mostly west of Cascades at elevations under 3,000'. East of Cascades along some watercourses in Chelan and Klickitat Counties. Near Peshastin and Entiat.

FORM: A massive, bushy tree. In the open, it grows to 80' high with a trunk to 2' thick, which soon branches into numerous upright limbs. Among forest trees it grows straight with a loose crown of up-pointing branches surmounting a clear trunk. Often forked or several trunks close together.

BARK: Finely roughened on trees to 6" in diameter. Then becoming furrowed into narrow, horny ridges. Drab, grey-brown in color.

LEAVES: The largest tree leaf in Washington, being on occasion to 16" long. Most commonly 6" - 10" long and divided into 5 prominent lobes. The brilliant fall coloring of the other two maples isn't shared—the leaves only turning a pale yellow.

FRUIT: Flowers appear with, or soon after, the leaves in April. They are quite prominent as pale yellow hanging clusters. Paired maple wings about 2" long and at 45° to 60° to one another are seen from late summer to early winter.

WOOD: Fine-grained and fairly dense. Very valuable for furniture, interior finish and other specialty uses.

DID YOU KNOW that thick moss and ferns often make their home on rough maple trunks and lower limbs?

QUICK CHECK: Large, 5 - lobed maple leaves.

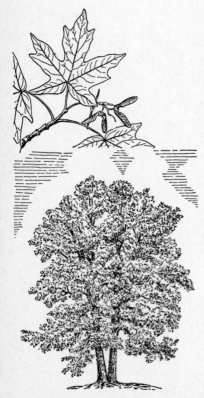

(48)

DOUGLAS MAPLE
(*Acer glabrum douglasii*)

Dwarf Maple - Rocky Mountain Maple

RANGE: Spotty occurrence along Coast southward from Alaska. Usually occurring at middle mountain elevations but liable to be found in any treed region of the State. Very abundant and widespread east of Cascades. Grows to over 4,000' in elevation. Stevens County, Olympics.

FORM: Sometimes a number of spreading stems up to 25' high and forming a loose, wide-spreading crown. Very often shrublike and under 10' high.

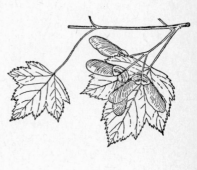

BARK: Smooth and grey-brown on main trunks. New twigs bright red.

LEAVES: A relatively small leaf 1" - 3" across and with 3 - 5 toothed lobes. Dark green in color but often blotched with vivid red dabs. The leaf stem is grooved and usually bright red. Produces very colorful red and crimson autumn foliage.

FRUIT: Pairs of maple "wings" about 1" long and almost forming a right angle to one another. Pinkish tinged during late summer.

WOOD: Not used because of small size of tree.

DID YOU KNOW that this maple leaf is quite like the shape of the "Maple Leaf of Canada"? The forked limbs provide very fine sling-shot crutches. None of the maple in Washington produce usable maple syrup.

QUICK CHECK: Small "maple" leaf with 3 - 5 toothed lobes.

VINE MAPLE
(*Acer circinatum*)

RANGE: Lower and middle elevations of Coastal region from Knight Inlet, B.C. southward to California. Sporadic occurrence in wetter places east of Cascades. Head of Lake Chelan. Also valley bottoms north of Peshastin. A tree of damp places along creeks or meadows where soils are fairly good. Very tolerant of shade and usually found growing under another tree.

FORM: Seldom found with a single trunk. More characteristically a bushy mass to 20' high from a number of stems 2" - 5" in diameter. If in the open it becomes a compact symmetrical shrub. Otherwise, as the name suggests, a straggly, crooked form is most common.

BARK: A smooth, pale green bark on trunk and limbs but occassionally becoming dull brown.

LEAF: A circular leaf with 7 - 9 short lobes like spread, blunt fingers. Lobes are sharply toothed. Leaves vary from 2" - 6" across.

FRUIT: Maple "wings" so widely spread as to be almost in a straight line. They vary from ¾" - 1½" long and are quite red when ripe.

WOOD: A surprisingly heavy wood of fine grain. Rots quickly when in contact with earth. Seldom used because of its small size, crooked form and weakness.

DID YOU KNOW that woodsmen use green vine maple for pot hooks and reflectors around campfires because it is almost impossible to burn? Vine maple has the most vividly colored autumn foliage of any Coastal tree or shrub.

IN SHADE   OPEN GROWN

QUICK CHECK: Leaf with 7 - 9 blunt, spreading fingers or lobes. Wide-spreading wings and limited range.

CASCARA
(Rhamnus purshiana)

RANGE: An infrequent tree often going unnoticed. Wide range but most abundant in low foothills of Coast below 2,500' and preferring shady, damp places. Sporadic along stream banks of Sagebrush, Bunchgrass and Yellow Pine Zones.

FORM: Older trees to 30' high and 10" in diameter seldom seen now. Often twisted and irregularly limbed if fighting for light. Young trees straight. Limbs relatively few and upright. Mostly shrub-like in eastern and southern Washington.

BARK: Smooth, slightly mottled grey bark resembling young red alder. Older trees tend to be scaly near their base.

LEAVES: Large, "cherry-like" leaves, quite distinctive by their shape and tendency to cluster. 2½" - 6" long, finely toothed and with prominent parallel veins. Paler green beneath. Leaf buds and uncurling leaves coppery in early spring.

GREEN, RED OR BLACK BERRIES

FRUIT: Clusters of small, greenish flowers usually go unnoticed in late spring. The plump, blue-black berries about ⅜" across are most prominent and seen in late summer. Several cluster together on short stems which branch from a longer main stem. The seedy berries are edible but not rated very highly.

WOOD: Light, brittle and of no value although during the last war tests were made on its drug content. The bark was harvested in great quantity during the war. Prices rose from 4c to 20c a pound.

DID YOU KNOW that the drug Cascara Sagrada is made from the bark? This laxative has been held in high regard by the medical profession for many decades.

QUICK CHECK: Large, ovalish, strongly veined leaves in loose whorls. Clusters of blue-black berries. Alderleaf buckthorn, a closely related shrub overlaps the range of cascara in northeastern Washington.

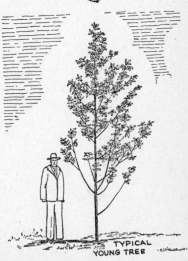

TYPICAL YOUNG TREE

(51)

4-6 SHOWY BRACTS

RED BERRIES

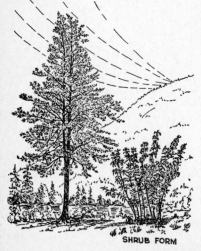

SHRUB FORM

PACIFIC DOGWOOD
(Cornus nuttallii)

Flowering Dogwood - Western Dogwood

RANGE: Fairly common along the Coastal region in a variety of soils—sometimes in rich valley bottoms and sometimes in rocky places. Upper elevation limit approx. 1,500'. Abundant vicinity Mt. Vernon.

FORM: Sometimes a bushy lop-sided tree to 12" in diameter and 30' high. Often has several trunks which are soon divided into heavy, upward-pointing limbs. Quite common as a very bushy shrub less than 10' high. Twigs are symmetrically branched opposite to one another and at right angles to the preceding pair.

BARK: Blackish-brown and smooth except on older trees which are finely ridged.

LEAVES: Glossy dark green above and much lighter below. Opposite, 3" - 4" long and with characteristic "dogwood veins" curving parallel to the leaf edge. In the fall, leaves generally are tinged with red.

FRUIT: Dogwood blossoms appear from April to June and sometimes again in September. The bloom is from 2½" - 5" across and may have from 4 - 6 white, showy bracts surrounding a rounded knob of greenish flowers. This central cluster turns into a compact group of red, bead-like berries thus adding gay color to the tree during August and September.

WOOD: A hard, fine-grained wood that has no particular use.

DID YOU KNOW that skewers or "dags" once were made from its wood, hence the name "dagwood" later popularized as "dogwood."

QUICK CHECK: Unmistakable "dogwood" leaves, flowers and fruit. In winter the symmetrical branching is sufficient.

ARBUTUS
(*Arbutus menziesii*)

Madrone

RANGE: A prominent tree of the Gulf Islands and usually associated with garry oak. Scattered trees along Coast in rocky exposed places. Isolated grove on bluffs along south fork of Snoqualmie River 30 miles east of Seattle.

FORM: A tree seldom more than 16" in diameter with twisting trunk and heavy irregular branches. When open-grown it assumes an irregular rounded outline but in shady surroundings there is a wide variation in shape.

BARK: An unusual and quite distinctive mottled, reddish-orange effect is produced by large, loose scales which curl raggedly and then drop. Sometimes the trunk is quite smooth if scales have fallen. Only native tree with this type and color of bark.

LEAF: Alternate, evergreen leaves from 3" - 6" long. They have a thick leathery texture and are glossy dark green above and whitish green beneath.

FRUIT: The clusters of creamy-white, bell-shaped flowers of May are followed in late summer by irregular masses of small, orange-red berries each about ⅜" across. They are seedy and not edible but much sought after by birds.

ORANGE-RED BERRIES

CREAMY "BELL" FLOWERS

WOOD: Although soft and easily worked when green it becomes extremely hard when dry. Its tendency to warp and check limits use to a few novelty items. The bright color of the bark is not retained to any degree by the brownish wood.

DID YOU KNOW that arbutus on most of its range is a good indicator of rock or a hard subsoil lying not far beneath the surface? The glossy leaves prevent water from remaining on them and thus, in winter, protect themselves from a damaging ice coating.

QUICK CHECK: A tree of limited range with exfoliating orange-red bark and thick, glossy, evergreen leaves.

OREGON ASH
(Fraxinus latifolia)
(Fraxinus oregona)

RANGE: West of the Cascades from sea level to near 3,000' elevation. A tree of the westerly part of the Coastal Forest Zone. Doesn't extend into British Columbia or to Olympic Peninsula. Abundant in Kings and Snohomish Counties. Prefers rich bottomland soils but grows well on poorer soils bordering streams. Usually scattered among other deciduous trees.

FORM: If open-grown, a rounded heavily foliated tree to 50' high. Limbs are stout and wide spreading. When competing for light with other trees it grows to 75' in height and has a short and narrow top of rather compact branches. Most trees seen now are under 2' in diameter but it can exceed this.

BARK: On young trees, grayish and blotchy and lightly roughened by welts. Old trees carry prominent criss-crossing fissures.

LEAVES: A particular gracefulness of foliage arises from the symmetry of opposite leaves. The main stems to a foot long are prominently grooved and carry 5 - 7 leaflets ranging from 3" - 6" long. These are a light green color and quite woolly beneath. A variety has been found which does not have hairy leaves.

FRUIT: Carried on female trees in noticeable large clusters of single wings. These are 1" - 2" long and ripen by late summer. The small flowers preceding the fruit are in bloom during March and April.

WOOD: Light brown in color and varying from medium to coarse grain. Sees limited use for tool handles, barrel, box and furniture making. Also fuel wood and shade tree purposes.

DID YOU KNOW that the ashes belong to the olive family which includes such popular garden shrubs as the lilacs, forsythias and sweet jasmines? All have their leaves opposite.

QUICK CHECK: Compound leaf with 5 - 7 leaflets, hairy below. Single winged seeds 1" - 2" long.

HACKBERRY
(Celtis reticulata)

RANGE: Limited occurrence in southeastern Washington to along the dry rocky banks of the Snake River and its tributaries. Sometimes on the edge of streams and also on adjacent rock bluffs. Noticeable in the vicinity of Clarkston, Pomeroy and Dayton. Reported many years ago as being found in the Puget Sound region.

FORM: In Washington a bushy tree often shrub-like in appearance. Seldom reaching over 30' high and 12" in diameter. A network of small twisting limbs and their many leaves accounts for the exceptionally heavy foliage. Often in rocky situations it bears a resemblance to a sturdy Saskatoon bush.

BARK: On the limbs it is a fine weave of grey and black tones from numerous thin fissures. Trunks are more deeply ridged.

LEAVES: Leaves have a lifeless appearance being heavy and thick, and dull green in color. They grow to 3" in length, have very heavy ribs on the undersurface, and are unpleasant to the touch. Note that the sides are of uneven length like their close relative, the elm.

FRUIT: Tiny, inconspicuous flowers are produced in spring. Those at the bases of the leaves near the ends of the branchlets develop into single, cherry-like fruits. These are about ¼" in diameter and range from a rusty brown to purple or black in color when ripe. Most of the berry is filled with a large hard seed. The edible fruit is dryish and sweet but not valued to any degree.

LEAVES TO 3" LONG
STIFF - COARSE

PEBBLY TWIGS

RUSTY BROWN
TO PURPLE
BERRY ¼" LONG

HEAVY RIBS BENEATH

WOOD: Heavy and brittle with low to medium hardness. Sapwood is slightly paler in color than the light yellow-brown heartwood. Because of its small size and limited range it is of no economic importance.

DID YOU KNOW that this shrub-like tree of Washington, when grown several hundred miles to the east, may reach 90' in height and over 2' in diameter?

QUICK CHECK: Very limited range. Uneven (elm) leaves and single cherry-like berries.

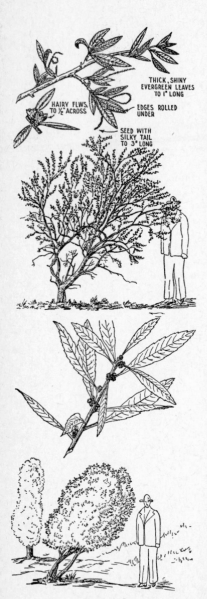

THICK, SHINY
EVERGREEN LEAVES
TO 1" LONG

HAIRY FLWS.
TO ½" ACROSS

EDGES ROLLED
UNDER

SEED WITH
SILKY TAIL
TO 3" LONG

CURL-LEAF MAHOGANY
(*Cercocarpus ledifolius*)

Mountain Mahogany

This is the only one of the mountain mahoganies in Washington although there are a number to the southward. They take their name from the hard, mahogany-colored wood. Because it is generally a much-branched shrub to 15' high it is described here as other shrubs, although technically it is a tree. Occasionally this mountain mahogany reaches to 20' high and forms a crooked squat tree with a trunk to 10" in diameter. Older twigs are marked by raised leaf scars. The trunk, measuring to 3" or 4" in diameter, is covered with irregular small greyish-brown scales. It is very spotty in occurrence and is usually found on dry open ridges as individuals or small groves.

The tiny leaves hardly clothe the limb framework. They vary from ½" - 1¼" long and have their margins tightly rolled over. The upper surface appears grooved because of the heavy midrib while beneath there is a fine mat of yellowish hairs.

From 1 - 4 hairy flowers form in the axils of the leaves and later change into spectacular seeds each carrying a silky tail to 3" long.

QUICK CHECK: Limited range and unmistakable rolled-over leaves.

RANGE: High open ridges of Blue Mountains.

WESTERN WAX MYRTLE
(*Myrica californica*)

Pacific Wax Myrtle
California Bayberry

Although classed as a tree, western wax myrtle as it occurs in Washington is generally shrub-like in form. Most frequently it is much-branched and not over 10' high. Its heavy foliage of dark green evergreen leaves sets it out from the dense Coastal shrubbery with which it is associated. Evergreen huckleberry is a common companion and somewhat similar in form.

Narrow leaves, slightly aromatic, average 2½" in length and have very small black spots on the undersurface. The long wedge-shaped base is characteristic of its close relative Sweet Gale. Teeth are shallow and well spaced.

Fruit forms in late summer as clusters of small round nuts. These are light gray in color from a waxy white covering over the purple berry-like nuts.

QUICK CHECK: Range is an important feature. Glossy evergreen leaves 2" - 4" long with long wedge-shaped base. Clusters of light grey berry-like nuts at base of leaves.

RANGE: Low hills and valley bottoms near the sea coast. Most abundant in southern region and particularly so along Oregon coast. Will grow in the open or in fairly heavy shade.

SHRUBS

KEY TO THE SHRUBS

Most keys are based on minute differences in flower or seed structure and may require in their use a fair knowledge of structural botany as well as several specimens showing these phases. Very often, a person finds shrubs without flower or seed and is at a loss for a clue. A simple method given here is the breaking of the shrubs into groupings by their general size and habitat. Besides the listings that follow a good deal of help can be obtained from "Nature's Calendar for Flowering Shrubs" page 192; the lists of the more common shrubs for each biotic zone, pages 7 - 13; and the altitudinal groupings, page 14.

ARMED SHRUBS

CREEPERS AND CLIMBERS

SHRUBS WITH EYE-CATCHING FEATURES

SHOWY FLOWERS

Broom (yellow)
Deer Brush (blue)
Elder (white)
Goats' Beard (white)
Hardhack (pink)
Mahonia (yellow)
Mock Orange (white)
Ninebark (white)
Ocean Spray (white)
Rabbitbrush (yellow)
Rhododendron (red)
Rhododendron (white)
Salmonberry (red)
Saskatoon Berry (white)
Shrubby Cinquefoil
   (yellow)
Snowbrush (white)
Thimbleberry (white)
Twin-flower (pink)

SHOWY BERRIES

Cranberry, high-bush (red)
Currant, Squaw (red)
Devil's Club (red)
Elder (red, blue, black)
Kinnikinnick (red)
Mahonia (blue-black)
Mountain Ash (red)
Red-osier Dogwood
   (dull white)
Rose, Wild (red)
Salmonberry
   (yellow to red)
Saskatoon Berry
   (blue to black)
Soopolallie (red)
Squashberry (red)
Thimbleberry (red)
Twinberry (red)
Waxberry (white)

UNUSUAL LEAVES

Azalea, False
   (white hairs)
Birch, Scrub
   (small, round)
Cinquefoil, Shrubby
   (3-7 fingers)
Golden Currant (3-lobed)
Labrador Tea
   (brown wool)
Mahonia (holly-like)
Ninebark (3-lobed)
Rhododendron, White
   (coppery hairs)
Soopolallie (brown rust)
Snowbrush (sticky)
Squashberry (3-lobed)

KEY TO THE SHRUBS

The following does not include the shrubs listed on page 57 as CREEPERS, CLIMBERS and ARMED SHRUBS. The groupings combine shrubs related in general form or growing together under similar conditions. The order of arrangement of the shrubs in this book follows as close as possible the divisions outlined on these facing pages.

UNDER 2' HIGH

EDIBLE BERRIES

	Page
Huckleberry, Dwarf	61
Huckleberry, Blue-leaved	61
Blueberry, Red Alpine	61
*Huckleberry, Black Mountain	89

SUB-ALPINE AND ALPINE

Heather, White, Moss	62
Heather, Red	62
Heather, Yellow	62
Crowberry	62

"SPIRAEA" LEAF

*Spirea, Flat-top	63
*Spirea, Mountain	63
*Spirea, Pyramidal	63

BOGS OR WET SLOPES

*Labrador Tea	76
*Labrador Tea, Mtn.	76
*Swamp-laurel	65

HAIRY RED BERRY

Teaberry, Mountain	70
Teaberry, Western	70

DRY INTERIOR ZONE

*Rabbitbush	93
*Tetradymia	93
*Pasture Wormwood	93
*Poison-Ivy	92

MISCELLANEOUS

*Dogbane, Spreading	74
*Cinquefoil, Shrubby	74
*Waxberry	75
*False Box	75

"HOLLY" LEAVES

*Mahonia (Oregon Grape)	73

*Usually over 1' high. Sometimes over 2'.

2' - 6' HIGH

LEAF WHORLS

	Page
Azalea, False	96
Copper Bush	96
Rhododendron, White	97
Rhododendron, Red	97

DRY INTERIOR REGION

†Antelope Bush	94
Sagebrush	94
Snowbrush	84
Ceanothus, Redstem	84
Soopolallie	85
Hop Sage	95
Currant, Squaw	86
†Sumac	86
Greasewood	95

SWAMPY GROUND

Hardhack	67
Sweet Gale	67
†Buckthorn, Alderleaf	68
†Birch, Scrub	68
†Dogwood, Red-osier	69

EDIBLE BERRIES

Huckleberry, Black Mtn.	89
Huckleberry, Tall Blue	89
Huckleberry, Red	90
Huckleberry, Evergreen	90

SHOWY FLOWERS

†Deer Brush	85
†Ocean Spray	87
†Mock Orange	87

† Often over 6' high.

2' - 6' HIGH

COAST

	Page
†Salal	79
†Indian-plum	79
†Hazel	80
Goats' Beard	80
†Thimbleberry	88
†Salmonberry	88
†Twinberry, Black	78
Currant, Red-flower	101
Currant, Sticky	101
Manzanita, Hairy	98
Gorse	98
Broom	98

MOUNTAIN SLOPES

Twinberry, Red	82
Honeysuckle, Blue Fly	82
Ninebark, Mallow	82
†Mountain Ash, Sitka	71
†Mountain Ash, Western	71
Squashberry	81
Cranberry, High-bush	81
Currant, Stink	100

† Often over 6' high.

OVER 6' HIGH

LARGE COMPOUND LEAF

Elder, Black-berry	72
Elder, Red-berry	72
Elder, Blue-berry	72

3-LOBED LEAF

Ninebark	69

HALF LEAF NOTCHED

Saskatoon Berry	83

DAMP GROUND

Dogwood, Red-osier	69
Dogwood, Western	69

Note: The following plants may be shrubby but usually are classed under Trees. Junipers, Dogwood, Sitka Alder, Hawthorn, Crab-apple and Cherries.

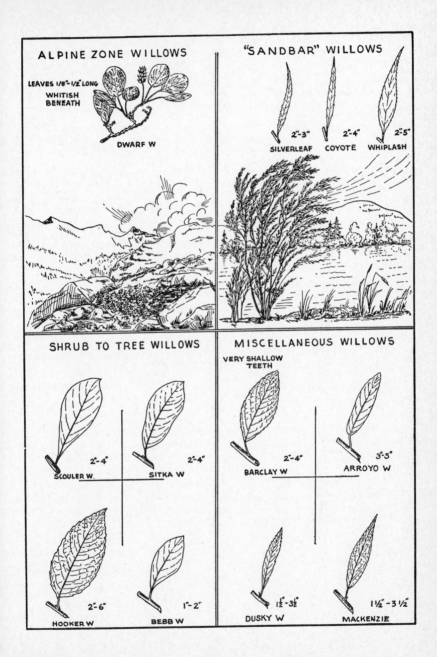

ALPINE ZONE WILLOWS

LEAVES 1/8"-1/2" LONG
WHITISH BENEATH

DWARF W

"SANDBAR" WILLOWS

2"-3"   2"-4"   2"-5"
SILVERLEAF COYOTE WHIPLASH

SHRUB TO TREE WILLOWS

2"-4"   2"-4"
SCOULER W.   SITKA W

2"-6"   1"-2"
HOOKER W   BEBB W

MISCELLANEOUS WILLOWS

VERY SHALLOW TEETH

2"-4"   3"-5"
BARCLAY W   ARROYO W

1½"-3½"   1½"-3½"
DUSKY W   MACKENZIE

(59)

WILLOWS
(Salix spp.)

Willows are one of the most familiar and widespread groups of shrubs in the State. Although most grow along creeks or rivers certain species are found high upon mountain slopes where they form a shrubby mat only a few inches high.

All willows like sunlight and seek open places. Their bark is exceptionally bitter. In spring and early summer each leaf stem has two shiny, false leaves growing at the base. Most willow leaves are long and graceful with smooth or slightly toothed edges. Winter buds have a single, hood-like scale. "Pussy willows" and white, fluffy catkins are very noticeable in the spring.

With thirty or more willows in Washington only a trained botanist can cope with their identification. This is because many species flower before the leaves appear; male and female flowers are on different shrubs; leaf and twig characteristics often vary greatly with age; and hybridization is common.

Two willows likely to reach tree size are Peachleaf Willow and Pacific Willow. They are described under TREES. The following is a selection of the more common and recognizable willows:

ALPINE WILLOWS
To 6" High, Shrubby, Mat-like

CASCADE W. (*S. cascadensis*)
Leaves 1/4"-3/4", glossy green. High Cascades, Mt. Rainier.

SNOW OR DWARF W. (*S. nivalis*)
Leaves 1/8"-1/2", silvery beneath. Olympics, High Cascades, Mt. Rainier.

ROCKY MTN. W. (*S. saximontana*)
Leaves 1/2"-1", strong vein network. Quite similar to Snow Willow and with same range.

SHRUBS TO SMALL TREES
Leaves Wide, Roundish

SCOULER W. (*S. scouleriana*)
Leaves 2"-4", 1/3 as wide, rounded or broad tip. Smooth on both sides. Sagebrush to Yellow Pine Zones, Olympics.

SITKA W. (*S. sitchensis*)
Leaves 2"-4" long, 1/3 as wide, rounded tip. Velvety with fine hairs beneath. Watercourses to middle elevations.

HOOKER W. (*S. hookeriana*)
Leaves 2"-6" long, 1/2 as wide, dull-pointed. Woolly hairs beneath. Wet or dry land, Coastal forests.

BEBB W. (*S. bebbiana*)
Leaves to 2" long, 1/2 as wide, round-pointed. Wet places, Sagebrush and Bunchgrass Zones.

"SAND BAR" WILLOWS
To 15' High, Slender Limbs, Narrow Leaves

SILVERLEAF W. (*S. argophylla*)
Leaves 2"-3", silvery with white hairs. Banks of Snake River and tributaries. Sagebrush and Bunchgrass Zones.

COYOTE W. (*S. exigua*)
Leaves 2"-4" long, 1/8"-1/4" wide. Silvery green. Range as above.

WHIPLASH W. (*S. caudata*)
Narrow leaves 2"-5" long, long tapering point. Green both sides. Fine teeth. Long brown "whips". Common along streams of Sagebrush and Bunchgrass Zones.

MISCELLANEOUS WILLOWS

BARCLAY W. (*S. barclayi*)
Variable leaves, 2"-4" long, ovalish, sharp-pointed, hairy above, bloom beneath. Sub-alpine. Mt. Rainier, Olympics.

DUSKY W. (*S. melanopsis*)
Shrub or small tree to 15' high. Leaves narrow, toothed near end. Stream edges of Sagebrush and Bunchgrass Zones.

ARROYO W. (*S. lasiolepsis*)
Bush or bushy tree to 30' high. Young leaves silky. Old leaves hairy beneath. Stream banks at low elevations of southeast Washington.

MACKENZIE W. (*S. mackenziana*)
Shrub or small tree. Leaves 1 1/2" - 3 1/2" long, sharp-pointed, rounded at base, "powdery" beneath. Stems hairy. Stream banks, Sagebrush and Bunchgrass Zones.

DWARF HUCKLEBERRY
(*Vaccinium caespitosum*)

Dwarf Bilberry — Dwarf Blueberry

Imagine a huckleberry bush only an inch high! Sometimes this dwarf bush is only this high but more often it is 4" - 8". The many thin round twigs carry a heavy mass of finely toothed leaves less than 1" long. The flowers are pinkish while the smallish solitary abundant berries are blue.

QUICK CHECK: A bushy shrub to 8" high. Leaves 1/4" - 1" long, widest above centre.

RANGE: Widespread throughout Wash. from sea level to alpine heights. Common on edges of swamps or in mountain meadows. Also on rocky ridges at high elevation.

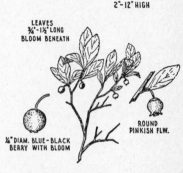

LEAVES 1/4"-1"

1"-8" HIGH

BLUE BERRY

4"-10" HIGH

BLUE-LEAVED HUCKLEBERRY
(*Vaccinium deliciosum*)

Delicious Blueberry

The rarified air of mountain meadows might account for the dwarf nature of this little huckleberry. Ranging from 2" - 1' in height the densely bushy shrub carries masses of toothed leaves from 3/4" - 1 1/2" long. These tend to have a whitish bloom beneath.

Single nodding flowers with stems as long as the flowers grow from the leaf axils. Pink to whitish flowers, almost spherical in form, are replaced by blue-black berries with a bloom.

QUICK CHECK: Alpine range. Small leaves with bloom beneath and single spherical flower.

RANGE: Sub-alpine and alpine meadows of Olympics and Cascade Mountains.

BOG BILBERRY (*V. occidentale*) to 2' high. Flower drooping, 1-2, berry black with bloom. Middle elevations on Cascade Mtns., Mt. Rainier.

LEAVES 1/2"-3/4"

FINELY HAIRY

BERRIES BLACK WITH BLUE BLOOM

2"-12" HIGH

LEAVES 3/4"-1 1/2" LONG BLOOM BENEATH

1/4" DIAM. BLUE-BLACK BERRY WITH BLOOM

ROUND PINKISH FLW.

RED ALPINE BLUEBERRY
(*Vaccinium scoparium*)

Grouseberry — Grouse Huckleberry

This, the smallest of the blueberries, may form a lacey green carpet 3" - 6" high over the dry gravelly forest soil. Very often it is the most abundant shrub over acres of ground. For some reason it is almost always found under lodgepole pine stands growing at elevations of 3,500' and up. There is a characteristic sour odor to these massed shrubs.

Each little bush is a network of kinky green twigs with oval leaves up to 1/2" long. The berries are from 1/8" - 1/4" in diameter, red and very pleasant to taste.

QUICK CHECK: Bushy little shrubs with green angled twigs and oval leaves less than 1/2" long. Small red berries. Grows under lodgepole pine.

RANGE: Generally above 3,500' elevations on easterly slope of Cascades. Wenatchee and Blue Mountains. Chinook Pass.

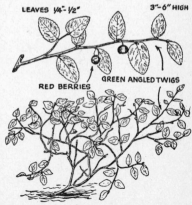

LEAVES 1/4"-1/2"

3"-6" HIGH

RED BERRIES

GREEN ANGLED TWIGS

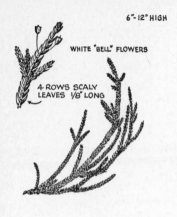

6"-12" HIGH

WHITE "BELL" FLOWERS

4-ROWS SCALY
LEAVES 1/8" LONG

WHITE MOSS HEATHER
(Cassiope mertensiana)

Once moss heather and heather are given a close look they never need be confused. Ordinary moss hasn't leaves and moss heather, for remembering purposes, hasn't them either. Actually the ridges of small scales are leaves but are pressed so closely that the twigs look like green pipe cleaners.

A common plant of sub-alpine and alpine areas it may grow in neat clumps several feet across and a foot high or in ragged sprawling masses over extensive areas of rock and ground. The small white flowers are bell-shaped and closely resemble those of yellow heather.

QUICK CHECK: A low matted plant with scales pressed to twigs. Small white bell flower.

RANGE: Sub-alpine and alpine heights of Cascades and Olympics.

ALASKA HEATH (*C. stellariana* or *Harrimanella stelleriana*) closely resembles the above except for grooves on the leaves. Sporadic occurrence as above. Mt. Rainier.

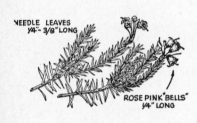

NEEDLE LEAVES
1/4"- 3/8" LONG

ROSE PINK "BELLS"
1/4" LONG

RED HEATHER
(Phyllodoce empetriformis)

A common low matted plant of the high mountains, sometimes almost the sole carpet for extensive alpine slopes. When in bloom it is topped with hundreds of rose-red "bell" blossoms —an ample reward in floral beauty for the mountain climber. The leaves are short and needle-like.

QUICK CHECK: A "heather" plant with short needle leaves. Rose-red flowers.

RANGE: Cascades and Olympics.

YELLOW HEATHER (*P. glanduliflora*) is very similar to the above except for the creamy flowers. Often the two mingle in a spreading mat with the contrast being shown in vivid fashion by the different blooms. The range is the same.

THICK SHINY LEAVES
1/8"-1/2" LONG

2"-6" HIGH

SMOOTH, BLACK BERRY

CROWBERRY
(Empetrum nigrum)

Crowberry differs from heather in having a number of small purplish flowers or round berries as black as a crow. Whereas the heathers usually grow in dry exposed places near timberline or above it, crowberry seeks shady places beneath the trees. Its leaves are about 1/4" long, thick and needle-like.

QUICK CHECK: Thick short "needle" leaves. Flowers, small, purple. Berries smooth and black.

RANGE: Moist shaded Cascade Mountains above 3,000' and extending to timberline. Sea coast to alpine slopes of Olympics.

FLAT-TOP SPIREA
(*Spiraea lucida*)

White Meadow Sweet — Birch-Leaf Spirea

This is a low spirea not over 2' high and very common throughout the drier, more open forests. The stem is slender and often has several branches. The leaves are rounded like a birch leaf and coarsely toothed along the upper two-thirds. Not all the shrubs bloom but those that do are capped with a dense flat-topped crown of small white flowers. Common associates are Douglas fir, larch, lodgepole pine, soopolallie and kinnikinnick.

QUICK CHECK: A low shrub with rounded spirea leaf. Flat white flower head on some. Don't confuse with scrubby Saskatoon berry.

RANGE: Mostly east of the Cascades in dry open mountain forests. Bunchgrass and Yellow Pine Zones. Vancouver, Wenatchee, Chelan, Pullman.

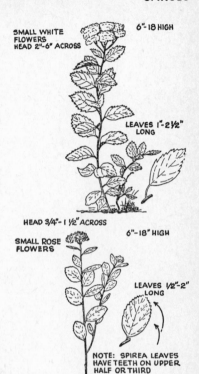

SMALL WHITE FLOWERS HEAD 2"-6" ACROSS

6"-18 HIGH

LEAVES 1"-2½" LONG

MOUNTAIN SPIREA
(*Spiraea densiflora*)

Pink Meadow Sweet — Sub-alpine Spirea

As the various names suggest this species is one of high mountain slopes. It is a typical spirea with a slender stem rarely over 2' high, very leafy with oval leaves to 2" long. The tiny pink flowers are massed in small heads ¾" - 1½" across. Although flowers are comparatively small in size, the color is so rich as to quickly catch the eye. Blooming time is early to mid-summer. Sub-alpine meadows throughout Washington are home to this trim little shrub. Olympics, Cascades, and Blue Mountains.

HEAD ¾"- 1½" ACROSS

SMALL ROSE FLOWERS

6"-18" HIGH

LEAVES ½"-2" LONG

NOTE: SPIREA LEAVES HAVE TEETH ON UPPER HALF OR THIRD

PYRAMIDAL SPIREA
(*Spiraea pyramidata*)

The 1" - 4" long pyramidal head of white or pinkish flowers and large leaves irregularly toothed on the top two-thirds will identify this shrub. Although not of common occurrence it is widely distributed east of the Cascades in the Yellow Pine Forest Zone. Ellensburg, Peshastin, Yakima, Kittitas County.

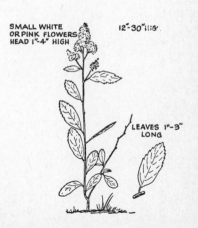

SMALL WHITE OR PINK FLOWERS HEAD 1"-4" HIGH

12"-30" HIGH

LEAVES 1"-3" LONG

(63)

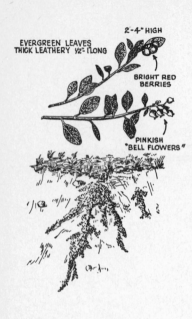

EVERGREEN LEAVES
THICK LEATHERY ½" LONG

2"-4" HIGH

BRIGHT RED
BERRIES

PINKISH
"BELL FLOWERS"

KINNIKINNICK
(*Arctostaphylos Uva-ursi*)

Bearberry

Kinnikinnick is one of the more common and widely distributed evergreen shrubs in the drier forests. Although small of leaf and trailing in habit it is brought to the attention by the bright red berries dotted among the glossy green leaves. These are very prominent from August to late winter and favored by grouse and bear.

Kinnikinnick may form a low green mat or extend exploring arms over rotten logs, rocks, or down the face of road cuts. The small evergreen leaves are leathery and grow alternately. The larger stems have reddish bark. Flowers are small, pinkish and bell-shaped.

The popular name kinnikinnick is an Indian word meaning a smoking mixture. Although the leaves of this plant were only one of the ingredients, the shrub has taken on this name.

QUICK CHECK: A trailing plant with ½" - 1" long, alternate, evergreen leaves. Bell-shaped pink flowers or mealy red berries.

RANGE: On exposed, well-drained soils from Coastal to sub-alpine levels and in Yellow Pine Zone.

PINEMAT MANZANITA (*A. nevadensis*) has leaves to ½" long with abrupt pointed tips. Rocky places in Cascade Mountains at middle elevation.

TWIN-FLOWER
(*Linnaea borealis*)

Twin-flower is so dainty and gay with flowers during summer months that it may be thought of as a flower although the woody vine brings it within the shrub grouping. A person won't go far into shady cool woods without seeing the thin spreading vines, perhaps 3' - 4' long, crawling over the forest floor. The little evergreen leaves are less than ½" long and almost round. Notice the several well-separated nicks or teeth along the upper half of the leaves. This feature will clear up any identification trouble.

In June and July numerous slender flower stems shoot up 2" - 4" from the vine. Each stem carries a pair of pink "twin" flowers so delicately scented their fragrance won't soon be forgotten. Linnaeus, the famous Swedish botanist and founder of the present system of botanical classification chose the twin-flower as his favorite plant.

QUICK CHECK: Slender vine with alternate, oval to round, evergreen leaves with few minute teeth on upper half. Pink "twin" flowers.

RANGE: Cool moist coniferous woods throughout Washington. From sea-level to timberline.

L. borealis longifolia has flowers about a third longer than the above.

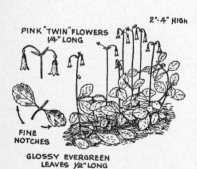

PINK "TWIN" FLOWERS
¼" LONG

2"-4" HIGH

FINE
NOTCHES

GLOSSY EVERGREEN
LEAVES ½" LONG

CRANBERRY
(*Vaccinium Oxycoccus intermedium*)

Although belonging to the blueberry family, this cranberry bears little resemblance to any of them. It is found in peaty, mossy bogs and consists of a very thin vine perhaps 4′ long and almost hidden in the moss. From the slender stem tiny evergreen leaves branch out. Often a hunt must be made to find one of its pink flowers or a berry which changes in color from white to red. Labrador tea and swamp laurel often hide this dainty cranberry from view.

Cranberries were much sought after by the first pioneers in America. They called them crane berries because of the fanciful resemblance of the flower to the head and neck of a crane.

QUICK CHECK: Very slender vine growing in bogs. Leaves alternate, sharp-pointed, evergreen and almost stemless. Flowers pink and berry white or red. Cloudberry which also grows in damp places has bristly hairs on the leaf.

RANGE: Boggy situations in the Coastal Forest Zone. Vicinity of Seattle and Tacoma.

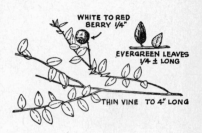

WHITE TO RED BERRY 1/4″

EVERGREEN LEAVES 1/4 ± LONG

THIN VINE TO 4″ LONG

SWAMP-LAUREL
(*Kalmia polifolia*)

American Laurel — Alpine Kalmia — Bog Kalmia

Watch for this dainty shrub if you are crossing a bog. The thin, twisting stems up to 2′ high and small, narrow leaves easily lose their identity in the thicker tangle of Labrador tea. Of course, if it is displaying its beautiful reddish-purple blossoms you will find it very quickly. The thick, leathery leaves look much like Labrador tea from above but are less than 1″ long, have their edges strongly rolled over, and a velvety whiteness beneath rather than the brownish wool.

The star-shaped flowers are worth examining for on some the anthers will be bent back and held by their tips in pits in the petals. Should an insect disturb these the elastic stalk will whip the anther up and spray the disturber with pollen.

QUICK CHECK: A bog shrub; pointed, tough leaves to 1″ long, edges rolled under, velvety white beneath. Pink, star flowers.

RANGE: Boggy situations and often occurring with Labrador Tea. Most common in lowlands of Coastal Forest Zone.

ALPINE SWAMP-LAUREL (*K. polifolia microphylla*) A miniature edition of the above growing in wet meadows at sub-alpine elevations. Flowers may be only 1/2″ above the moss. Leaves are from 1/4″-1/2″ long. Most frequent in Cascade Mountains.

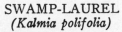

LEAVES TO 1″ LONG

ROSE FLOWERS 1/2″ ACROSS

(65)

TRAILING RUBUS
(*Rubus pedatus*)

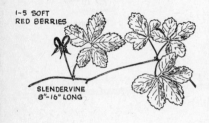

1-5 SOFT
RED BERRIES

SLENDERVINE
8"-16" LONG

This tiny trailing plant hiding under false azalea, white rhododendron and huckleberry bushes on the higher mountain slopes could be regarded as one of the more obscure shrubs in the State. However its relative abundance under certain conditions, the display of symmetrical leaves against a mossy background, and the tiny red jewel-like berries all contribute in enhancing its appearance.

The wire-thin woody vine may be 8" - 16" long. At intervals an unusual leaf branches off. It has 3 rounded leaflets, 2 of which may be so deeply lobed as to look like 5 complete leaflets. The small white raspberry-like flowers grow singly and are replaced by several clear red berries.

QUICK CHECK: Slender vine with rounded "leaflet" leaf about 1" across. One to several clear red berries.

RANGE: Shady mossy places in sub-alpine elevations of Cascade and Olympic Mountains.

PURPLE HONEYSUCKLE
(*Lonicera hispidula*)

Hairy Honeysuckle

This is one of the group of honeysuckles that either climbs or creeps rather than forming an erect woody shrub. Its slender twining stems seldom get far off the ground although they may extend to a length of 10' or more.

Often several pairs of the upper leaves are joined at the base while those lower on the stem may be heart-shaped and have little "ears" at the base of their stems. Most leaves aren't over 2" long and while slightly hairy above have a thin white bloom beneath.

Flowers are clustered on several stems at the top of the branchlets. Each cluster carries from 2 - 6 purplish-red trumpets with a yellowish tinge inside. Each trumpet is from 1/2" - 3/4" long and the stamens and style protrude very noticeably. The berries are red.

QUICK CHECK: A creeper or climber with joined upper leaves. Purplish-red flowers with long extended stamens and style.

RANGE: Open woods and dry situations along Coastal region.

PURPLISH-RED
FLWS. 1/2-3/4 LONG

UPPER LEAVES
JOINED

STAMENS
& STYLE
PROTRUDING

WHITISH BLOOM

"EARS"

HARDHACK
(*Spiraea douglasii*)

Steeple Bush — Douglas Spirea

Hardhack usually masses in dense clumps around wet places and is crowned with such a showy display of fluffy pink plumes that it can't help but be noticed. Its slender reddish-brown stems some 3' - 4' high show up like a miniature forest during winter months. At this time the pyramidal brownish husks are very noticeable and possibly give rise to the common name. In summer the twigs are covered by narrow oblong leaves with coarse notches on the top half. The coarse teeth on the upper part of the leaf are characteristic of the spireas. Hairy twigs and leaves hairy beneath are features of hardhack which always favors open places where there is plenty of light.

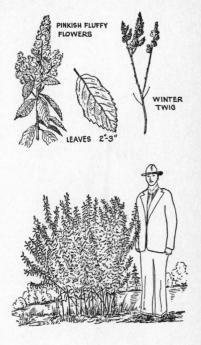

PINKISH FLUFFY FLOWERS

WINTER TWIG

LEAVES 2"-3"

QUICK CHECK: In winter, thin reddish-brown stems with dry pyramidal husk. In summer, upright pink plumes of tiny flowers. Spirea leaf toothed on upper half, woolly beneath.

RANGE: Margins of ponds and meadows at low elevations throughout Coastal Forest Zone. Mountains of Stevens County.

MENZIES SPIREA (*S. menziesii*) has smooth leaves. It is less common than the above.

SWEET GALE
(*Myrica Gale*)

There is a good possibility that sweet gale will never be noticed unless a special effort is made to find it. Because it prefers a moist humid climate and a damp habitat, sweet gale is found along swamps and lake margins on Gulf Islands and at low elevations along the Mainland. It closely resembles hardhack in form and often loses its identity with the showier shrub.

The slender reddish stems grow up to 4' high. The thin wedge-like leaves, ½" - 2" long, are coarsely notched along their upper third and have a whitish tinge on the undersurface. Before the leaves appear, clumps of greenish catkins form along the ends of the branches. These later change to brown, cone-like husks.

FORM AS ABOVE

GREENISH CATKINS

LEAVES ½"- 2" LONG

QUICK CHECK: See habitat limitations. Unmistakable catkins and "cone" seeds.

RANGE: Margins of ponds, bogs and lakes in Coastal and Mountain Forest Zones. Ocean City, Lake Quinault.

ALDERLEAF BUCKTHORN
(*Rhamnus alnifolia*)

Buckthorn

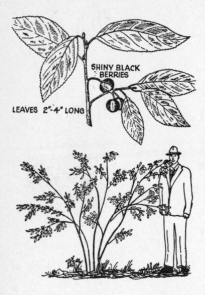

SHINY BLACK BERRIES

LEAVES 2"-4" LONG

Alderleaf buckthorn hasn't thorns and probably takes the buckthorn part of its name from related species to the south. It is a shrub that one might look for in vain unless knowing that it is confined to marshy places like wet meadows. Here where it grows with scrub birch, red-osier dogwood and twin-flower, it may be quite plentiful.

Most shrubs aren't over 5' high and have a loose limb structure something like red-osier dogwood. The symmetrical, 2"-4" long, dark green leaves with their fine teeth may be noticed before the small greenish flowers or scattered black berries. These plump three-seeded berries usually grow singly and, although juicy, are very bitter.

QUICK CHECK: Marsh habitat. Distinctive symmetrical leaf heavily veined beneath. Small greenish flowers or single black berries in axils of the leaves.

RANGE: Very limited in range to wet brushy places in eastern Washington. Yellow Pine and Mountain Forest Zones.

SCRUB BIRCH
(*Betula glandulosa*)

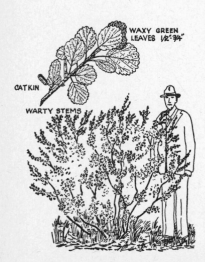

WAXY GREEN LEAVES 1/2"-3/4"

CATKIN

WARTY STEMS

"Any resemblance to any birch living or dead is purely co-incidental" might be the descriptive theme for scrub birch. True enough the smooth bark with dull white markings bears some similarity to water birch and there are birch catkins. However, its leaves catch the attention more than anything else for they are almost round and no larger than 10c or 25c coins. Heavy veins give them a ribbed look and add to the thick leathery texture. They turn coppery red in the fall.

Scrub birch brings a picture of wet meadows and swamps sometimes covered almost completely by this shrub. It seldom grows as a lone individual. From the rather compact base a dozen or more crooked branches raise and spread outward to form a loose sprawling top.

The slim brown catkins less than 1" long give a colorful touch in late fall to an otherwise drab shrub. Labrador tea and buckthorn often keep it company.

QUICK CHECK: A limby shrub of swamps and low grounds. Leaves thick and round, up to 1" across. Twigs rough and sticky.

RANGE: Sporadic occurrence in Coastal Zone and edges of Mountain Forest Zone. Also in Klickitat County in Yellow Pine Forest Zone.

RED-OSIER DOGWOOD
(*Cornus stolonifera*)

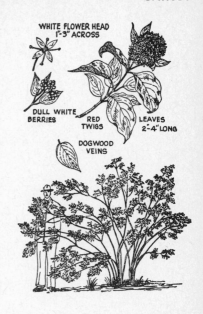

WHITE FLOWER HEAD 1"-3" ACROSS

DULL WHITE BERRIES

RED TWIGS

LEAVES 2"-4" LONG

DOGWOOD VEINS

Red-osier dogwood has three eye-catching features. In winter and spring the shiny, bright red bark of the thin stems and symmetrically arranged branches provides welcome color. During June the round heads of dainty flowers are startlingly white against the rich green background of leaves. The graceful vein network of the leaves, characteristic of dogwoods, is the third point.

Usually the red-osier dogwood is massed with other shrubs and trees and so in the summer almost loses its identity in the floral picture. In August it attracts attention by the unusual lead-white color of its berries. Look for this attractive shrub in the Interior along shady creek courses or damp lowlands and mixed with poplar, water birch and willow. Fall weather brings a reddish tint to some of the leaves similar to those of dogwood.

QUICK CHECK: In winter red twig ends and characteristic branching. In summer, "dogwood" leaf.

RANGE: Widespread east of the Cascade Mountains. Found from valley bottom to near timberline.

WESTERN DOGWOOD (*C. occidentalis*) so closely resembles the above that the name red-osier dogwood is generally used for both. However this shrub has leaves with hairs on the underside. It is most abundant west of the Cascades.

NINEBARK
(*Physocarpus capitatus*)

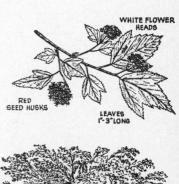

WHITE FLOWER HEADS

RED SEED HUSKS

LEAVES 1"-3" LONG

Ninebarks receive their name from the supposedly nine thin layers of shreddy bark on the main stems. In Coastal regions ninebark is a rather dense upright shrub 6'-12' high with long arching branches. Usually it is well scattered and growing with thimbleberry, red-osier dogwood, and other damp-ground shrubs.

The eye-catching, 3-lobed leaves which are quite similar to squashberry, often bring ninebark to notice. During May and into June it is artistically dappled with white rounded balls formed by masses of tiny flowers. By July 15 these have made a startling change to a reddish clump of rough seed husks. The color lasts until August when the seeds are ripe. Mallow ninebark is a small shrub of the Interior. See page 82.

QUICK CHECK: 3-lobed, deeply veined, alternate leaves with fine hairs on undersurface. Shreddy loose bark.

RANGE: Damp places Coastal region and in upper edge of Yellow Pine Zone. Blue Mountains.

SHREDDING BARK

SHRUBS

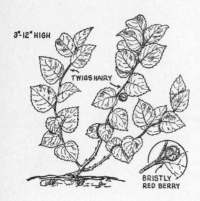

3"-12" HIGH

TWIGS HAIRY

BRISTLY
RED BERRY

WESTERN TEABERRY
(Gaultheria ovalifolia)

Bush Wintergreen — Oregon Wintergreen

It requires more than casual observation to find this small sprawling shrub. Even its red berries pass unnoticed for they are hidden beneath the trim little leaves. Western teaberry is a shallow-rooted plant with several thin kinky branches reddish in color. The heart-shaped leaves from ½" - 1½" long are artistically arranged in alternate fashion on the hairy twigs. The leaves are minutely toothed and shiny waxy green above but dull beneath. The small white flowers grow singly while the bright red berries are quite unusual being grooved into segments and covered with fine hairs. They are edible.

A preference is shown for dry semi-open forest land above 2,000' elevation in the Coastal Forest Zone with a similar habitat east of the Cascades. Lodgepole pine, white pine and Douglas fir with a sparse undergrowth of false box and twin-flower make a common setting for western teaberry.

QUICK CHECK: Low shrub less than 12" high. Alternate glossy green, heart-shaped leaves on hairy red twigs. Single red berries.

RANGE: Locally abundant in suitable habitat but one of less frequently encountered shrubs. Olympics and Cascade Mountains above 2,000' and up to 6,000'. Mt. Rainier, Mt. Adams.

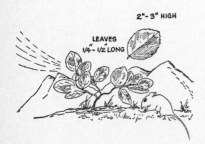

2"-3" HIGH

LEAVES
¼" - ½" LONG

MOUNTAIN TEABERRY
(Gaultheria humifusa)

Western Wintergreen

This miniature edition of the above usually is found in damp locations at sub-alpine and alpine elevations. It seldom reaches 3" in height. The small leaves from ¼" - ½" long are rounded and very finely toothed. Flowers and fruit are similar to western teaberry.

QUICK CHECK: Note range limitation. Low shrub 1" - 3" high with several short crooked stems. Alternate rounded leaves finely toothed. Red berry.

RANGE: A near timberline plant in the Cascade and Olympic Mountains. Mt. Rainier, Mt. Angeles.

SITKA MOUNTAIN ASH
(Sorbus sitchensis)

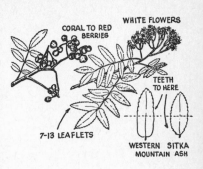

CORAL TO RED BERRIES

WHITE FLOWERS

TEETH TO HERE

7-13 LEAFLETS

WESTERN SITKA MOUNTAIN ASH

The use of mountain ash as an ornamental tree makes most people familiar with the tree form. The large bunches of red berries which hang on after the leaves have fallen distinguish this tree or shrub from any other.

Along the Coast, trees up to 20' high will be noticed. These are one of the two native mountain ash and only here do they attain a definite tree size. Otherwise they are shrubby growths of the higher mountains.

Sitka mountain ash is the most common and comes into fair abundance on high mountain slopes where the trees begin to thin out—approximately 3,000' at the Coast, 4,000' in the Interior. Sometimes there are only several thin stems up to 8' high with a sparse display of leaves and berries near the top. Under more favorable conditions a brushy thicket is found. In either case an open spot is chosen such as the edge of a meadow or rockslide. The compound leaf has 9 - 13 leaflets which carry coarse teeth almost to the base. Flowers are small, white, and carried in flat-topped clusters 2" - 4" across. These masses of blooms are quite prominent in the high mountains during June. The berries are bright red and suitable for making jelly although having a sour mealy taste when raw.

September sees them at their peak but some hang on until October. Migrating birds sometimes pick off astounding quantities of the berries.

QUICK CHECK: Compound leaf with 9 - 13 leaflets toothed to near base. Flower clusters 2" - 4" across. Berries coral-red.

RANGE: Most abundant above 3,500' on Cascade Mountains. General throughout in the Mountain and Sub-Alpine Zones. Spotty in the Olympics and Blue Mountains.

WESTERN MOUNTAIN ASH (*S. occidentalis*) is very similar to the above but has 7 - 11 bluish-green leaflets with serrations near the tip only. The flower clusters are usually less than 2" across. The berries have a purplish rather than a coral tinge. The two species occasionally grow together. Western mountain ash is more apt to be found on the west slopes of the Cascade Mountains although it has been recorded on the east side. Quite common in Olympics. Mt. Rainier, Mt. Adams, Stevens Pass.

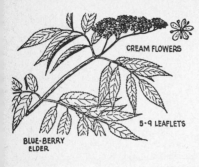

BLUE-BERRY ELDER

CREAM FLOWERS

5-9 LEAFLETS

BLUE-BERRY ELDER
(Sambucus glauca)

The names of the elders show that they may be distinguished by their berries. Otherwise the individual habitats, ranges and time of blooming can be definite helps. All elders have a large soft pith.

Blue-berry elder partly overlaps red-berry elder in range but grows on dry open situations. Leaflets are generally in nines although fives and sevens often occur. The flower head is white, flat and from 5" - 8" across. This one blooms through the summer and may continue into late August. The berries, in flat-topped clusters, are tinged with a lighter bluish-bloom.

QUICK CHECK: Large flat-topped blooms in June, July and August. Masses of small blue berries August and September.

RANGE: Dry places and low elevations along Coastal region and Olympics. Most abundant in dry localities of eastern Washington. Vicinity creeks in Sagebrush, Bunchgrass, and Yellow Pine Zones.

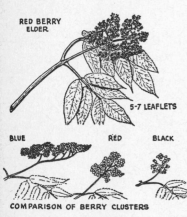

RED BERRY ELDER

5-7 LEAFLETS

BLUE   RED   BLACK

COMPARISON OF BERRY CLUSTERS

RED-BERRY ELDER
(Sambucus callicarpa)

Red-berry elder is a common shrub along the Coast and in the wetter regions of the Interior, where it raises a spreading mass of stout stems 10' - 20' into the air. The leaves are opposite and formed of 5 - 7 toothed, sharp-pointed leaflets. Vigorous young shoots sometimes have 9 leaflets. The small yellowish-white flowers in their rounded head are in bloom throughout May. The smooth berries tinge with red in early June. They are not edible and even reputed to have poisonous properties.

QUICK CHECK: Compound leaf with 2" - 5" long, toothed, pointed leaflets. Yellowish-white flowers in rounded or pyramidal head. Berries bright red.

RANGE: Coastal Forest and both slopes of Cascade Mountains below 3,000'.

RED BERRY ELDER

BLACK-BERRY ELDER
(Sambucus melanocarpa)

Black-berry elder is seldom over 8' high. It has the typical ascending spread and similarity in leaf and bark. Confusion can usually be avoided by noting the high mountain range limitation. The flower cluster differs from the red-berry elder in being more rounded and looser.

QUICK CHECK: Loose flower head. Shiny black berries. Leaflets 5 - 7.

RANGE: Mostly on eastern slopes of the Cascades from 3,000' to timberline. Blue Mountains. Mountain Forest Zone.

MAHONIA
(Mahonia spp.)
(Berberis spp.)

Oregon Grape — Holly Grape

Mahonia or Oregon grape is immediately distinguished by its evergreen, "holly"-like leaflets for no other shrub in the State bears any resemblance to it. There may be considerable variation between two of the three species but the main characteristics, "holly" leaf, bright yellow flowers, or waxy blue berries are standard features.

OREGON GRAPE (*M. nervosa*): Has leaflets dull both sides, 11 - 21 per leaf. Three central veins. Prefers forest shade. It displays little variation in shape being under 2' high with several fern-like sprays of leaflets. Generally confined to lower elevations in Coastal forests.

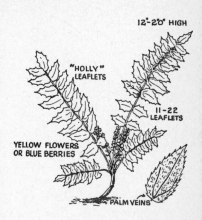

TALL MAHONIA (*M. aquifolium*): Has leaflets shiny both sides, 5 - 11 per leaf. Main central vein. Favors exposed situations like road edges and stony clearings. This species is the one most commonly noticed. Sometimes thick, irregular stems reach 3' - 5' in height but more often a low sprawling shrub is found. Bright yellow flowers are prominent in clusters along the stem during May 15 - June 15. Dark blue berries with whitish bloom are well formed by August 15 and hang on until late fall. They make good jelly when dead ripe or touched with frost. Indians used the bright yellow wood in making a yellow dye. The attactive foliage, flowers, and berries together with the brilliant autumn coloring make it a desirable ornamental. This is the State flower of Oregon. Wide distribution through Washington on exposed situations with poor rocky soils. Tonasket, Republic, Spokane, Chelan, Wenatchee Mountains, White Salmon, Tacoma.

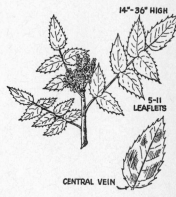

CREEPING MAHONIA (*M. repens*): Has leaflets dull beneath, 2 - 7 per leaf. Main central vein. Very similar to *M. aquifolium* but less than 1' high. The spines are thinner and weaker. The underside of the leaflets has a whitish tinge. Widely scattered throughout Washington on dry places to 5,000' elevation. Bunchgrass and Yellow Pine Forest Zones. Ellensburg, Wenatchee, Spokane, Pullman.

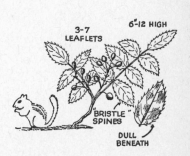

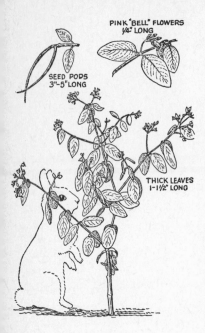

PINK "BELL" FLOWERS
1/4" LONG

SEED PODS
3"-5"LONG

THICK LEAVES
1-1½" LONG

SPREADING DOGBANE
(*Apocynum androsaemifolium*)

The dogbanes send up new stems each year but look so much like shrubs with their fibrous branching stems up to 16" high that they are so treated here. The name results from an unfounded superstition that dogs were repelled by this plant.

If the smooth reddish stem is broken a sticky, milky juice appears as with sumac. The dry exposed habitat along road edges and the prolonged blooming of the end clusters of small, pinkish, bell blossoms help in giving it individuality.

The rather thick, egg-shaped leaves are sharp-pointed and opposite. The fragrant flowers are in bloom from May to July due to the successive development of new clusters. Bees produce a very fine grade of honey from these. The seed pods are an amazing affair being shaped like a smooth, curved green bean 3" - 5" long. This brownish husk splits open to allow silky seeds to escape.

QUICK CHECK: A low 2 or 3-branched shrub with opposite, thickish leaves. Milky juice exudes from broken stems.

RANGE: Patchy distribution on dry exposed soils throughout Wash. From sea level to 3,000' in the Cascade Mountains.

INDIAN HEMP (*A. cannabinum*) is a big brother to the above being up to 3' in height. The flowers differ in being greenish and slightly smaller than the above. The stems of Indian hemp were once picked in the fall by the Indians, shredded and woven into fishing lines and small ropes. Throughout eastern Washington in Sagebrush, Bunchgrass, and Yellow Pine Zones.

Four other species or varieties have minor differences not likely to be noticed by the amateur botanist.

VELVETY LEAVES
3-7 FINGERS

YELLOW FLOWER
3/4" ACROSS

SHRUBBY CINQUEFOIL
(*Potentilla fruticosa*)

Being abundant only in certain localities or under favorable conditions, shrubby cinquefoil is a common plant to many but a total stranger to others... It is a fine-limbed, sprawling shrub up to 2' high with velvety, "3 - 7 fingered" leaves and bright yellow, "buttercup" flowers.

QUICK CHECK: Velvety "3 - 7 finger" leaves and "buttercup" flowers.

RANGE: Cascade and Olympic Mountains. Exposed places from sub-alpine to alpine elevations. Mt. Angeles, Mt. Rainier.

WAXBERRY
(*Symphoricarpus albus*)
Snowberry

Everyone will remember waxberry (often called snowberry) for its clumps of waxy, white berries during early winter months. Even after leaves and berries have fallen the thin twigs branching opposite to one another, provide identification.

Waxberry is one of the most widespread shrubs in Washington. Once started it widens its hold until a low bushy thicket 2' - 3' in height is formed.

The opposite leaves, thin and without teeth are roughly oval in shape and on some plants are irregularly lobed. They show a fine hair on the undersurface. The pinkish, bell flowers are usually clustered near the end of the twigs and in all stages of growth from bud to berry during June and July. The clusters of white, soft berries, irregular in shape and waxy to the touch, don't appear to be sought after by bird or rodent.

QUICK CHECK: A slender-stemmed shrub less than 3' high, locally abundant. Thin, opposite leaves, hairy beneath. Clumps of pinkish, bell flowers or white, waxy berries.

RANGE: Wide range of habitat but not in extreme shade. Throughout Washington but usually limited to approximately 2,000' in Coastal forests and 4,000' in eastern Washington.

WOLFBERRY (*S. occidentalis*) has leaves usually not hairy beneath. Stamen and styles are longer than petals. Sporadic occurrence.

Other closely related species may be trailing and have leaves finely hairy on both surfaces.

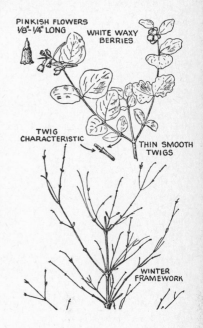

PINKISH FLOWERS 1/8"- 1/4" LONG

WHITE WAXY BERRIES

TWIG CHARACTERISTIC

THIN SMOOTH TWIGS

WINTER FRAMEWORK

FALSE BOX
(*Pachystima myrsinites*)
Mountain Lover — Myrtle Box Leaf

Although lacking in conspicuous flowers or leaves, false box makes up for these shortcomings by its abundance in certain forest regions. It is a characteristic evergreen plant of Douglas fir, lodgepole pine or Engelmann spruce forests. In the shade it grows loose and sprawling but rarely reaches a height of 2'. On rocky slopes it forms attractive compact balls of greenery. The opposite, thick, evergreen leaves are comparatively small, 1/4" - 1" long, and grow on thin, angled branches.

The small flower clusters are an inconspicuous greenish or reddish color and usually go unnoticed cradled between branch and leaf stem.

QUICK CHECK: Small, opposite, evergreen leaves on thin, angled twigs. Comparatively abundant in its range.

RANGE: Widespread throughout Washington in damper coniferous forests from sea level to timberline. Coastal, Mountain, Sub-Alpine Zones. Spotty in Yellow Pine Zones.

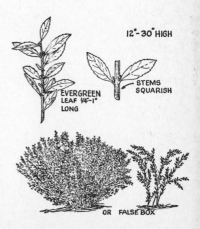

12"- 30" HIGH

EVERGREEN LEAF 1/4"-1" LONG

STEMS SQUARISH

OR FALSE BOX

(75)

LABRADOR TEA
(*Ledum groenlandicum*)

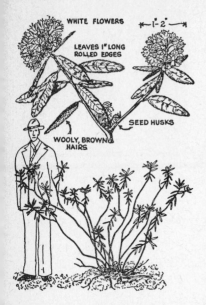

WHITE FLOWERS

← 1'-2" →

LEAVES 1" LONG
ROLLED EDGES

SEED HUSKS

WOOLY, BROWN
HAIRS

Labrador tea is widely distributed across Canada and the United States. Eastern Indian tribes used it for making a tea and this practice was copied by early explorers and settlers. There is little record of this use in the West. The leaves are picked and left to dry before being crushed and steeped like tea.

Found generally on mossy, spongy bogs it sometimes occurs on wet, rocky sidehills at high elevations. Its thin, twisting stems, seldom over 3' high, and thick, narrow leaves with their woolly mat of reddish hairs on the undersurface are quite distinctive. This wool and the rolled-over edges of the evergreen, leathery leaves are Nature's way of preventing the loss of water from the underside of the leaves. Although Labrador tea usually grows in a bog the water is so cold that the plant may be unable to absorb much and so adopts a highly specialized leaf to conserve it. The leaves are grouped to give a rough whorl effect.

During June and July, depending on altitude, the twisted little shrub raises a showy head of white, star-like blossoms. These are replaced by clusters of dry husks that often hang on until the following spring. Common associates are swamp laurel, scrub birch and willow.

QUICK CHECK: Thick rusty wool on underside of leaves.

RANGE: Bogs in Coastal and Mountain Forest Zones. Sometimes at higher elevations. Vicinity Seattle and Tacoma. Humptulips, Mt. Rainier.

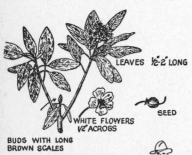

LEAVES ½-2" LONG

WHITE FLOWERS
½" ACROSS

SEED

BUDS WITH LONG
BROWN SCALES

MOUNTAIN LABRADOR TEA
(*Ledum glandulosum*)

Although slightly larger than the former, this shrub is quite similar in the crooked branching, white flowers, and leaf-whorl characteristics. It lacks the reddish wool beneath the leaves and grows on shady, damp mountain sides where it often forms a brushy tangle. The leaves are deciduous.

QUICK CHECK: Leaf whorls and slightly rolled over edges.

RANGE: Most abundant east of the Cascades on moist mountain slopes. Found up to 5,000' and associated with swamp gooseberry and Engelmann spruce.

WHITE CLEMATIS
(Clematis ligusticifolia)

Travellers' Joy

Travellers' Joy is an apt descriptive name for this vigorous climber which so artistically decorates the landscape throughout the drier parts of the State. It often chooses fences to climb on but when these are not convenient a tree or shrub becomes the support. The slender vines may reach 40' in length and bunch to form mat-like festoons. In spring these owe their beauty to the numerous clusters of small white flowers which are gradually replaced by soft fluffy masses of silver fleece. New shoots with their flower bunches prolong the blooming season from the middle of June to the middle of August, when both flowers and fleece decorate the same vine. The fluffy seed masses last until late October or possibly over winter.

This white clematis chooses the tree-fringed valleys of the Sagebrush, Bunchgrass, and Yellow Pine Zones for its home. Most vines contrive to get their roots into fair soil such as waste places along the edge of farms. Ponderosa pine, black cottonwood and choke cherry, usually grow in the vicinity.

QUICK CHECK: A vigorous climber with leaflets in threes, clusters of small white flowers or white fluffy masses of seeds.

RANGE: Republic, Wenatchee, Spokane, Pullman, Yakima, Pomeroy, Dayton, Pasco.

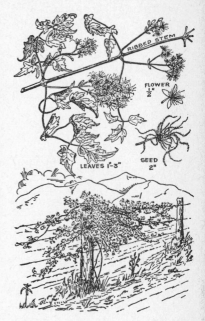

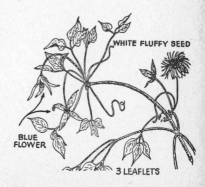

BLUE CLEMATIS
(Clematis columbiana)

Virgins' Bower

Blue clematis is a rather uncommon shrub. Its slender twining form is all but lost on the bushes upon which it climbs. Were it not for the large, showy, blue flowers or white, fluffy seeds it might never be noticed by the casual observer. The shoots branch from the main stems in very symmetrical fashion and carry the tendrils by which it clings to its support. Leaflets are in threes. Unlike the sturdy, white-flowering clematis, this one only raises a few feet into the air. The flowers, set off by a yellow centre, may be 2" - 4" across. Seeds are white and fluffy like miniature dust mops.

QUICK CHECK: A short, slender climber with large blue flowers or fluffy, white "dust mop" seeds.

RANGE: Wide altitudinal range in shady mountain slopes or valley bottoms east of the Cascades. Upper edge of the Yellow Pine Forest Zone, and extending into the Mountain Forest Zone. Spokane, Mt. Carlton.

(77)

ORANGE HONEYSUCKLE
(Lonicera ciliosa)

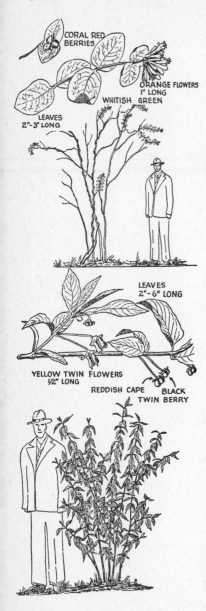

CORAL RED BERRIES

ORANGE FLOWERS 1" LONG
WHITISH GREEN

LEAVES 2"-3" LONG

LEAVES 2"-6" LONG

YELLOW TWIN FLOWERS ½" LONG

REDDISH CAPE   BLACK TWIN BERRY

Orange honeysuckle is a vine that rises from the ground in several thin stems and climbs up shrubs and trees by spiralling tightly around the branches. Sometimes the stems extend 30' in the air.

The oval, entire leaves are opposite as in all the honeysuckles and have a whitish bloom beneath which rubs off. The twin end-leaves are joined to make an irregular disk with the stem coming through the centre. Orange honeysuckle breaks into leaf early in the season closely following the Indian-plum or oso-berry. During May its clusters of tube-like, orange-red flowers attract attention but then it fades into the background until September when the tidy bundles of orange berries become prominent. Usually 3 or 4 of the berries develop at the expense of the others. They are filled with a reddish pulp and a number of large, yellow seeds.

QUICK CHECK: A supple vine tightly twisted around shrubs or trees. Leaves opposite and with white bloom. Orange-red flowers and orange berries.

RANGE: Particularly abundant below 2,000' elevation west of Cascades. Shady places at upper elevations of Yellow Pine Forest Zone. Spokane, Blue Mountains.

BLACK TWINBERRY
(Lonicera involucrata)

Bearberry Honeysuckle

Black twinberry is a shrub 3' - 10' high growing on damp ground. After becoming familiar with its yellow twin-flowers, black twin-berries, and long, light green leaf you will find its presence can almost always be anticipated in the proper habitat.

On Coastal slopes it may be overshadowed in the luxuriant growth of thimbleberry, red-osier dogwood and Pacific crab-apple. East of the Cascades it grows in more open situations with salmonberry, red-osier dogwood, water birch and cow parsnip.

The ½" long, yellow twin-flowers in May and June, and berries with their sticky reddish cape during July and August provide excellent identification features. The long, tapering, opposite leaves are equally good once recognized.

QUICK CHECK: Yellow twin-flowers or shiny, black twin-berries with sticky black or reddish cape.

RANGE: Wet lands throughout Washington but especially abundant in Coastal regions. Ranges from sea level to mountain forests. Olympics, Cascades and Blue Mountains. Coastal, Mountain, and Yellow Pine Zones.

SALAL
(*Gaultheria shallon*)

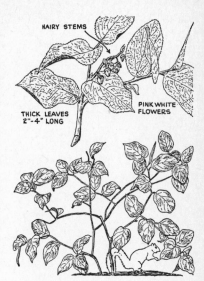

Salal is the Coast Indian word for this plentiful shrub. To them it was of high importance for the dark, mealy berries were made into a syrup or dried in cakes.

Possibly the most abundant shrub of the Coastal Forest Zone, salal may vary from a low sparse growth to an impenetrable tangle 10' or more in height. The pointed, egg-shaped leaves are thick, tough and evergreen and the stems strong and flexible so that the plant can survive the heavy wet snows which may flatten it to the ground.

The pinkish, bell- or urn-shaped flowers hang like beads along the twigs and may be found in bloom from May 15 to July 1. The blackish berries are ripe by August 15 and like the flowers have a very long season.

QUICK CHECK: An abundant shrub with leathery, evergreen leaves, 2" - 4" long. White or pink bell flowers; hairy, blackish berries.

RANGE: Coastal forests to approximately 2,500' elevation.

INDIAN-PLUM
(*Osmaronia cerasiformis*)

Oso-berry — Bird Cherry — Skunk Bush

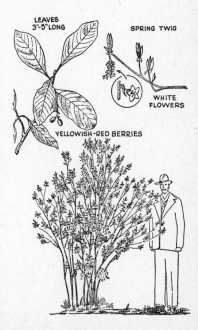

In March the Indian-plum is the first shrub at the Coast to herald spring. From each separate cluster of leaves there hangs 4-9 small, white flowers in various stages of opening. The flowers have a peculiar odor likened by some to watermelon rind. The crushed leaves also have a pungent smell and the torn bark emits an odor like wood alcohol.

The tapering leaves grow to 3" - 5" in length and show prominent raised veins on their light undersurface. Having such an early start in the spring they are the first to yellow, some as early as July. A scattered string of yellowish-red, plum-like berries replaces the flowers. These ripen to a bluish-black color with a dark blue bloom. A large seed and a flat flavor result in the berries being left for the birds.

Indian-plum develops a bushy, erect form in the open but, if shaded by trees, is sprawling and up to 10' high.

QUICK CHECK: Upright leaf clusters and string of white flowers in early spring. Peculiar flower, leaf and bark smell. Long, tapering leaves and oval berries in summer.

RANGE: Coastal plains and low mountain forests, west of Cascades. Bellingham, Seattle, Montesano.

HAZEL
(Corylus cornuta californica)

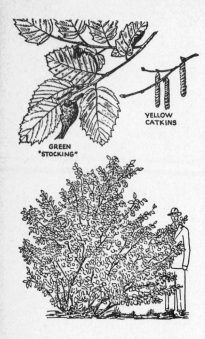

GREEN "STOCKING"

YELLOW CATKINS

Within its rather wide Coastal and Interior range it grows abundantly, equally at home on exposed rocky places or in shady glades.

Its numerous slender stems spread in graceful fashion to form a rounded, bushy shrub with heavy foliage. Hazel may reach 20' in height but generally is from 5'-12' tall.

During February and March conspicuous slender, yellow catkins hang from the slight twigs and so distinguish this shrub from its neighbors. By July the hazel nut is taking shape and is enclosed by a green, stocking-like husk which blends perfectly with the leaves. The edible nut, ripe by fall, is very popular with squirrels.

QUICK CHECK: Yellow catkins in early spring; green "stocking" husk in summer and fall.

RANGE: Coastal Forest Zone ranging from sea level to 2,500'. Upper elevations of Yellow Pine Zone. Teiton River, Kittitas County, Chinook Pass, Kings County.

GOAT'S BEARD
(Aruncus sylvester)

PENCILS" OF WHITE FLOWERS OR BROWN SEEDS

LEAFLETS FRINGE-LIKE

RIBBED STEMS

Goat's beard dies to the ground each year and isn't a true shrub. Its vigorous growth and shrub-like appearance warrant grouping it here.

Goat's beard is found in Coastal regions in shady, forest borders where the damp soil also supports salmonberry, thimbleberry and red-berry elder. Its common name probably arises from the long, white plumes that make such a showy display during May and June. The 3'-7' high shrub often has a foot or two of its tip in many unmistakable, pencil-like strings of very small flowers. However, the leaves with their short side branches often carrying three leaflets might be mistaken for salmonberry although the golden satiny color of salmonberry bark is quite distinctive.

The thin flower plumes of goat's beard gradually fade from white to a dirty brown as the seeds are formed. These brown strings last until late summer and, although not very conspicuous, do serve as a means of rapid identification from a distance.

QUICK CHECK: Pencils of small white flowers or brown seeds.

RANGE: Low elevations in Coastal Forest Zone. Sporadic on eastern slope of Cascades in high passes. Clallam County, Montesano, Chinook Pass, Mt. Angeles.

SQUASHBERRY
(Viburnum pauciflorum)

VARIABLE LEAVES

BRIGHT RED BERRIES

Squashberry is usually drawn to the attention through its crinkled, three-lobed leaves or group of bright red berries. In fall the leaves turn crimson and accurately mark its position in the floral picture. Perhaps the rather straggling growth and low height of from 2' - 6' keep it from being noticed by many persons. At higher elevations it grows in more open situations and frequently among rocks.

The leaves are long-stemmed and grow opposite from one another. Most are three-lobed but young ones often are quite variable in shape. Fine hairs and prominent ribs are characteristics of the underside. The small, white flowers make a cluster an inch or so across. Two to five bright red berries usually mature. They are bitter to the taste and have a large, flat seed in them. Berries often hang long after leaves have fallen.

QUICK CHECK: Rounded, 3-lobed leaves, opposite, usually hairy beneath. Flower cluster approximately 1" across. Several smooth, red berries. Ninebarks have somewhat similar leaves but they are alternate.

RANGE: Damp, shady locations in Mountain Forest Zone. More exposed at higher elevations in the Sub-Alpine Zone. Drops to low Coastal elevations on west side of Olympics. Lake Chelan, Mt. Adams, Stevens Pass, Simcoe Mountains.

HIGH-BUSH CRANBERRY
(Viburnum trilobum)

WHITE FLOWERS

LEAVES 2"-4" LONG

This shrub is so scarce that it will be missed by most people. In general form it closely resembles the above except for leaves and size of flower clusters. The flowers are yellowish white and very showy in their broad clusters.

Central flowers are small while the outer sterile ones are large and showy.

The fruit is bright red and very tart. If cooked it closely resembles cranberry sauce in flavour. Like squashberry the seeds are particularly large.

Shady, brushy thickets along streams is the preferred habitat.

QUICK CHECK: Leaves strongly 3-lobed. White flower clusters 2" - 4" across.

RANGE: Although found east of the Cascades in British Columbia, it generally is listed as only occurring west of them in Washington. The rarity of this shrub accounts for so little information on its range.

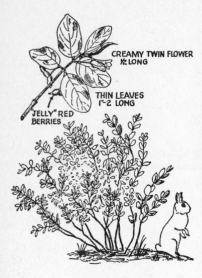

CREAMY TWIN FLOWER
½ LONG

THIN LEAVES
1"-2 LONG

"JELLY" RED
BERRIES

RED TWINBERRY
(*Lonicera utahensis*)

The long, thin stem and opposite leaves of red twinberry are an indication that it belongs to the honeysuckle family. Most shrubs are from 2'-5' high with a number of irregular "spray" branches. Its straggly limbs, small leaves and dirty, dead-looking bark give it a nondescript appearance only enlivened by the twin, yellowish-white flowers or jelly-like, red berries. Very often one flower grows at the expense of the other and results in one berry being much the larger. Flowers are out as early as May at low elevations but might be delayed a month or more on mountain heights. The 1"-2" long leaves are very thin and variable in shape. They do not have teeth.

QUICK CHECK: Thin opposite, ovalish leaves with smooth edges. Twin white to yellow flowers or pulpy red berries, one usually undeveloped.

RANGE: Widely distributed in mountains from valley bottom to timberline east of the Cascades but also occurring at sub-alpine elevations in the Olympics. Spokane and Blue Mountains.

BLUE FLY HONEYSUCKLE (*L. coerulea*) Very similar to above. Low, erect shrub to 2' high with reddish bark. Leaves 1"-1½", opposite, oval and hairy beneath. Yellow flowers in pairs. Twinberry, blue-black. Sporadic occurrence in Cascades. Range little known.

MALLOW NINEBARK
(*Physocarpus malvaceus*)

This shrub, because of its drabness and possible confusion with a currant is not very familiar to most people. However, in September when the foliage turns a bright russet red it becomes very attractive and noticeable on semi-open, rocky side-hills. There is considerable similarity to squash-berry at this time of the year.

Most shrubs are from 2'-4' high, stout and bushy, and might easily be taken for a currant from the 3-5 lobes and palmate veination of the leaves. The main stems are light grey in color with shreds of loose bark hanging on them. Rounded masses of small, white flowers appear at the twig-ends in June and by August have changed to a cluster of brown seed husks.

Mallow ninebark is often associated with Douglas fir, yellow pine, larch, Douglas maple, Saskatoon berry, mahonia (Oregon grape) and waxberry.

QUICK CHECK: Shreddy bark on stems; leaves alternate, 3-5 lobed; white flower head or mass of brown seed husks.

RANGE: Very abundant on dry hillsides east of the Cascades. Bunchgrass and Yellow Pine Zones. Ferry and Stevens Counties, Blue Mountains, Spokane, Kamiak Butte.

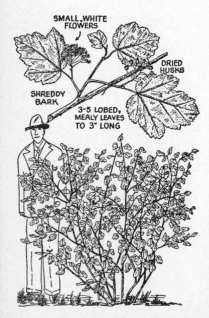

SMALL, WHITE
FLOWERS

DRIED
HUSKS

SHREDDY
BARK

3-5 LOBED,
MEALY LEAVES
TO 3" LONG

SASKATOON BERRY
(Amelanchier spp.)

June Berry — Shadbush — Service Berry

Saskatoon berry when either in blossom or fruit can be recognized easily but at other times may be so dwarfed or misshapen from the typical form as to cause confusion. It is under these circumstances that the small, rounded leaf with its big notches on the top half will provide the necessary clue.

Being easily damaged by grazing animals or other means this shrub may often be found less than 2' high All variations in shape are liable to occur but where left undisturbed it forms a loose bush with the upright limbs fanning outward at the crown. It may reach 15' in height but the average is from 6' - 12'. The loose spreading framework, made more noticeable by the small leaves, provides positive identification from the distance.

The fragrant clusters of white blossoms are very abundant and dot the bush from top to bottom during April and May. Berries start to form soon after and by July are a dull red which shades to the ripe black fruit in early August. Unfortunately many of the berries are wormy and their use as an edible fruit has not been popularized. Indians were not so fussy and mixed them with pounded meat to make pemmican. Bears find them a favorite delicacy.

Three or more species are often listed as occurring in Washington. The two most important are *A. cusickii* and *A. florida*. The former is supposed to have the leaves toothed from near the base or middle while the latter has its leaves toothed above the centre. Some authorities fail to distinguish any repeatedly marked difference in leaves, blossom or fruit among the species.

QUICK CHECK: Clusters of fragrant blossoms during April and May. Many red or half-black, seedy berries during summer and fall. Typical round leaf notched on top.

RANGE: Widespread through North America and Washington. Generally below 2,000' west of the Cascades. Very abundant on rocky slopes in all drier regions of eastern Washington.

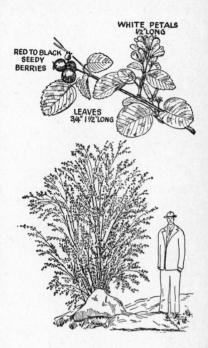

WHITE PETALS 1/2" LONG

RED TO BLACK SEEDY BERRIES

LEAVES 3/4" 1 1/2" LONG

SNOWBRUSH
(Ceanothus velutinus)

Mountain Balm — Sticky Laurel — Buckbrush

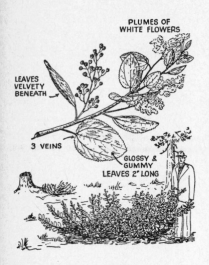

PLUMES OF WHITE FLOWERS

LEAVES VELVETY BENEATH

3 VEINS

GLOSSY & GUMMY LEAVES 2" LONG

Snowbrush grows very abundantly on certain sites. Generally it seeks semi-barren gravelly flats or slopes where sunlight is at a maximum. Here the brushy, sprawling shrub may form extensive, irregular mats. The smooth, forked limbs twist upward and carry thick, evergreen leaves about 2" long. These have a glossy but gummy surface which gives rise to the name of sticky laurel. In contrast the undersurface is soft and velvety. The leaf has 3 main veins like central fingers. When the summer's heat becomes intense the leaves curl lengthways along their centre and thus prevent water loss as well as minimizing surface exposure.

During June soft, white heads of tiny flowers rest amongst the glossy green leaves and later turn to small, hard husks. The flowers will make a soapy lather with water and some Indian tribes once used the leaves for a tobacco.

QUICK CHECK: Glossy, evergreen leaves with gummy surface and three main veins.

RANGE: Infrequent west of Cascades but very common in Yellow Pine Zone. Spotty occurrence lower slopes of Olympics. Ferry and Stevens Counties, Chinook Pass, Chelan County, Blue Mountains.

REDSTEM CEANOTHUS
(Ceanothus sanguineus)

SMALL, WHITE FLOWERS

REDDISH BARK

3 VEINS

Redstem ceanothus is a nondescript, bushy shrub. With dead limbs and twigs poking out here and there it gives a first impression of being damaged and unhealthy. Preferring semi-shade and well-drained soils it is found along the edge of road clearings, forest openings and rock slides.

This loose ragged shrub may be from 2'-6' high. Its oval, deciduous leaves have the characteristic 3 main veins evident also in its evergreen relative, snowbrush. The soft, fluffy masses of small, white flowers near the twig ends are out in June. Hard seed pods persist to the following year.

In spring the new twigs have a spicy flavour, and then take on a reddish coloring which leads to the name. It is found growing with Douglas maple, hazel, ocean spray, Saskatoon berry and snowbrush.

QUICK CHECK: Deciduous, toothed leaves with 3 main paralleling veins.

RANGE: Scattered occurrence west of Cascades in Coast forests. From Bunchgrass Zone to upper limits of Yellow Pine Forest Zone. Ferry, Spokane and Chelan Counties.

DEER BRUSH
(*Ceanothus integerrimus*)

Mountain Lilac

2"-6" LONG
CLUSTER OF SMALL
BLUISH FLOWERS

LEAVES ALTERNATE, 3-RIBBED, TO 2" LONG

SEED POD ⅓" ACROSS 3-DIVISIONS EACH WITH ONE HARD SEED

This loosely branched shrub with its slender spreading greenish limbs might be almost lost in the general floral picture were it not for the delicately scented clusters of pale blue to white flowers. These are at their best in early May when their misty quality compliments the release of spring.

The characteristic 3 veins of the ceanothus are evident here in the rather narrow oval leaves which seldom reach 2" in length. The small flowers bunch in a short plume much like that of a miniature lilac. Often a number of limbs branch into twigs each carrying its own cluster of 5-petalled flowers.

The seeds are carried in dry capsules, each having 3 sections and bearing a seed apiece.

QUICK CHECK: Tall shrub with narrow, oval, 3-veined leaves.

RANGE: Generally on exposed places such as along road edges or rockslides but tolerant to a fair amount of shade. Lower elevations of easterly slopes of Cascades. Klickitat County.

SOOPOLALLIE
(*Shepherdia canadensis*)

Soap Berry — Canada Buffalo Berry —
Russet Buffalo Berry

COPPERY DOTS

DARK GREEN LEAVES 1"-2½" LONG

BRIGHT RED BERRIES

Soopolallie berries when rubbed between the hands make a soapy froth, hence the Indian name: (soop - soap; olallie - berry). When growing in the semi-open it is bushy, upright and 3' - 4' in height. On wetter and more shady slopes a higher, more sprawling form is common. Soopolallie grows abundantly in semi-open forests at medium elevations.

The leaves are opposite, entire, roughly egg-shaped and from 1" - 2½" long. Although dark green above, the undersurface is a combination of silvery hairs and rusty brown spots. Twigs are pebbled with the same brown rust. The small, yellowish-brown male and female flowers are borne on separate bushes. The orange-red, almost transparent fruit grows in small clusters along the stem and twigs.

QUICK CHECK: Dark green, opposite leaves with silvery hairs and rusty brown spots on undersurface. Twigs pebbly with rust. Berries orange-red, transluscent.

RANGE: Generally east of the Cascades but isolated occurrences in Olympics and Gulf Islands. Okanogan and Stevens Counties.

(85)

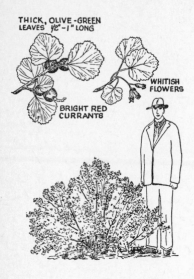

THICK, OLIVE-GREEN
LEAVES ½"–1" LONG

WHITISH
FLOWERS

BRIGHT RED
CURRANTS

SQUAW CURRANT
(*Ribes cereum*)

Wax Currant

Only the driest and hottest of climates suit this shrub. Here along the foot of rocky slopes or on almost barren benches the squaw currant can be recognized by its compact rounded outline, seldom 4' high, and the drab olive-green of its small leaves. By August most shrubs are bright with hundreds of small, red currants.

The crooked, upright stems are brushy toward the top and the bark is greyish with reddish tones and dull white markings. Leaves have a dull, olive sheen to them and vary between the size of a 10c and 25c piece.

QUICK CHECK: Bushy shrub with small, olive-green leaves. Smooth red currants in August and September. With rabbitbush, white clematis and poison ivy.

RANGE: Sagebrush and Bunchgrass Zones. Tonasket, Republic, Yakima and Chelan Counties. Blue Mountains.

GOLDEN CURRANT *(R. aureum)* with yellow berries and strongly lobed leaves is reported near Princeton.

SUMAC
(*Rhus glabra*)

Smooth Sumac

Sumac is a picturesque, many-branched shrub found in the drier regions of the State. Usually a loose thicket develops since new plants shoot up from the long, rambling roots.

In the north it seldom grows over 3' high but along the Columbia River a tree-like form to 20' high is quite common. The crooked, twisting limb structure looks like some Oriental dwarf shrub. Each stout leaf carries from 13 - 21, long, toothed leaflets which give the plant its characteristic "plume" foliage. Some plants have a conspicuous conical mass of round seeds near their top. In September and October the seeds are rich red in color from their plush-like covering.

During October the leaflets and stem turn a bright crimson bringing a vivid red rash to lower mountain slopes. Sumac surely leads the way in its flaunting colors of autumn.

Sumac exudes a milky juice when bruised. Some species are used in preparing waxes, dyes and varnishes. "Indian lemonade" is made from the velvety seeds. The husks are steeped in hot water, then the water is strained, sweetened and let cool.

QUICK CHECK: Stout leaf bearing 13 - 21, toothed leaflets. POISON SUMAC, a native of the Eastern States, does not occur in Washington.

RANGE: Sagebrush, Bunchgrass, and occasionally on edge of Yellow Pine Forest. Okanogan River, Snake River and tributaries. Ferry, Yakima and Chelan Counties.

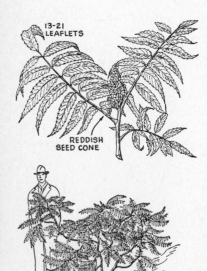

13-21
LEAFLETS

REDDISH
SEED CONE

MOCK ORANGE
(Philadelphus lewisii)
(Philadelphus gordonianus)

Syringa — Bridal Wreath

Mock orange with its showy "orange" blossoms is one shrub that invariably arouses the curiosity during June.

P. gordonianus, which is the Coastal species, often forms a slender, spreading shrub up to 12' high. It seeks out shady places with fairly good soils. In the Interior, *P. lewisii* seldom grows over 6' high and often is a small, ragged shrub niched into clefts on dry, rocky sidehills.

The profusion of "orange" blossoms are out during June and can hardly be confused with those of any other shrub. The Coastal species is very fragrant, the eastern one almost without perfume. The light green leaves are quite distinctive with a few points or teeth on each side of the leaf and the peculiar arrangement of the three main veins. Bark on new twigs is a bright chestnut brown but on older stems is often broken and loose.

QUICK CHECK: White "orange" flowers in June. Points on leaves and vein arrangement.

RANGE: Generally shrub of lower elevations. Sagebrush, Bunchgrass, and Yellow Pine Zones for *P. lewisii*. Spokane, Yakima, Blue Mountains, and Coastal Forest Zone for *P. gordonianus*.

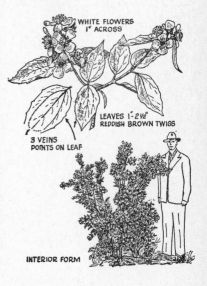

WHITE FLOWERS 1" ACROSS

LEAVES 1"-2½" REDDISH BROWN TWIGS

3 VEINS POINTS ON LEAF

INTERIOR FORM

OCEAN SPRAY
(Holodiscus discolor)

Arrow-wood

Although dogwood has a showier bloom, ocean spray is more widespread and possibly the most abundant flowering shrub we have. Nearly every dry forest opening or roadside in western Washington is softened during June by masses of loose, creamy plumes. With erect, spreading shrubs to 15' in height almost completely covered with bloom no one can fail to notice ocean spray. In easterly regions it is not so abundant and only reaches 6' - 8' in height.

In winter months the sparse limb framework still retains a loose cluster of dried husks, a good identifying feature. If before blooming time, the unusual leaves provide the clue. Note how severely the base is wedge-shaped and how coarse are the teeth. Straight young limbs were a source of arrow material for the Indians.

QUICK CHECK: In winter, end twigs with dry husks. Wedge leaves or sprays of small, white flowers.

RANGE: Dry land shrub of forested areas at lower elevations. Mountain and Yellow Pine Forest Zones. Ferry, Stevens and Spokane Counties.

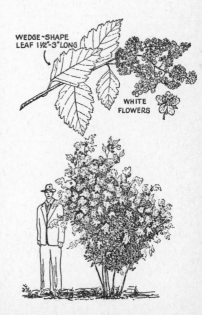

WEDGE-SHAPE LEAF 1½"-3" LONG

WHITE FLOWERS

SHRUBS

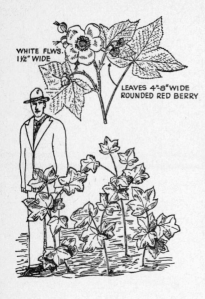

WHITE FLWS. 1½" WIDE

LEAVES 4"-8" WIDE ROUNDED RED BERRY

THIMBLEBERRY
(Rubus parviflorus)

Thimbleberry, a widespread shrub, is particularly noticeable because of its large "maple" leaves often 8" across.

In the Coastal Forest Zone thimbleberry masses in dampish places along the edge of roads or forest openings. East of the Cascade Mountains the same shrub will be found in quite dry places although creek bottoms are preferred.

Ranging from 4' high at the Coast to 2' in the Interior, thimbleberry is an erect, unarmed shrub with short, branching limbs. The stark white flowers, almost 2" across, show up very dramatically from May to July against the background of interlocked leaves, and serve as a means of ready identification. The berries are not "thimble" shaped but round and lumpy. These are bright red and insipid to the taste although sought after by birds and bears during July and August.

QUICK CHECK: Large white flowers or soft, red, rounded berries. "Blotting paper" maple leaf.
RANGE: Widespread in damp shady places. Coastal, Mountain and Yellow Pine Forest Zones.

SALMONBERRY
(Rubus spectabilis)

Salmonberry, a common shrub of the Coastal forest, is found usually in bottomlands or around the edges of marshes and creeks. In winter its golden, satiny bark with scattered weak spines marks it quite distinctly. Then in early April, it puts forth small bundles of fresh green leaves soon followed by a delicate red flower over 1" wide. As the leaves grow larger the flowers lose their prominence in the landscape, but as new buds develop, continue to bloom an amazingly long time. Flowers might be seen by April 1 and as late as June 1 with berries almost ripe on the same bush. The tender young shoots were eaten raw by Indians and early explorers.

Shrubs usually grow in an erect, branching form 6' - 8' high but where soil conditions are favorable, salmonberry can produce a thicket that would stop Paul Bunyan in his tracks.

The leaflets are mostly in threes and in this respect different from any other native shrub except the thorny blackberries and raspberries. The soft insipid fruit is shaped like a logan or boisonberry and may vary in color from yellow to red. Berries are often ripe by July 1.

QUICK CHECK: Satiny brown stems with very sparse thorns. Leaflets in threes, red "tissue paper" flower 1" across or salmon to red, rounded berry.
RANGE: Wet places below 3,000' in Coastal Zone and Gulf Islands.

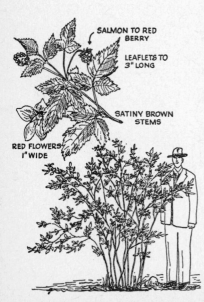

SALMON TO RED BERRY

LEAFLETS TO 3" LONG

SATINY BROWN STEMS

RED FLOWERS 1" WIDE

BLUEBERRIES, HUCKLEBERRIES
and WHORTLEBERRIES
(*Vaccinium spp.*)

These three names together with bilberry and cranberry are used in the common naming of the genus *Vaccinium*. A great deal of confusion exists in the names and the following is an attempt to use the more common ones of some descriptive significance.

BLACK MOUNTAIN
HUCKLEBERRY
(*Vaccinium membranaceum*)

Big Whortleberry — Thin Leaf Huckleberry

As the name suggests this is a shrub of the mountains. At elevations greater than 2,800' west of the Cascades and 4,000' to the east, black mountain huckleberry is often the most common shrub. Tall blue huckleberry may be mixed in with it but is distinguished by the entire leaves.

Black mountain huckleberry ranges from 5' in height at lower elevations to 1' near timberline. It is a crooked plant with smooth limbs and slightly angled twigs. Sometimes a few twisting stems make up its sparse form but often it is a bushy shrub. Leaves are from ½" - 1½" long, pointed at both ends and finely toothed. Small, whitish flowers in May and June turn to black berries by September. The leaves turn a beautiful red and purple color in late fall.

QUICK CHECK: Thin leaves with fine teeth. Smooth, black berries. Note approximate elevation ranges.

RANGE: Common throughout on higher slopes of Olympics, Cascade and Blue Mountains. Mountain Forest Zone.

TALL BLUE HUCKLEBERRY
(*Vaccinium ovalifolium*)

Tall Huckleberry — Oval Leaf Whortleberry

This huckleberry is commonly found to 6' high where conditions are ideal. Being in the shade for the most part it develops a scraggly form. The pinkish "bell" blossoms grow singly from the axils of the leaves. Berries are ripe by September. Leaves sometimes toothed.

QUICK CHECK: Egg-shaped leaf usually with smooth edges. Berries with bluish bloom.

RANGE: Widespread west of Cascades throughout cool, shady forests. Most abundant in Mountain Forest Zone at elevations from sea level to sub-alpine heights.

THIN LEAVES ½" - 1½" LONG

SMOOTH BLACK BERRY

GREENISH-WHITE FLOWER

TWIGS SLIGHTLY ANGLED

FORM AS

VERY THIN TWIGS

BLUE-BLACK BERRIES WITH BLUE BLOOM

OVAL LEAVES ½" - 1½" LONG

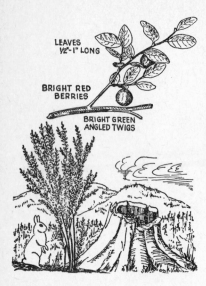

LEAVES ½"-1" LONG

BRIGHT RED BERRIES

BRIGHT GREEN ANGLED TWIGS

RED HUCKLEBERRY
(*Vaccinium parvifolium*)

There is no mistaking this lacey, bright green bush even though its bright red berries are not present. It appears limited to cool Coastal forests at elevations below 1,500'. Sometimes 6' in height it grows in a compact upright form, a mass of small oval leaves less than 1" long. On rare occasions they may be toothed. The twigs are as green as the leaves and sharply angled. Sometimes red huckleberry grows in fairly shady places but more often it seeks out the edges of forest openings and roadsides. Old stumps are a favorite perch.

QUICK CHECK: Note range. Angled, green twigs, and tart red berries. Quite common.

RANGE: Most common in Coastal forests below 1,500' in elevation. Olympics.

EVERGREEN HUCKLEBERRY
(*Vaccinium ovatum*)

Scattered specimens of evergreen huckleberry will be found along the north coastal region but as one proceeds southward it becomes increasingly abundant and vigorous. Single shrubs are replaced by thickets tightly laced together with salal. Rocky or gravelly soils are preferred.

Indians called the fruit shot-oolalie or shotberry on account of its size and shape.

Most shrubs are bushy and thick. Many are 6' high. There is a superficial resemblance to manzanita in that both have thick evergreen leaves, very hairy young twigs and a general similarity in flowers and berries. The crooked, reddish limbs and rounded outline of manzanita quickly distinguish it however.

The fine-toothed leaves are mostly less than 1" long, sharp-pointed, and with very short stems. The many small, pink flowers grow in groups along or near the end of the branches. The abundant berries are small and shiny black. Their sweet flavour makes them very desirable for pies and other domestic uses.

QUICK CHECK: Small sharp-pointed, toothed, evergreen leaves and woolly twigs. Clusters of pink, "bell" flowers during May; shiny, black berries in October and on to mid-November.

RANGE: Scattered through Coastal Forest Zone. Olympia, Tacoma, and low elevations of Olympics.

THICK WAXY-GREEN LEAVES ½" 1" LONG

FLOWERS PINK-WHITE

HAIRY, REDDISH TWIGS

BLACK RASPBERRY
(*Rubus leucodermis*)

Black Cap

NOTE: Raspberries come off a central core while blackberries are picked with the core.

Not all raspberries are red as this particular shrub will show once the flavorful fruit is fully ripe. Most of the summer its "raspberry" look will serve for rough identification. Many of the shoots are quite straight and may reach 5' in height. Other stems bend over and droop to the ground. Stout thorns with their points turned back bristle on the branches and even creep up on the leaf stems. The white flowers with 5 petals bunch together in small clusters and are out from April to June. The fruit looks like a common raspberry until late summer when it turns almost black. The sharp-pointed, crinkly leaflets are in threes or fives and their contrasting silvery under-surface provides a fairly reliable identity check.

Black raspberry wants lots of sunlight and a coarse dry soil for its roots. Road clearings, forest openings and logged-over areas are favored places.

QUICK CHECK: A mostly upright shrub, thorny, 3 - 5 leaflets with very silvery undersurface. Petals are shorter than hairy, reflexed sepals. Blackish fruit with bloom when ripe.

RANGE: Wide distribution throughout Cascade and Blue Mountains. Snake River, Seattle. Sagebrush to Mountain Forest Zone.

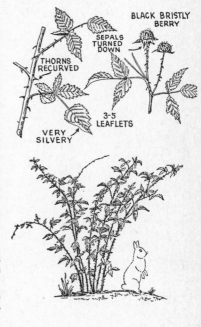

RED RASPBERRY
(*Rubus idaeus*)

Beyond the fact that this raspberry is red when ripe there is a great similarity in form and leaf to black raspberry. However, the range of red raspberry is east of the Cascade mountains and its preference for very dry places such as rock-slides helps distinguish it. Many plants have a very noticeable blue bloom over the brownish stalks. The leaves are hairy beneath but not with the high silvery sheen of black raspberry.

QUICK CHECK: Similar to black raspberry with sepals longer than petals but not folded back. Blue bloom on many stalks. Fruit red. Watch range limitations.

RANGE: Widely distributed east of Cascade summit in Bunchgrass and Yellow Pine Forest Zones.

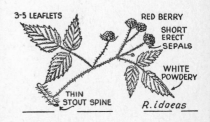

POISON-IVY
(Rhus radicans rydbergii)

12"-20" HIGH

DULL
WHITE BERRY

3 GLOSSY-GREEN
LEAFLETS

Despite the abundance of poison-ivy in certain regions of Washington and the publicity given its poisonous properties, there are comparatively few people who can make definite recognition. Being a sun-loving plant poison-ivy is found in a specialized habitat where the careful observer quickly comes to look for it. In the hot climate of central and eastern Washington, rock slides, stony places and road edges are brightened by patches of this low, glossy-leaved shrub. In southern areas it is often 3' - 5' high.

Its large, wavy-edged leaves in threes and whitish berries in loose clusters part way up the stem are positive identifying features. In the fall the plant turns a colorful scarlet and soon loses its leaves although the berries may remain all winter.

The poison which causes severe irritation to the skin is an oil contained in all parts of the shrub. Poisoning may result from contact with shoes or clothes that have been worn around the shrub or from smoke from the burning plant.

If exposure is suspected, thorough washing in several changes of very soapy water is recommended. A coating of soft soap or a strong solution of Epsom salts over the affected parts are good home antidotes. The standard remedy is calomine lotion obtainable at all drug stores. The poison runs its course and usually clears up in several days' time.

Strangely enough sheep, goats and cattle graze on poison-ivy without harm and may help in its eradication.

QUICK CHECK: Glossy green leaves in threes. Dull white berries close to stem.

RANGE: Sagebrush and Bunchgrass Zones and edge of Yellow Pine Zone. Spokane, Wenatchee, Yakima, Oroville, Ferry County, Snake River, White Pass.

GREENISH WHITE
BERRIES

GLOSSY, LEATHERY
LEAFLETS
VARIABLE IN SHAPE

POISON-OAK *(Rhus diversiloba)*, fortunately enough is comparatively rare in Washington. Poison-oak may be a straggly, erect shrub or more commonly a stout climber. The three leaflets are roughly round in outline but sometimes irregularly lobed or toothed often causing a superficial resemblance to an oak leaf. Vicinity of Seattle, Tacoma, Hoodsport. Coastal Forest Zone.

LEAVES IN THREE, LET IT BE!

RABBITBUSH
(Chrysothamnus nauseosus)

Rabbitbush is often confused with sagebrush because of its similarity in appearance and habitat. From August 15 to September 15 the compact, grey-green plant is topped by a mass of small, yellow flowers whereas sagebrush isn't in drab bloom until the end of September.

Rabbitbush is a compact, olive-green shrub about 2' in height. Numerous finely hairy, erect stems give it a trim look whereas sagebrush has a thick, twisting trunk. Pasture wormwood with which it may be confused also is softer in color and has a much lighter twig framework.

QUICK CHECK: Massed head of yellow flowers from August 15 - September 15. Leaves thin, velvety, and not notched at tip.

RANGE: Sagebrush Zone north and south of Yakima. Whitman County. Extends into Bunchgrass Zone.

C. viscidiflorus has stems and leaves not hairy. Wide distribution in Sagebrush and Bunchgrass Zones. Oroville, Clarkston.

TETRADYMIA *(T. canescens)* resembles rabbitbush but can be identified by the 4 oblong bracts surrounding the flower head. Leaves are only about half as long. Rocky plateaus and slopes from Spokane south. Also Ellensburg, Wenatchee. Sagebrush Zone.

THIN, YELLOW FLOWERS

VELVETY STEMS AND LEAVES 1"-1½" LONG

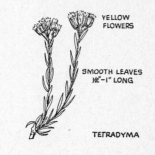

YELLOW FLOWERS

SMOOTH LEAVES ½"-1" LONG

TETRADYMA

PASTURE WORMWOOD
(Artemisia frigida)

Fringed Sagebrush — Arctic Sagebrush

This beautiful little shrub mingles with sagebrush and rabbitbush but can be picked out by its smaller size (4" - 20" high) and softer shade of color. The "sage" smell of the crushed leaves is very pungent. The leaves differ from rabbitbush in being finely hairy and divided into 2 or 3 thin, fringe-like leaflets. The small, dull flowers cluster along the thin flowering twigs and won't be noticed unless closely examined.

QUICK CHECK: Note limited range. Low shrub less than 20" high with finely divided and hairy leaves, silvery, olive-grey in color and with "sage" smell.

RANGE: Although ranging widely throughout the dry interior of B.C., this shrub occurs infrequently in Washington. Okanogan and Ferry Counties have the greatest abundance. A specimen collected 150 years ago in Siberia led to name *"frigida"*.

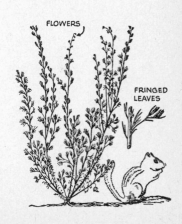

FLOWERS

FRINGED LEAVES

(93)

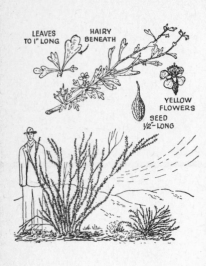

LEAVES TO I" LONG
HAIRY BENEATH
YELLOW FLOWERS
SEED 1/2" LONG

ANTELOPE BUSH
(*Purshia tridentata*)

Bitterbrush — Greasewood

The dull green color of this shrub blends very well with the neighboring sagebrush. Actually it is quite different in form having a spreading structure of stiff, awkward branches. The thin, notched leaves are so tiny that the outline of the fibrous limbs is quite distinctive. In some regions it may grow 8' high but in other areas it may seldom reach 4' and may be brushy in shape.

In early spring the bush is dotted with small, yellow blossoms that go unnoticed unless a limb is examined.

Greasewood is a common name and arises from the fact that the shrub, even when green, burns with much spitting and crackling. A dark, greasy smoke helps lend authority for this name.

QUICK CHECK: Note limited range. Short leaves up to 1" long, triple notched like sagebrush. Yellow flowers or "tear-drop" seeds on limbs.

RANGE: Sagebrush and Bunchgrass Zone in vicinity of Wenatchee, Ellensburg, and Yakima. Walla Walla County, Gifford Ferry, Peshastin, Entiat.

SAGEBRUSH
(*Artemisia tridentata*)

Sagebrush with its usual thin, triple or "trident" notched leaves can easily be identified by this one feature. Occasionally there are 4 or 5 unequal lobes. Its gnarled form is so characteristically massed over barren, arid waste land that it just naturally has to be sagebrush. The "sage" smell to its foliage and the twisted, loose bark are other noticeable points. The flowers are extremely small and drab in color and bloom from September 15 to October 15. See page 184 for a further sagebrush.

Although under favorable conditions it will reach 8' in height the average shrub is about half that high. Sagebrush is considered an intruding weed plant in overgrazed or otherwise impoverished soils. A rather interesting feature is its occurrence almost always on soils of volcanic origin and seldom on those of granitic formation.

QUICK CHECK: A gnarled, grey-green shrub 2' - 5' high with thin, "trident" leaves.

RANGE: Westerly portion of Sagebrush Zone and scattered in Bunchgrass Zone. Not in the Snake River Canyon nor channeled scablands.

A. trifida, sometimes given as a sub-species, differs principally in having the leaves quite deeply notched. The shrub is smaller and generally more bushy.

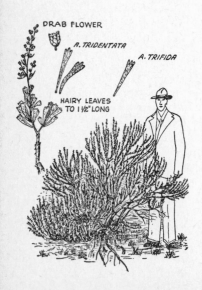

DRAB FLOWER
A. TRIDENTATA
A. TRIFIDA
HAIRY LEAVES TO 1 1/2" LONG

HOP SAGE
(Grayia spinosa)

This is a bushy shrub associated with the sagebrush desert country. Although from 1' - 4' high it most commonly forms a tousled much-branched shrub around 2' in height. In spring it is quite conspicuous for twig ends carry dense clusters of fruiting bracts or scales which are often decoratively tinged with red.

The leaves, like most dry land plants, are comparatively small being seldom over 1½" long and more commonly around ½" in length. They are thick and tend to be rough to the touch. Hidden among them are sharp spines formed on twig ends. Older branches have a dark brown shredding bark.

QUICK CHECK: Seldom found in anything but Sagebrush Zone. Only one of common group i.e. sagebrush, rabbitbush, antelope bush, greasewood that has spines. Fruiting scales distinctive.

RANGE: Mostly in south central Washington in Sagebrush Zone of Douglas, Yakima and Franklin Counties. Also found near Grand Coulee.

SPINES

DULL GREEN LEAVES TO 1½" LONG

THIN GREENISH TO RED SCALES

GREASEWOOD
(Sarcobatus vermiculatus)

In certain sagebrush areas of Washington a person will see rather similar shrubs intermingled with the sagebrush. However their dark green color separates them very clearly from the grey of the common range plant. A further clue to watch for is the presence of alkali, as shown by a white pasty substance on the ground, for greasewood is very partial to this situation. Spiny twig ends are a further feature in clinching its identity.

Growing from 2' - 8' high, greasewood forms a stout spiny shrub. Unlike sagebrush it has a smooth light gray bark. Leaves are plentiful but narrow and thickish and taper inwards at their base.

The same shrub carries two types of flowers during mid-summer. One looks like a small catkin because its flower parts are hidden by numerous small scales. The other type of flower usually occurs as a single bloom which, as it goes to fruit, displays a heavily veined wing with a ragged edge.

QUICK CHECK: Usually with or near sagebrush. Alkaline habitat. Spiny twigs and distinctive flowers.

RANGE: Widely scattered in suitable localities throughout the Sagebrush Zone. Grand Coulee, Moses Coulee, Coulee City, Pasco, Yakima.

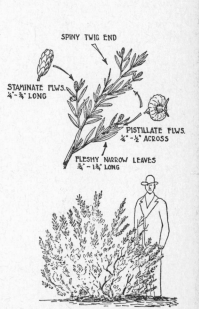

SPINY TWIG END

STAMINATE FLWS. ¼" - ¾" LONG

PISTILLATE FLWS. ¼" - ½" ACROSS

FLESHY NARROW LEAVES ¾" - 1¾" LONG

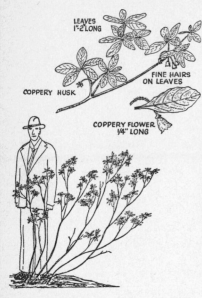

LEAVES 1"-2" LONG

FINE HAIRS ON LEAVES

COPPERY HUSK

COPPERY FLOWER 1/4" LONG

FALSE AZALEA
(*Menziesia ferruginea*)

Fool's Huckleberry.

False azalea, although much larger in size than cultivated azalea, bears a resemblance in its loose whorls of small leaves. It is a common shrub on Coastal mountains and, where moist conditions prevail, often dominates the undergrowth. Usually 2'-6' high, its slender, ascending limbs support an artistic pattern of blue-green leaves. Young twigs are often coppery in color possibly leading to some confusion with copper bush. The leaves have fine hairs on both surfaces and the base tapers to clasp the stem. In color they are bluish-green on top and light, whitish-green underneath. The bell-shaped flowers, carried on long stems, are an unusual copper color. Shrubs often found with false azalea are copper bush, white rhododendron and black mountain huckleberry.

QUICK CHECK: Leaves 1" - 2" long, in rough whorls. Fine hairs on both sides. Copper bush hasn't hairs on the old leaves. White rhododendron has most leaves over 2" long.

RANGE: Moist slopes in the Mountain Forest Zone. Olympics, Cascades, Mason County, Hoquiam, Skomania County, Mt. Adams, Mt. Rainier, Stevens Pass.

LEAVES 1/2"-2" LONG

HAIR ON YOUNG LEAVES

SEED STAGES

SHREDDY COPPERY BARK

COPPERY "BELL" 1/4" LONG

COPPER BUSH
(*Cladothamnus pyrolaeflorus*)

This is a not too common shrub of Cascade Mtn. forests above 2,500' elevation. It mingles with white rhododendron and false azalea to form dense thickets. Being 3' - 5' high, bushy, and with its leaves in rough whorls it might be passed up for one of its neighbors. Look closely and you will see it has stout stems with loose coppery bark. The numerous branching twigs have smooth leaves 1/2" - 2" long which, when young, are covered with fine, white hairs. Veins show up very prominently on young leaves and older ones have a very noticeable main rib on the underside.

If copper bush is in flower or fruit you will know it immediately by its round coppery flower with the curved, protruding anther. The bumpy, green seed also has this curved protrusion.

QUICK CHECK: Loose coppery bark on shoots. Old leaves not hairy like false azalea or white rhododendron. Copper flower with curved anther. Berry similar in general shape.

RANGE: Most abundant with mountain hemlock and yellow cedar forest type. Sub-alpine Zone in Olympics and northerly portion of Cascade Mountains.

WHITE RHODODENDRON
(Rhododendron albiflorum)

Cascades Azalea

Hikers often are so overwhelmed by its tangle of uncompromising branches that the descriptive name, "Mountain Misery," is hardly out of place. This 3' - 6' high shrub favors the high damper slopes of the Olympic and Cascade Mountains.

The noticeable, rough whorls of 5 - 7 leaves might be confused with false azalea or copper bush. However, turn the thin leaves so the sunlight glances across the surface. Look closely for fine, coppery hairs glinting in the sun. The main rib on the underside of the leaf is clad in white hairs. Young twigs are hairy also.

In late spring handsome, bell-like, white flowers in clusters of one to three blossoms provide an unmistakable feature. Then the flowers change into dry, brown husks which hang on until next spring.

Many shrubs have yellow mottlings on the leaves, particularly on mature foliage. Associated shrubs are copper bush, false azalea and mountain ash.

QUICK CHECK: Leaves 1" - 3" long in rough whorls. Copper-colored hairs on leaf. White flowers in late spring.

RANGE: From 3,500' elevation to near timberline on Coastal slopes. On shady, moist mountains throughout the Cascade and Olympic Mountains. Sub-Alpine Zone. Clallam County, Mt. Adams, Mt. Rainier, Stevens Pass.

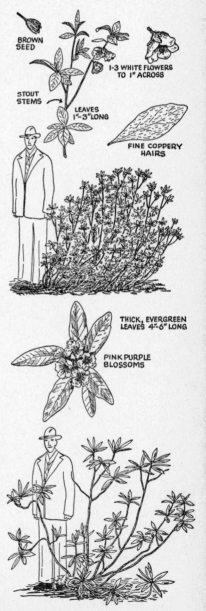

BROWN SEED

1-3 WHITE FLOWERS TO 1" ACROSS

STOUT STEMS

LEAVES 1"-3" LONG

FINE COPPERY HAIRS

THICK, EVERGREEN LEAVES 4"-6" LONG

PINK PURPLE BLOSSOMS

RED RHODODENDRON
(Rhododendron macrophyllum)

Red rhododendron is very similar to the cultivated shrub except for its larger, more sprawling form which may reach 10' into the air. Generally extensive patches grow under the trees rather than widely spaced individuals.

The pink-purple blossoms form in June in round masses strikingly set off by the loose rosettes of long, shiny, evergreen leaves. Sometimes the flower bunches are 6" across and provide a display of color and beauty surpassing all other native shrubs. It well deserves the honor of being the State flower of Washington.

QUICK CHECK: Note range. Evergreen leaves 4" - 6" long with whitish bloom beneath. Large masses of pink-purple flowers.

RANGE: Abundant in Skagit Valley bordering British Columbia. South-east flank of Olympics. Seattle, Whidby Island. Coastal Forest Zone.

MANZANITA

VERY HAIRY TWIGS

OLIVE-GREEN LEAVES
1/2"- 1 1/2" LONG

WHITE
FLOWERS

CROOKED
RED LIMBS

HAIRY MANZANITA
(*Arctostaphylos columbiana*)

Hairy or woolly manzanita with its dull green foliage is usually found on stony slopes or rocky bluffs where the sun's heat is at a maximum.

It is a rounded, bushy, evergreen shrub seldom reaching 6' in height. The strikingly crooked branches are smooth and have a rich reddish-brown color. Young twigs and leaves are very hairy. The urn-shaped, whitish flowers resemble those of salal and arbutus. In bloom during May they later develop into a blackish-red, mealy berry. Few people know of their edible qualities although they were gathered by the Indians and either eaten raw or cooked.

QUICK CHECK: A compact shrub with thick, evergreen leaves. Twigs and young leaves very hairy. Limbs crooked, reddish-brown.

RANGE: Gulf Islands, Olympics, Seattle, and ranging south to Columbia River. Generally west of Cascades in Coastal Forest Zone.

BROOM
(*Cytisus scoparius*)

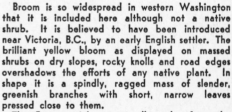

GROOVED GREEN
BARK

HAIRY PODS

3/4" LONG YELLOW FLOWERS

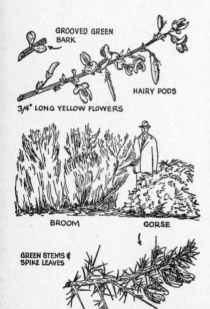

BROOM   GORSE

GREEN STEMS &
SPIKE LEAVES

Broom is so widespread in western Washington that it is included here although not a native shrub. It is believed to have been introduced near Victoria, B.C., by an early English settler. The brilliant yellow bloom as displayed on massed shrubs on dry slopes, rocky knolls and road edges overshadows the efforts of any native plant. In shape it is a spindly, ragged mass of slender, greenish branches with short, narrow leaves pressed close to them.

The flowers stick out at all angles from the stem and are at their best during May. Some limbs flower as late as July 1. However, by this time most bushes are hung thickly with small pea pods having many hairs along the edges. Some blooms show red and purple shades.

QUICK CHECK: Squarish, green twigs with small leaves, yellow flowers or small, hairy pea pods. Note range limitation.

RANGE: Roadsides and waste places throughout western Washington.

GORSE (*Ulex europaeus*) is an introduced shrub somewhat resembling broom by reason of its bushy green form and yellow flowers which often are out in January. It is low and sprawling with sharp-pointed needle leaves. The range is more limited, being along Puget Sound and the west side of the Olympic Peninsula.

DEVIL'S CLUB
(*Oplopanax horridus*)

Devil's club stands out because of its large, maple-like leaves and thick, spiny stems. In the mottled shadows of cedar swamps, Devil's club grows abundantly wherever the ground is black, soft and damp. Its light brown stems rise in crooks and twists to support large, exotic leaves which spread like green platters to catch the filtered sun's rays. Long, yellowish spines bristle from the stems and sparse, thin thorns project from the underside of leaf and stem. Terminal clusters of white flowers appear in June. They later change to a pyramid of bright red berries very noticeable during August.

QUICK CHECK: Coarse stems about 1" thick, bristling with light brown, needle-like spines.

RANGE: Generally wherever red cedar grows. From sea level to approximately 4,500' in Coastal and Mountain Forest Zones.

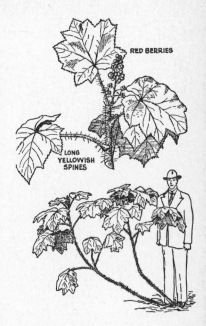

RED BERRIES

LONG YELLOWISH SPINES

WILD ROSES
(*Rosa spp.*)

Wild roses are recognized the country over but as individuals only an expert can tell the difference between them. Over 100 different kinds grow in North American and at least 8 in Washington. Each features white to deep rose flowers with a fragrant perfume. The leaves have an odd number of leaflets and a wing-like sheaf clasps the base of the leaf. The fruit or "hips" which hang on all winter are almost as well known as the flowers. Most roses have thorny stems. The following are three of the more common.

COMMON WILD ROSE (*R. nutkana*): Probably the most common bush rose. A bushy shrub to 10' high and armed with stout prickles beneath each leaf. Showy flowers often 2" across, either singly or with one or two others. Fruit, a large showy, scarlet hip. Blooms from May to July. Prefers fairly rich soils. Ranges throughout Washington, generally at lower elevations.

DWARF ROSE (*R. gymnocarpa*): A spindly shrub to 4' high with slender stems prickly with weak straight spines. Leaflets 5 - 9 and pale pink flowers ½" - ¾" across. Fruit smooth and orange in color. Found on rocky exposed situations, it ranges at lower elevations across Washington.

SWAMP ROSE (*R. pisocarpa*): Weakly armed with straight spines. Leaflets 5 - 7. Several flowers in twig-end clusters. Fruit smaller than *R. nutkana*. Throughout Washington at lower elevations.

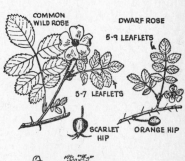

COMMON WILD ROSE

DWARF ROSE

5-9 LEAFLETS

5-7 LEAFLETS

SCARLET HIP

ORANGE HIP

CURRANTS AND GOOSEBERRIES
(Ribes spp.)

Currants and gooseberries have a close resemblance in leaf and fruit to the cultivated variety. The leaves are 3 - 5 lobed, usually toothed and have prominent veins radiating from the base to all the lobes. The pungent, currant smell of the crushed leaves is a help if in doubt. Currants are unarmed while gooseberries carry spines.

STINK CURRANT
(Ribes bracteosum)

Blue Currant

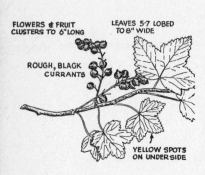

FLOWERS & FRUIT
CLUSTERS TO 6" LONG

LEAVES 5-7 LOBED
TO 8" WIDE

ROUGH, BLACK
CURRANTS

YELLOW SPOTS
ON UNDERSIDE

This currant is a more or less erect shrub to 8' high with a few sprawling branches. The large "currant" leaves up to 8" in width are wider than long with from 5 - 7 sharp-tipped lobes. Yellow resin ducts are scattered on the under-surface. The erect, green, saucer-shaped flowers and rough, black fruit in a loose, long cluster of two or three dozen are quite different than the small number of fruit on other species. The smell of the leaves is very pronounced and accounts for the common name.

QUICK CHECK: Large, blue-green leaves, 5 - 7 lobed. Flowers and fruit in 4" - 6" long cluster. Strong currant smell to leaves.

RANGE: Most common at low elevations in Coastal Forest Zone, but extending up mountain slopes to near sub-alpine elevations.

GOLDEN CURRANT
(Ribes aureum)

YELLOW FLW.
⅜" LONG

SMOOTH BERRIES
YELLOW TO
REDDISH-BLACK

LEAVES ½"- 2" WIDE
WAXY BENEATH

Here's a shrub that catches the eye during May when its clusters of bright yellow flowers adorn the slender branches. Fortunately for the amateur botanist its identity can be determined easily for the yellowish-green, 3-lobed leaves aren't duplicated by any other native shrub.

The majority of plants are 4' - 6' high and favour lowland thickets and damp places. However specimens are seen now and then in rocky surroundings. The yellow flowers in clusters of from 6 - 15 are slightly less than ½" long. They are much favored by insects. Petals may have a red or purplish tinge.

The smooth berries are ¼" in diameter and have a long chaffy protuberance. Although the berries most often are yellow in color they can range to red and almost black.

QUICK CHECK: Distinctive three-lobed leaves, flowers and berries.

RANGE: A relatively common shrub of brushy damp places in the Sagebrush Zone and extending to the Bunchgrass Zone. Spokane, Almota, Yakima, Wenatchee, Ellensburg.

RED-FLOWER CURRANT
(Ribes sanquineum)

Winter Currant

To persons west of the Cascades, this currant will be the one surely to be known. True enough it has only a brief few weeks of glory but it is at a time in early spring when color is much appreciated. The small, red flowers in drooping clusters attract the first migrant humming birds about April 1 but blooms may be seen as late as May 15.

Red-flower currant consists of several crooked stems supporting a loose bush. Cultivated shrubs reach 10' in height but in the woods most are not over 5'. Dry, open woods, logged areas or roadsides are places to look for this shrub. The dull green, mealy leaves are from 1" - 3" across and matted on the undersurface with almost invisible hair. The fruit is a globular, blue-black berry with a whitish, waxy bloom.

QUICK CHECK: Roundish, 3 - 5 lobed currant leaves with fine white hairs beneath. Red flower clusters.

RANGE: Low elevations in Coastal Forest Zone. Gulf Islands, Seattle, Tacoma, Silverton.

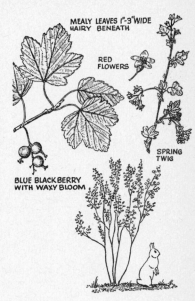

MEALY LEAVES 1"-3" WIDE HAIRY BENEATH

RED FLOWERS

SPRING TWIG

BLUE BLACKBERRY WITH WAXY BLOOM

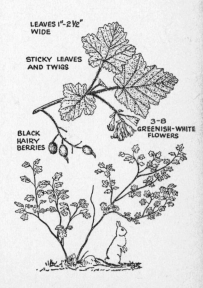

STICKY CURRANT
(Ribes viscosissimum)

Most bushes are from 2' - 4' high, the few stems twisted and stout at the base. The stems are without thorns but with rather shreddy bark on older branches. Sticky currant grows in semi-open forests on mountains east of the Cascades. Although individual shrubs are well separated the range often covers extensive mountain slopes.

The most noticeable feature is the sticky pores and hairs on the leaves, twigs and fruit. The greenish-white flowers with pinkish tinge are in clusters of from 3 - 8. For some reason very few berries form but those that do are black and covered with short, stiff hairs.

According to an early explorer, David Douglas, 2 or 3 berries will cause vomiting.

QUICK CHECK: "Currant" leaves; twigs, leaves and fruit sticky, hairy.

RANGE: Semi-open mountain slopes from 1,800' to 6,000' from Cascades eastwards. Yellow Pine and Mountain Forest Zones.

A number of other currants are found in the State but are confusing unless flowers and berries are present. The most important are *R. petiolare, R. reniform, R. laxiflorum, R. aceriflorum (R. howelli).*

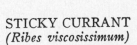

LEAVES 1"-2½" WIDE

STICKY LEAVES AND TWIGS

3-8 GREENISH-WHITE FLOWERS

BLACK HAIRY BERRIES

WILD GOOSEBERRY
(*Ribes divaricatum*)

Wild Gooseberry

LEAVES 3-5 LOBED, HAIRY 1"-1½"LONG

SINGLE THORNS

GREENISH OR PURPLISH FLOWERS

PURPLE BERRIES

Common Gooseberry

This shrub sends up several sturdy, "whip" limbs that may reach 6' in the air before bending over. Most of the stem is unarmed but at every joint a single spine (occasionally 2 or 3) is found. Greenish or purplish flowers have five, petal-like lobes that hang down. There may be from 1-4 flowers to a cluster. The berry is smooth and wine-colored.

QUICK CHECK: Single thorn at joints. Drooping petal-like lobes on flower.

RANGE: Coastal Forest generally below 2,000' elevation. Hoquiam, Puget Sound, Seattle, Port Ludlow.

SWAMP GOOSEBERRY
(*Ribes lacustre*)

A very plentiful shrub in damp, shady places in the higher mountains. Here it may form an extensive low thicket of weakly upright, spiny stems several feet high. Young stems are bristly with 3-7 heavier spines at the nodes. Older branches are almost smooth. The whitish flowers tinged with red are about ¼" across, saucershaped, and in clusters of from 5-12. The berry is black, bristly and bitter.

QUICK CHECK: Young stems bristly. Flowers and berries as described.

RANGE: Mountain slopes from Coast to 6,000' throughout. Port Ludlow, Olympics, Mt. Adams, Wenatchee and Blue Mountains.

Swamp Gooseberry

LEAVES 1"-2½" WIDE

3-7 SPINES

5-12 WHITISH FLOWERS

BRISTLY, BLACK BERRY

UNRIPE GREEN BERRIES

OTHER GOOSEBERRIES
(*Ribes spp.*)

GUMMY GOOSEBERRY (*R. lobbii*): Noticeable in spring because of its handsome flowers with red petals. Spiny stems up to 4' high with 3 large spines at nodes. Leaf deeply 3-lobed and up to 1" across. Leaf and stem sticky. Berry large, hairy and purple. Range—shady forests in Coastal Forest Zone.

MOUNTAIN GOOSEBERRY (*R. irriguum*): Resembles *R. divaricatum* except for fine thorns all along branches and 1-3 large ones at joints. Greenish white flowers, 1-3. Berry smooth and purple. Range—along streams in mountains of Bunchgrass and Yellow Pine Zones. Spokane, Blue Mountains.

SNAKE RIVER G. (*R. niveum*) also known as snowy gooseberry because of its showy blossoms is a shrub to 8' high. Leaves are 3-5 lobed. Clusters of 2-5 flowers. Berry blue-black with a bloom. Snake River Canyon and tributaries.

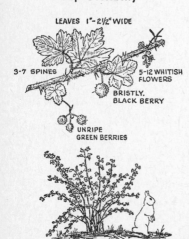

TRAILING BLACKBERRY
(Rubus vitifolius)

Here's a long, thorny creeper that has a habit of abruptly bringing itself to one's attention. Its foot-catching and thorn-sticking capabilities might be twined over 15 or 20 feet of ground or draped artistically over logs or rock outcrops. This tough, sinewy shrub is the most abundant and widely distributed blackberry on the Coastal slopes. It shows a very definite preference for recently logged or burned-over forests and comes in with bracken and fireweed as pioneer growth.

During June some confusion as to identity might arise because male and female flowers are carried on separate plants. The male flower is much larger and showier being about 1½" across as compared to ¾" for the female. New runners are often unbranched the first year but thereafter have numerous short side branches.

Most of the dark green, alternate leaves carry 3 leaflets but occasionally 5 are seen. Thorns are stout and curved back at the tip. The glossy black fruit ripens in August and is much sought by humans, bears, birds and even deer.

QUICK CHECK: A slender thorny crawler with alternate, 3-leaflet leaves. Fruit, glossy and black.

RANGE: Most abundant in the burns and logging of the Douglas fir Coastal forests. Altitude range to 3,500' in the Cascades. Also reported in the Moscow Mountains of Idaho and northwards.

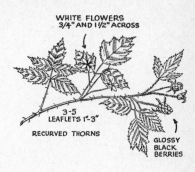

WHITE FLOWERS
3/4" AND 1½" ACROSS

3-5
LEAFLETS 1"-3"

RECURVED THORNS

GLOSSY
BLACK
BERRIES

SUB-ALPINE BLACKBERRY
(Rubus nivalis)

This slender trailer with slightly woody stems only grows a few feet long. It is usually armed with numerous, small, weak, recurved prickles. The "blackberry" leaves may be 3-lobed or have three leaflets... Flowers are usually solitary with white or purple petals. The fruit is a finely hairy, red berry.

QUICK CHECK: Note range. Short, prickly trailer with red berry.

RANGE: Most general on dry exposed places at middle elevations of Cascade Mountains.

EVERGREEN BLACKBERRY (*R. laciniatus*) is a common escape from cultivation in western Washington. It has very stout stems with strong, recurved thorns. Dense thickets are a common sight along roadsides.

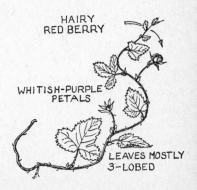

HAIRY
RED BERRY

WHITISH-PURPLE
PETALS

LEAVES MOSTLY
3-LOBED

FLOWERS

SCORCHED PENSTEMON
(Penstemon deustus)

For general features of the penstemons see page 173. Scorched penstemon is the only white-flowered species liable to be encountered. Sometimes there may be a yellow or purplish tinge. The plant has a branching form to 2' high with stout erect stalks. Leaves are dull green, about 1½" long, and variable in shape with distinct jagged teeth. The flowers form clusters along the top 3" - 6" of stem. Each bloom is ½" long and has a hairy throat. It flowers during May and June.
RANGE: Rocky places in Sagebrush and Bunchgrass Zones. Wenatchee.
YELLOW P. *(P. confertus)* has 3 - 4 clusters of small yellow flowers. Bunchgrass Zone to mountain slopes.

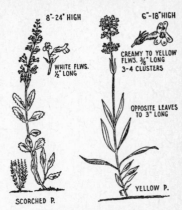

VARIED-LEAVED PHACELIA
(Phacelia heterophylla)

Varied-leaved phacelia is a tousled plant to 16" high with a dense cluster of low leaves greatly varying in shape but deeply veined and hairy. Dry banks are a favored habitat.

Flowers are usually white but may have a light purplish blush. They too are hairy and grouped in thick fuzzy clusters. The blooming time is middle to late summer depending on elevation.
RANGE: Mostly Sagebrush and Bunchgrass Zones. Wenatchee, Pasco.
WHITE-LEAVED PHACELIA *(P. leucophylla)* is quite similar but has silvery leaves from dense hairs. The leaves are not lobed or "winged". Dry slopes of Sagebrush and Bunchgrass Zones.

ELEGANT MARIPOSA LILY
(Calochortus elegans)

Elegant Star Tulip
Cat's Ear, Three Spot

The name "Elegant" is well chosen for the white petals are lushly carpeted with white hairs which become yellow in the throat of the flower. Embellishing this is a purple-violet pouch near the base of each petal, thus the name of Three Spot.

This lily, one of seven in Washington, is 6" - 16" in height and carries from 1 - 3 blooms. A ribbed basal leaf provides suitable balance. A few small leaves adorn the upper stem and there is a scattering of purple dots near the base of the sepals. Late June into July is the blooming time.
RANGE: Dryish flats of Bunchgrass and Yellow Pine Zones. Wenatchee, Pullman.
BAKER'S MARIPOSA LILY *(C. apiculatus)* to 16" high, differs in having pale yellow petals densely covered with yellow hairs on the lower half. The gland is round and blackish. Blooms late June into July. Open grassland or Yellow Pine Zone in northeastern Washington.

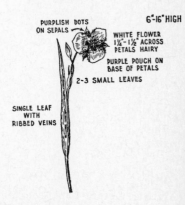

4"-10" HIGH
5 WHITE PETALS "3-FINGERED"

FRINGE CUP
(Tellima parviflora)
(Lithophragma parviflora)

Fringe cup is one of the early spring wild-flowers that can be confused with several plants with small white flowers such as field chickweed, Siberian miner's lettuce and montia. If you think of the "fringe" part of the name while looking at the five petals, each so deeply fringed as to look like three separate parts, you should be able to remember the name. Fringe cup grows on fairly open ground, such as swales and forest borders. It is one of the first flowers and blooms from April to June. The flowers look like large symmetrical snowflakes with a pinkish tinge. Blooms and buds cluster in profusion at the top of thin stems.

RANGE: Open places on Gulf Islands. Generally east of Cascades in Bunchgrass and Yellow Pine Zones.

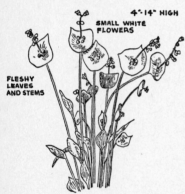

4"-14" HIGH
SMALL WHITE FLOWERS
FLESHY LEAVES AND STEMS

MINER'S LETTUCE
(Claytonia perfoliata)
(Montia perfoliata)

Miner's lettuce is a significant name for it means what it says. Indians first used the fresh plant for food. Then the early miners, prospectors, and trappers, often at a loss for green vegetables copied the Indians and found it was a tasty succulent green. Several other related species may be called miner's lettuce also. The plant is in bloom and suitable for eating during April and May.

The unusual feature about this species is the saucer-shaped upper leaves through which the stem protrudes. The small white flowers grow along thin stems rising from the centre of the leaf discs. The lower leaves are of more ordinary design and have long stems.

RANGE: Coastal Forest Zone. Blue Mountains. Sporadic in wet shady places at low elevations east of Cascades.

5"-12" HIGH
5 WHITE NOTCHED PETALS WITH RED LINES

SIBERIAN MINER'S LETTUCE
(Claytonia sibirica)

You don't have to go to Siberia to find this plant although that is where it was first discovered. It differs from miner's lettuce in not having the upper pair of leaves form a disk. However, they are short-stemmed while the lower leaves have long stems.

The flowers, on long thin stems, have 5 petals quite noticeably notched and sometimes pinkish from red lines on them. During April and May you will find this flower in the rich moist soil of meadows or road ditches. Like miner's lettuce it is excellent for salad greens.

RANGE: Common in wet places of Coastal regions. Yellow Pine and Mountain Zones.

LEPTARRHENA
(Leptarrhena amplexifolia)
(Leptarrhena pyrolifolia)

This plant is most prominent just as the snow leaves the soggy meadows at and above timberline. Then its leathery, glossy green leaves make a vivid mat pattern against the dead grasses of the past year. It also finds a suitable habitat along the banks of small creeks. Leaves are 1" - 3" long, with a sheath-like base clasping the short and thick main stem. A marked difference is seen in the dark green surface of the leaf and the whitish green tone displayed beneath.

In early summer the plant is found by its 6" - 12" high stalks carrying dense clusters of small white flowers at their tips. One or two thickish leaves occur on the flower stem.

As frosts grip the meadows, this member of the saxifrage family adds its final decorative touch, a beautiful purplish-red seed stem with a tight packed cluster of seeds of the same brilliant hue.

RANGE: Sub-alpine and alpine meadows of Olympic and Cascade Ranges. Mt. Rainier.

BUCKBEAN
(Menyanthes trifoliata)

The fact that buckbean grows in water enables a person to find it without too much trouble. Marshy places like bogs or around the borders of shallow lakes are a favoured habitat. Its 3-parted leaves are unmistakable. Note how the thick fleshy stems are sheathed at their bases.

The stout flower stem to a foot high carries a dozen or more heavy flowers. These are about 1/2" long and vary from a drab white to a pale purplish tinge. The five petals have a fuzzy appearance from fine hairs on their surface. Usually the petals curve back disclosing a hairy throat.

Buckbean blooms in May and June.

RANGE: Marshy places across the State.

BANEBERRY
(Actaea arguta)

Baneberry is a leafy plant to 3' high with an erect stem holding 2 or 3 leaves broken into divisions of three, or ternately compound. Leaves are crinkled and coarsely and sharply toothed.

Small white flowers in a dense cluster make a fuzzy white ball because of the many protruding stamens. Watch for the bloom of this easily recognized plant from April into June. Do not confuse it with a false bugbane. See Page 114. By August, handsome scarlet berries, smooth and firm, flaunt their charms. Occasionally white ones are produced. There is a strong possibility that baneberries are poisonous.

RANGE: Moist shady places from sea level to mountain forests. Also Yellow Pine Zone.

CLUSTER OF SMALL WHITE FLOWERS — 6"-12" HIGH — PURPLISH-RED SEEDS & STEM — THICK LEATHERY LEAVES TO 3" LONG — WET GROUND

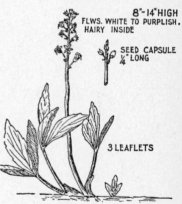
8"-14" HIGH — FLWS. WHITE TO PURPLISH, HAIRY INSIDE — SEED CAPSULE 1/4" LONG — 3 LEAFLETS

SCARLET OR WHITE BERRIES — 1'-3' HIGH — DENSE CLUSTER OF SMALL WHITE FLOWERS (MANY STAMENS) — LEAVES COARSE-TOOTHED — LEAVES 2-3 TIMES DIVIDED IN 3's

2"-4" HIGH
WHITE 'STAR'
FLWS. ¼" ACROSS

LEAVES
⅛"-¼" LONG

TOLMIE SAXIFRAGE
(*Saxifraga tolmiei*)

Alpine Saxifrage

The saxifrages represent a very widespread group of flowers. Characteristics are basal leaves, sepals in a 5-lobed sheath, 5 entire petals, and generally 10 stamens. A large number of species are less than 6" high and the habitat is mostly on rocky places.

Tolmie saxifrage is quite common on dryish, exposed places above timberline. The leaves form a compact shrubby mat from which slender flower stems rise from 2"-4". Leaves are evergreen, mealy, ⅛"-¼" in length, round-tipped, and with a tendency to roll over on the edges. One or several small star-like flowers adorn the stems.

RANGE: High alpine slopes of Olympic and Cascade mountains.

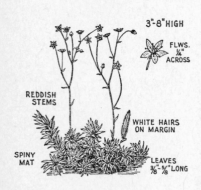

3"-8" HIGH

FLWS.
¼"
ACROSS

REDDISH
STEMS

WHITE HAIRS
ON MARGIN

SPINY
MAT

LEAVES
⅜"-⅞" LONG

SPOTTED SAXIFRAGE
(*Saxifraga bronchialis*)

Common Saxifrage

This plant is somewhat similar to the above in mat-like growth but the leaves are spiny and sharp, ¼"-½" long, and with hairy margins. The small white flowers form a galaxy of sparkling stars atop slim stems. Look closely and you will see that the tiny white petals are artistically speckled with distinct maroon and yellow dots.

There are two varieties, *austromontana* and *vespertina*, distinguished by their range. The former is very abundant in rocky places near and just above timberline. Olympic and Cascade mountains.

VESPER SAXIFRAGE (*S. bronchialis* var *vespertina*) grows in exposed places along the edge of cliffs and rock slides. Seldom does it ever extend to timberline. The range is not well known. Coot Mountains, Mt. Baldy.

3"-6" HIGH

WHITE FLWS.
10 ORANGE STAMENS

HAIRY,
PURPLISH

LEAVES
RED WOOLLY

RUSTY SAXIFRAGE
(*Saxifraga rufidula*)

Red Woolly Saxifrage

This plant takes its name from the red woolly appearance of the underside of the leaf. The stem helps the idea along by having a purplish hue. Leaves are thick, leathery, and coarsely but regularly toothed. The branched stem carries a number of white flowers beautified by 10 orange stamens. Blooming time is May to August.

RANGE: Alpine Zones of Cascades and Olympics. Also Columbia R. gorge.

SAXIFRAGE
(Saxifraga integrifolia)

This particular saxifrage is common west of the Cascades. It is found on mossy exposed places during March and April with other early spring flowers such as peacocks, satin flower, and spring gold. The stem is reddish and hairy and the small white flowers form a not too attractive packed cluster. Leaves are thick and shallowly notched. Many are reddish beneath. Other species show a great variety in leaf, some being notched and others lobed.

RANGE: Open places at low elevations west of Cascades. Puget Sound, Tacoma.

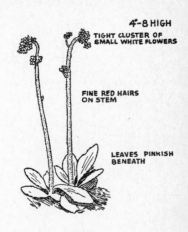

4"-8 HIGH

TIGHT CLUSTER OF SMALL WHITE FLOWERS

FINE RED HAIRS ON STEM

LEAVES PINKISH BENEATH

FIELD CHICKWEED
(Cerastium arvense)

Star of Bethlehem

This fresh white little flower rising on a thin stem from a mat of leaves has a world-wide distribution but nevertheless makes a convincing display at being a native wildflower.

Each flower is about ½" across and has 5 petals which are so deeply cleft in two that they are easily mistaken for a total of 10. The hairy stems carry narrow sharp-pointed leaves but a leafy mat-like growth is not uncommon. Field chickweed often is found with other spring wildflowers which grow on the drier rockier places. It has a prolonged blooming season from April into June.

RANGE: Sporadic across Washington from low to alpine elevations.

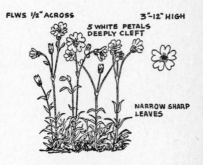

FLWS ½" ACROSS

3"-12" HIGH

5 WHITE PETALS DEEPLY CLEFT

NARROW SHARP LEAVES

WILD LILY-OF-THE-VALLEY
(Maianthemum unifolium dilatatum)

The twisting veiny leaves are sufficient aid in recognizing this small plant which generally masses together in shady places. Each short stem holds one or two waxy leaves. During May a 2"-4" long spike of small white flowers rises above the leaves. This display is short-lived but even so is embellished by each flower having knobby protruding anthers and a delicate scent. The berries that follow are first mottled with brown but later change to ruby beads.

RANGE: Common at low elevations of Coastal region.

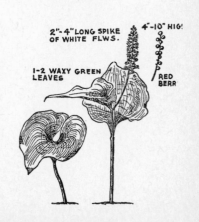

2"-4" LONG SPIKE OF WHITE FLWS.

4"-10" HIGH

1-2 WAXY GREEN LEAVES

RED BERR

FLOWERS (WHITE)

6"-12" HIGH

6 WHITE PETALS

GOLDEN ANTHERS

B ROWN MOTTLING ON SHINY GREEN LEAVES

EASTER LILY
(*Erythronium oregonum*)

Dog-tooth Violet

In spring many forest glades are carpeted by this regal white lily. Almost as showy as the flower are the mottled glossy leaves. Well out of sight deep in the ground is a bulb which requires 5 - 7 years to develop before raising its first flower stem. Seed dropped from the flowers accounts for the great masses of lilies often seen in secluded surroundings.

The Easter lily blooms in April and is particularly abundant in some localities. This condition can hardly be expected to continue for many unthinking people go to great trouble to pick every flower they can find.

RANGE: Coastal Forest Zone. Another species with pink anthers is found in eastern Washington.

PINK EASTER LILY (*E. revolutum*) has pink petals and grows sparsely in Coastal forests.

WHITE OR PINK FLWS 1 1/2" - 2" ACROSS

6"-24" HIGH

WESTERN TRILLIUM
(*Trillium ovatum*)

Wake Robin

There is no chance of confusing the trillium with any other flower. Its stout stem carries three large, net-veined leaves which form a whorl to cradle the short-stemmed white flower. There are three petals from 1" - 2" long and 6 dark, fuzzy stamens in the centre. The pure white flower undergoes a change to purple or pink as it ages. The blooming season is from mid-April to the end of May. See page 175 for a purple trillium.

RANGE: Coastal Forest Zone and upward to middle mountain elevations. Yellow Pine Forests of eastern Washington.

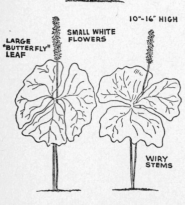

10"-16" HIGH

SMALL WHITE FLOWERS

LARGE "BUTTERFLY" LEAF

WIRY STEMS

VANILLA LEAF
(*Achlys triphylla*)

May Leaves — Sweet-after-death

The masses of large 3-winged "butterfly" leaves will be seen here and there at lower elevations throughout shady coniferous forests. A thin wiry stem about a foot high holds a single leaf artistically divided into 3 wavy-edged segments. The leaves start to take shape by mid-April and in May a thin flower stem unerringly pokes its way between a narrow leaf cleft to hold aloft a spike of small white flowers.

The name comes from the faint vanilla odor of the dried leaves as does sweet-after-death, another name sometimes used. A bundle of dried leaves hung in a room is supposed to repel flies.

RANGE: Low and middle elevations in Coastal Region.

BUNCHBERRY
(Cornus canadensis)

Pigeon Berry

Bunchberry is a relative of the flowering dog-wood tree. In its few inches of height are contained all the dogwood tree features except size. See how similar are the leaves with their parallel curved veins. The "flower" too has a greenish centre of tiny flowers surrounded by a number of showy white bracts. This produces the effect of a white blossom about 1" across.

Bunchberry is one of the more abundant forest flowers and carpets many forest dells and glades. Sometimes it will grow on old stumps and logs where soil has collected. Flowers may be well out in May and, like the tree dogwood, the tiny plant sometimes blooms again in late summer. By August most plants have developed a cluster of brilliant red berries, a showpiece more impressive than the flowers. These, although insipid and mealy, are in no way poisonous.

RANGE: From sea level to sub-alpine heights in moist forests. Most common in Mountain Forest Zone.

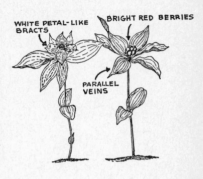

3"-8" HIGH

WHITE PETAL-LIKE BRACTS

BRIGHT RED BERRIES

PARALLEL VEINS

QUEEN'S CUP
(Clintonia uniflora)

Alpine Beauty

Queen's Cup is a widespread forest flower that is bound to come to the attention of every mountain hiker. Its two or three shiny green leaves from 4" - 8" in length mark it immediately. From May to July a slender stem about 6" high carries one pure white flower about 1" across. This is followed by a most unusual oval berry. Its deep, china-blue color is one not often seen in nature.

RANGE: Most abundant at middle mountain elevations where it may carpet the mossy forest floor. It ranges across the State.

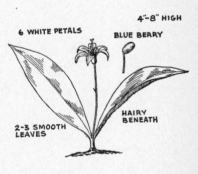

4"-8" HIGH

6 WHITE PETALS

BLUE BERRY

2-3 SMOOTH LEAVES

HAIRY BENEATH

RATTLESNAKE PLANTAIN
(Peramium decipiens)
(Goodyera decipiens)

Mossy but fairly dry places in coniferous forests are home to this plant with the peculiar name and leaves. The long ovalish leaves which grow close to the ground are a dark green color laced with a criss-cross network of white. This marking is supposed to resemble that on a rattlesnake.

Often the leaves are the only feature to be seen for the plant does not bloom every year. When it does it produces a thickish stalk with small greenish-white flowers loosely scattered along the spike. There is a tendency for the flowers to favor one side of the stem. The blooming time is midsummer.

RANGE: Coastal region and dry coniferous forests across Washington at middle elevations.

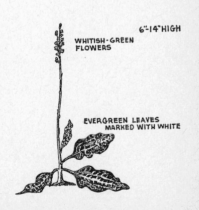

6"-14" HIGH

WHITISH-GREEN FLOWERS

EVERGREEN LEAVES MARKED WITH WHITE

[111]

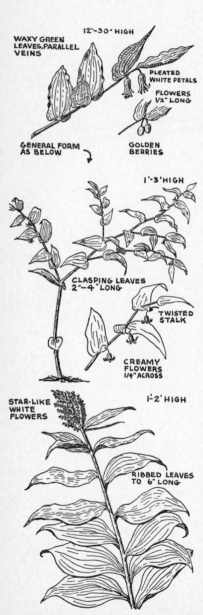

WAXY GREEN LEAVES, PARALLEL VEINS

12"-30" HIGH

PLEATED WHITE PETALS

FLOWERS 1/2" LONG

GENERAL FORM AS BELOW

GOLDEN BERRIES

1'-3' HIGH

CLASPING LEAVES 2"-4" LONG

TWISTED STALK

CREAMY FLOWERS 1/4" ACROSS

STAR-LIKE WHITE FLOWERS

1'-2' HIGH

RIBBED LEAVES TO 6" LONG

OREGON FAIRY BELLS
(Disporum oregonum)

Smooth Fairy Bells

Glossy veined leaves cover its several branches and effectively hide the creamy 2-3 flowers. During May and June look for the pairs of drooping, bell-shaped flowers near the tips of each branch. After the flowers are over an oblong smooth berry will form. It varies from yellow to orange and its pulpy centre surrounds several large seeds. The berry looks edible but its taste doesn't bear out the appearance.

RANGE: Lower elevations of Coastal Forest and moist woods of Yellow Pine and Mountain Forest Zone east of Cascades.

ROUGH FAIRY BELLS (*D. trachycarpum*) has larger and more greenish flowers than the above. The berry is more rounded and has a velvety fuzz to it. When ripe it turns a rich red color. The range is east of the Cascades in the Yellow Pine Forest Zone.

TWISTED STALK
(Streptopus amplexifolius)

Twisted stalk gets its name from the curious sharp twist in the hair-like stems carrying the flowers and berries. This oddity of structure serves for immediate identification whereas the leaves are confused easily with other plants. The alternate leaves clasp the stem and grow so close together they often hide the flowers or berries. The white or cream-colored flowers which hang one to the stem, are about 1/4" long and will be found in bloom during May and June. Even when the oblong bright red berries are formed the kink in the stems still remains.

RANGE: Shady damp woods across Washington at middle elevations.

FALSE SOLOMON'S SEAL
(Smilacina amplexicaulis)

False Solomon's seal may attract the attention by reason of its size, the large glossy leaves, or plume of creamy flowers. Each stout unbranched stem carries two rows of opposite broad leaves from 2½" - 5" long. These clasp the stem at their base. Parallel veins impart a touch of the exotic. The small whitish flowers are packed into a pyramidal cluster which emits a sweet scent. They will be found from May into June. Later in the season mottled greenish-red berries are carried which slowly turn an unusual red color. They are edible but rather tasteless with one or two seeds.

RANGE: Damp shady habitat throughout Washington.

STAR - FLOWERED SOLOMON'S SEAL
(*Smilacina stellata*)

This plant, because of similarity of name or leaf, is liable to be confused with twisted stalk, fairy bells and false Solomon's seal. The plant is fairly uniform in size being a single stem 1'- 2' high. The thin leaves 2"- 5" long clasp the main stem and point upward. It gets its name from the several white, star-like flowers at its tip. From April until June these tiny sprites make their appearance. Later, the berry becomes green with darkish stripes and slowly changes to bright red.

RANGE: Moist woods throughout Washington.

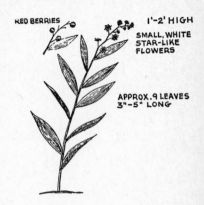

RED BERRIES
1'-2' HIGH
SMALL, WHITE STAR-LIKE FLOWERS
APPROX. 9 LEAVES 3"-5" LONG

LADIES' TRESSES
(*Spiranthes romanzoffiana*)

The distinguishing feature about ladies' tresses is the 3 vertical rows of flowers which spiral around the central stem. The suggestion of the twisting of a hair braid has led to the common name. The white or pale cream flowers are almost ½" long and have a sweet fragrance. It bears a slight resemblance to white rein orchis. The blooming season is July to August.

RANGE: Most common in Coastal Zone, but also in N. E. Washington and Blue Mountains.

WHITE BOG ORCHID
(*Habenaria dilatata*)

About half a dozen bog orchids or rein orchis are found in Washington. The Latin, *habena* means a bridle or rein alluding to the narrow lip of some species. The beautiful little orchids vary from white to greenish-yellow in color. The white bog orchid has flowers of the purest white and a perfume to match. Most species are lovers of moist soils thus leading to the common name of bog orchid.

RANGE: Medium to high elevations throughout.

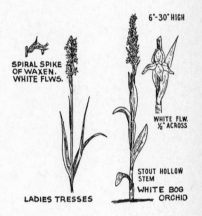

6"-30" HIGH
SPIRAL SPIKE OF WAXEN. WHITE FLWS.
WHITE FLW. ½" ACROSS
STOUT HOLLOW STEM
LADIES TRESSES
WHITE BOG ORCHID

INDIAN PIPE
(*Monotropa uniflora*)

A person finding Indian pipe for the first time is sure his senses are deceiving him. The waxy white clump of "pipes" can hardly be likened to any other growing plant. The stout brittle stems twist over at the tip and droop in a massed cluster of thick waxy scales. The leaves are white also and press closely to the stem. Indian pipe may be found in late spring or midsummer. It gets its nourishment from growing on decaying matter from other plants.

RANGE: Shady place in Coastal regions. Occasionally found east of Cascades.

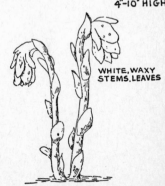

4"-10" HIGH
WHITE, WAXY STEMS, LEAVES

(113)

FLOWERS (WHITE)

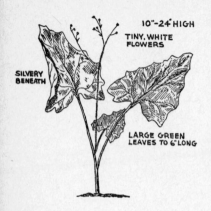

10"-24" HIGH

TINY, WHITE
FLOWERS

SILVERY
BENEATH

LARGE GREEN
LEAVES TO 6" LONG

SILVER - GREEN
(*Adenocaulon bicolor*)

Pathfinder

The most noticeable feature about silver-green is the contrast in color between the two sides of the leaf. Its alternate name of pathfinder comes from the marked path that is left when a person disturbs these plants. The dark green weedy leaves when turned over attract immediate attention by their silvery sheen and can be seen from afar. The flashing color comes from a mat of fine white hairs.

The small white flowers on their thin stems aren't noticed very often but later may prove an annoyance through the sticky seeds catching in the clothing.

RANGE: Coastal forests and moist woods at middle elevations east of Cascades.

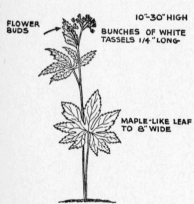

FLOWER
BUDS

10"-30" HIGH

BUNCHES OF WHITE
TASSELS 1/4" LONG

MAPLE-LIKE LEAF
TO 8" WIDE

FALSE BUGBANE
(*Trautvetteria grandis*)

False bugbane prefers shady moist places giving rise to luxuriant vegetation. For this reason the plant is usually hidden except for its head of small white bristly flowers. The bristles are formed by tufts of long stamens which are a good distinguishing feature. After blooming during late spring, bright red berries are formed.

The single leaves are maple-like and from 2" - 6" across. Generally they are wider than long and have from 5-9 lobes. Stem leaves are few and short stemmed.

RANGE: Coastal Forest Zones from low to sub-alpine elevations.

The true bugbane or baneberry is described on page 107.

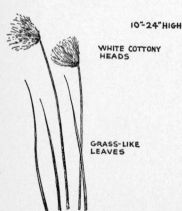

10"-24" HIGH

WHITE COTTONY
HEADS

GRASS-LIKE
LEAVES

COTTON GRASS
(*Eriophorum chamissonis*)

Although there are several species of cotton grass in B.C. the peculiar white cottony head and swamp habitat dispel any doubts as to general recognition. Often wet meadows are covered so thickly with this sedge that they appear like a field of cotton.

The springy green stems from 1' - 2' high carry a puffy ball of cotton which obscures the small flowers hidden in its depths. Leaves are short and grass-like. Cotton grass has a wide altitudinal range being found from sea level to sub-alpine meadows.

RANGE: Sedgy, wet meadows throughout Coastal Region. Sometimes east of Cascades.

FOAM FLOWER
(*Tiarella unifoliata*)

Laceflower

The fine erect stems carry only a single leaf on them but the plant is provided with a group of long-stemmed leaves growing from its base. Often masses of this delicate flower are found in favorable locations. The tiny white flowers dance on the ends of short wire-like branchlets grouped airily near the top of the stem. They have a prolonged blooming season during May to July.

RANGE: Mostly middle and high elevations in damp coniferous forests across Washington.

T. trifoliata has 3 leaflets instead of a single leaf. Coastal forests.

SMALL - FLOWER ALUMROOT
(*Heuchera micrantha*)

Alumroots with creamy or yellow flowers are given on page 159.

Alumroots are quite easily recognized from their basal group of long-stemmed, oval to heart-shaped leaves with irregular lobes and rounded notches. Long tap roots with an astringent, alum taste make a firm anchor. Often alumroot is the first plant of any size to establish itself on inhospitable cliffs. The leaves have rounded lobes and a heart-shaped base. The slender stems are reddish from fine hairs. Tiny white globes on short, delicate side branches bloom from May to July.

RANGE: Common alumroot west of Cascades.

ALUMROOT (*H. glabra*) has sharp-pointed leaf lobes and smooth stems. Abundant in Coastal Forest Zone, and up to sub-alpine elevations.

SUNDEW
(*Drosera spp.*)

The low tuft of small leaves are bristly with reddish hairs each with a tiny sticky globe at its tip. This secretion attracts insects which are caught fast when they alight and absorbed into the leaf. The inconspicuous white flowers droop near the tip of one or more thin stems. They only open in strong sunlight. The blooming period is from late spring to midsummer.

RANGE: Coastal regions and northeastern Washington.

ROUND LEAF SUNDEW (*D. rotundifolia*) has small round leaves. Sphagnum bogs.

SUNDEW (*D. anglica*) has long narrow leaves shaped like a canoe paddle. It too is found mostly in bogs or wet soils around the shores of lakes. Often occurs to sub-alpine elevations.

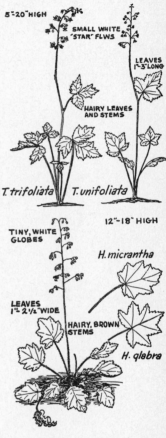

5"-20" HIGH

SMALL WHITE "STAR" FLWS

LEAVES 1"-3" LONG

HAIRY LEAVES AND STEMS

T. trifoliata   *T. unifoliata*

12"-18" HIGH

TINY, WHITE GLOBES

H. micrantha

LEAVES 1"-2½" WIDE

HAIRY, BROWN STEMS

H. glabra

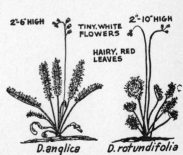

2"-6" HIGH

TINY, WHITE FLOWERS

2"-10" HIGH

HAIRY, RED LEAVES

D. anglica   *D. rotundifolia*

(115)

FLOWERS (WHITE)

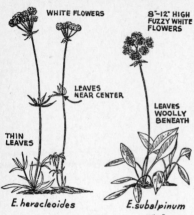

WHITE FLOWERS

8"-12" HIGH FUZZY WHITE FLOWERS

LEAVES NEAR CENTER

LEAVES WOOLLY BENEATH

THIN LEAVES

E. heracleoides

E. subalpinum
2"-8" HIGH

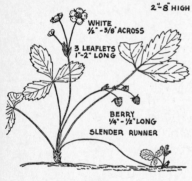

WHITE
½" - ⅜" ACROSS

3 LEAFLETS
1"-2" LONG

BERRY
¼" - ½" LONG

SLENDER RUNNER

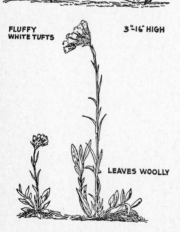

FLUFFY WHITE TUFTS

3"-16" HIGH

LEAVES WOOLLY

TALL WHITE ERIOGONUM
(Eriogonum subalpinum)

Eriogonums have a shrubby, mat-like base and white hairs on one or both sides of the leaves. The flowers are in shades of white, cream or yellow but often a reddish tinge is seen toward the end of the season.

Tall white eriogonum raises a stout stem from a dense mat of ovalish leaves which are noticeably woolly beneath. The small, white to cream flowers bunch in a compact rounded cluster supported by a series of short umbrella stems. Flowers are on display from June to August.

RANGE: On rocky or poor soils at middle to sub-alpine elevations throughout Washington.

E. heracleoides has a wisp of leaves near the centre of the stem. It grows at lower elevations and is quite common on poor soils in open places throughout the Dry Interior Zone.

See page 152 for two eriogonums with yellow flowers.

WILD STRAWBERRY
(Fragaria spp.)

The wild strawberries are much like the cultivated varieties except for their sparseness and smaller size, particularly that of the berry. Of possibly 6 different species in Washington, *F. chiloensis* is common throughout while *F. bracteata* grows west of the Cascades.

There is no plant stem for everything seen above ground is either a flower, leaf stem or runner since these branch almost directly from a scale cluster attached to the roots. The flowers have 5 white petals and later produce a very small but sweet berry.

RANGE: Widespread from low to high elevations.

WHITE PUSSYTOES
(Antennaria spp.)

White pussytoes attracts attention in the spring because of its odd woolly head. The tight ball of flowers is dry and furry and very soft to the touch. There are over a dozen species but all of these flannelly plants seek out rocky, dry places on which to grow. The leaves are alternate and entire with wider leaves at the base of the stem. Some species are so woolly as to appear quite white. One has very attractive pink flowers (page 139) and all possess "everlasting" qualities after being picked.

RANGE: Dry exposed places throughout Washington from sea level to mountain tops.

PEARLY EVERLASTING
(*Anaphalis margaritacea*)

This is a vigorous roadside plant with a flat-topped mass of white flowers. It waits until the more colorful spring flowers have faded and then in July bursts into bloom. The stems and the underside of the long thin leaves are covered with a white wool which is usually hidden from sight by the bushy mass of dark green leaves.

The tightly packed flower head, perhaps 6" across, is worth more than a passing glance. Each pearly white ball has a yellowish or brownish centre flanked by a large number of beautifully arranged parchment-like scales of delicate pastel shading. The flowers, if picked in full bloom, remain without wilting thus leading to "Everlasting" as an alternate name.

RANGE: Throughout Washington. Often seen along roads and wherever there is settlement.

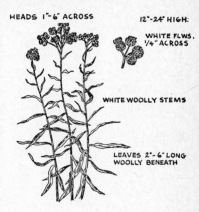

HEADS 1"-6" ACROSS

12"-24" HIGH:

WHITE FLWS. 1/4" ACROSS

WHITE WOOLLY STEMS

LEAVES 2"-6" LONG WOOLLY BENEATH

YARROW
(*Achillea millefolium*)

This plant may be thought of as a flower or weed depending on the ideas of the individual. Perhaps the weed concept arises from the wide range of yarrow over waste areas and on the poorer soils.

Arching from its stout unbranched stem are a number of leaves so finely divided into fringes that they look like large fuzzy pipe cleaners. These have a very pungent odor if crushed. The flower head of numerous small flowers is from 2" - 4" across and slightly rounded. A casual glance shows small, scaly, white flowers with yellow centres. Actually each tiny part of the flower is itself a complete flower. Both the white "ray" flowers and the yellow "disk" flowers produce seed. Yarrow blooms about June at the Coast and August elsewhere.

RANGE: Throughout Washington on dry and poor soils.

8"-20" HIGH

FLAT, WHITE FLOWER HEAD 2"-4" ACROSS

MEADOW SPIREA
(*Lutkea pectinata*)
(*Spiraea pectinata*)

This small plant, so abundant in damp open places in sub-alpine and alpine regions, differs greatly in outward appearance from the several other common spireas in the Province. The fresh green clumps only several inches high are composed of a large number of individuals. Leaves are so divided as to appear fringed like those of a fern. The slender stems carry small white flowers in bloom during midsummer.

RANGE: High mountains of Olympics, Cascades, and Blue Mountains. Extends to Alaska.

2"-4" HIGH

SMALL, WHITE FLOWERS

FRINGED LEAVES

FLOWERS (WHITE)

FLWS 1½"2" ACROSS

1'-2' HIGH

WHITE "DAISIES" WITH YELLOW CENTERS

OXEYE DAISY
(Chrysanthemum leucanthemum)

The feeling that this flower would look quite at home in a garden is perfectly right for it is a naturalized plant now widely distributed.

Its erect graceful stems, branching near the top, carry symmetrical white daisies. The combination of yellow centre and white ray petals make up a gay bloom almost 2" across. The leaves are dark green and lobed.

Sometimes entire fields are taken over by the oxeye daisy. Then the massed blooms, all at an even height, present an unforgettable sight as they shimmer in the sunshine or ripple to the touch of a breeze. The blooming season is from May to July, after the bulk of spring flowers has passed.

RANGE: Spotty occurrence in roadsides and fields of Coastal Zone. Infrequent east of Cascades. OLYMPIC ASTER *(A. paucicapitatus)* has showy white flowers on long, leafy stems. Sub-alpine meadows of Olympic Mountains.

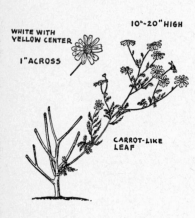

WHITE WITH YELLOW CENTER

1" ACROSS

10"-20" HIGH

CARROT-LIKE LEAF

FIELD CHAMOMILE
(Anthemis arvensis)

This flower also is daisy-like in appearance and an introduced plant but differs from the oxeye daisy in not having such large crisp flowers. It is more tousled in form being much branched and lacking the long erect stems. The white flower, about 1" across, has a yellow centre. New buds are continually developing and so lead to a prolonged blooming season during June and July. The leaves are shredded like those of carrots.

RANGE: Waste places such as roadsides here and there in Coastal region, and spotty occurrence in Bunchgrass Zone.

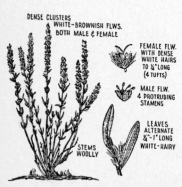

DENSE CLUSTERS WHITE-BROWNISH FLWS. BOTH MALE & FEMALE

FEMALE FLW. WITH DENSE WHITE HAIRS TO ⅛" LONG (4 TUFTS)

MALE FLW. 4 PROTRUDING STAMENS

LEAVES ALTERNATE ¼"-1" LONG WHITE-HAIRY

STEMS WOOLLY

WINTERFAT
(Eurotia lanata)

White Sage, Winter Sage

This is an important nutritive range plant during winter months. Watch for it in extensive patches on low ground showing signs of alkali. The overall whitish or heavy appearance comes from an abundance of white hairs on twigs and leaves.

Winterfat is a shrubby plant from 1'-3' high. The erect stems carry a sparse amount of small flat leaves with curled-over edges. A fuzzy appearance is imparted to the top half of the shrub through dense clusters of very hairy flowers in the leaf axils. Usually both male and female flowers occur on the same plant. The female flowers are very attractive with 4 dense tufts of white to brown silky hairs.

RANGE: Alkaline soils at low elevations east of the Cascades. Douglas and Yakima Counties.

THREE-LEAVED ANEMONE
(Anemone deltoides)

Western White Anemone

This easily recognized plant has a large white bloom closely resembling a thimbleberry blossom. Three leaves just above the half-way point on the stem are arranged in a whorl like those of trillium. The 5 sepals vary a great deal in size and shape but are ornamented by a bright green raised center serving as a base for numerous white stamens. Flowers such as this that grow in shady places often are white. This gives them the maximum of contrast with their surroundings.

RANGE: April and May in moist woods at lower elevations west of the Cascades.

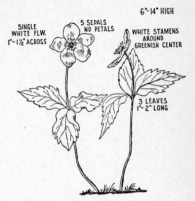

6"-14" HIGH
SINGLE WHITE FLW. 1"-1½" ACROSS
5 SEPALS NO PETALS
WHITE STAMENS AROUND GREENISH CENTER
3 LEAVES 1"-2" LONG

OREGON OXALIS
(Oxalis oregana)

There are three distinct oxalis or wood-sorrels in Washington. Leaves, when not neatly folded, look very much like those of clover. A single white or pinkish flower is carried on a stem shorter than the leaves. May is the most common blooming month.

RANGE: Damp shady woods at lower elevations west of the Cascades.

GREAT OXALIS *(O. trilliifolia)* has a cluster of several flowers with notched petals. Damp shady places to higher elevations than the above.

WESTERN YELLOW OXALIS *(O. suksdorfii)* has a bright yellow flower. Less common than the above two it favors more open ground. Coastal forest area.

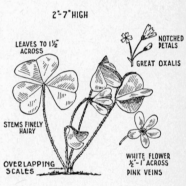

2"-7" HIGH
LEAVES TO 1½ ACROSS
NOTCHED PETALS
GREAT OXALIS
STEMS FINELY HAIRY
OVERLAPPING SCALES
WHITE FLOWER ½"-1" ACROSS PINK VEINS

YERBA BUENA
(Satureja douglasii)
(Micromeria chamissonis)

This is an intriguing little creeper both from its attractive form and historical associations. The aromatic leaves with their purplish tinge beneath are neatly arranged in pairs. From their axils arise the tiny white flowers with the 2-lobed and 3-lobed lips. Look for these blooms from May to late July depending on the locale and elevation.

Its name of Yerba Buena, or 'good herb' was given by early Spanish priests in California. Later its aromatic dried leaves were used for tea by the early settlers, a use the Indians had discovered long previous. San Francisco's main center was first known as Yerba Buena after this common little trailer.

RANGE: Lower forest elevations west of the Cascades.

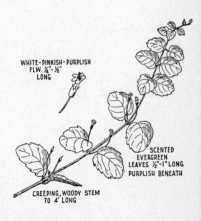

WHITE-PINKISH-PURPLISH FLW. ¼"-½" LONG
SCENTED EVERGREEN LEAVES ½"-1" LONG PURPLISH BENEATH
CREEPING, WOODY STEM TO 4' LONG

(119)

FLOWERS (WHITE)

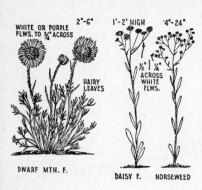

WHITE OR PURPLE
FLWS. TO 3/4" ACROSS

2"-6"

HAIRY
LEAVES

DWARF MTN. F.

1'-2' HIGH

1/2" 1/4"
ACROSS
WHITE
FLWS.

DAISY F.

4"-24"

HORSEWEED

DWARF MOUNTAIN FLEABANE
(*Erigeron compositus*)

This dainty flower with either white or purple ray petals is less than 3/4" across and has a yellow center. Generally low and many branched, the leaves are velvety and branch into thin fingers. Blooming time is from mid-summer on. There are several varieties with minor changes in leaves and hairyness.

RANGE: Dry gravelly soils of Sagebrush and Bunchgrass Zones. Spokane.

DAISY FLEABANE (*E. ramosus*) grows to 2' high and has white or creamy flowers about 1/2" across. Leaves are scant and from 1" - 1 1/2" long. It blooms in July and occurs spasmodically across the State. Wenatchee, Pullman, Spokane.

HORSEWEED (*E. canadensis*) is a common weed growing stiffly erect with a many branched stem carrying a large number of white "fleabane" flowers about 1/4" across. Leaves are slender and up to 2 1/2" long. Mostly Sagebrush and Bunchgrass Zones.

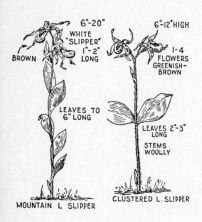

6"-20"
WHITE
"SLIPPER"
1"-2"
LONG

BROWN

LEAVES TO
6" LONG

MOUNTAIN L SLIPPER

6"-12" HIGH

1-4
FLOWERS
GREENISH-
BROWN

LEAVES 2"-3"
LONG

STEMS
WOOLLY

CLUSTERED L. SLIPPER

MOUNTAIN LADY'S SLIPPER
(*Cypripedium montanum*)

This exotic plant supports large waxy green leaves with parallel veins. Surmounting this are 1 - 3 pure white slippers veined with purple and sometimes reaching 2" in length. Several long brown petals and sepals are twisted like coppery ribbons.

There is an exquisite perfume to this unusual flower.

RANGE: Mountain Forest and Yellow Pine Zones.

CLUSTERED LADY'S SLIPPER (*C. fasicidulatum*) is a very unusual greenish brown color streaked with dull purple veins. Upper edge of the Yellow Pine Zone and extending from the Wenatchee Mountains to near the Columbia River.

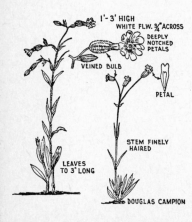

1'-3' HIGH
WHITE FLW. 3/4" ACROSS

DEEPLY
NOTCHED
PETALS

VEINED BULB

PETAL

STEM FINELY
HAIRED

LEAVES
TO 3" LONG

DOUGLAS CAMPION

NIGHT-FLOWERING CATCHFLY
(*Silene noctiflora*)

The catchfly's or campions are a widespread group of about a dozen rather weedy plants all with prominently veined bulbs formed by the 5-lobed calyx beneath the flowers. The five petals are either lobed, divided or fringed and have a scale at their base which gives the appearance of an inner row of shorter petals. Flowers may be white, pink or red. There are 10 stamens and the leaves are opposite. This catchfly is hairy throughout with white petals deeply cut into the two lobes.

RANGE: Sparse in Coastal areas but common east of Cascades particularly in Bunchgrass Zone.

DOUGLAS CAMPION (*S. douglasii*) is a high mountain species from 2" - 2' high. Flowers are white, notched, and usually 3 to a stem. Sagebrush Zone to mountain forests.

WHITE MARSH MARIGOLD
(Caltha leptosepala)

Frigid ice water trickling about its roots does not discourage this succulent plant with its stout fleshy leaves and reddish flower stems, nor its companions, the snow lily, western anemone, buttercup and globe flower. The abundant leaves, 2″ - 4″ long are characteristically folded and twisted. They are a light waxy green color. The showy flowers are from ¾″ - 1¼″ across and average about 8 white petals tinged blue on the underside. The flower center is greenish-yellow from a large number of yellowish stamens.

RANGE: Wet places above timberline on Olympic and Cascade Mountains.

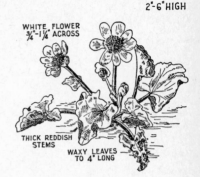

2″-6″ HIGH

WHITE FLOWER ¾″-1¼″ ACROSS

THICK REDDISH STEMS

WAXY LEAVES TO 4″ LONG

GLOBE FLOWER
(Trollius laxus)

Globe flower sometimes even pokes its precocious way through the melting snow of alpine meadows. It superficially resembles the above and should not be confused with the anemones which have a bluish tinge to the outside of the petals.

The white flower 1″ - 1½″ across has a beautiful golden center. This collar of gold is a circlet of from 15 - 25 tiny petals while the showy white bloom is composed of 5 to 6 sepals. These soon discolor and wilt. Leaves are deeply lobed. Note the group of leaves just below the flower.

RANGE: High mountains of Olympics and Cascades.

4″-20″ HIGH

SEED HEAD BROWN AND GREEN

WHITE FLOWER 1″-1½″ ACROSS GOLDEN CENTRE

AMERICAN BISTORT
(Polygonum bistortoides)

Mountain Dock
Mountain Meadow Knotweed

The white "bottle brush" about 1″ long and ½″ thick is formed of tightly packed small white flowers with protruding stamens.' The flower stem is wiry and jointed below each of the several small tapering leaves, a characteristic of the *Polygonum* or knotweed family. Blooming time is during July and August. There are several dozen knotweeds in Washington. See also pages 134 and 136.

RANGE: Alpine meadows of Olympics and Cascades. Also moist meadows in Bunchgrass and Yellow Pine Zones.

ALPINE BISTORT (*P. viviparum*) seldom exceeds 12″ in height. Its flowers vary from white to rose and are loose-clustered. Protruding stamens impart a fuzzy look. Small reddish bulblets form close to the stem below the flowers. Alpine meadows of Coast mountains in northern Washington.

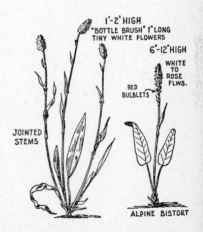

1′-2′ HIGH

"BOTTLE BRUSH" 1″ LONG TINY WHITE FLOWERS

6″-12″ HIGH

WHITE TO ROSE FLWS.

RED BULBLETS

JOINTED STEMS

ALPINE BISTORT

FLOWERS (WHITE)

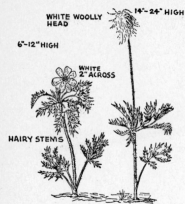

WHITE WOOLLY HEAD

6"-12" HIGH

14"-24" HIGH

WHITE 2" ACROSS

HAIRY STEMS

WESTERN ANEMONE
(*Anemone occidentalis*)

Tow-head Baby

Most people never see the flower because the plant pops up immediately the snow has left the ground. The thick stems are hairy and the leaves finely divided. A typical anemone flower with white sepals tinged with blue on the outside adorns the top of the stem. Seed is a fluffy "dust mop."

RANGE: Sparse in Olympics. Common in Cascades. Sub-alpine and alpine elevations.

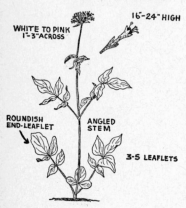

WHITE TO PINK 1"-3" ACROSS

16"-24" HIGH

ROUNDISH END-LEAFLET

ANGLED STEM

3-5 LEAFLETS

MOUNTAIN VALERIAN
(*Valeriana sitchensis*)

Among the gay alpine blooms the sweet-scented valerian raises its head of tiny white or pinkish flowers. One of the more common plants at sub-alpine and alpine heights, the blooming period may be any time during the summer. The flowers have a very fragrant perfume which is in strong contrast to the disagreeable smell of the roots.

RANGE: Approximately from 4,000' to 7,000' in Olympics, Cascades and Blue Mountains.

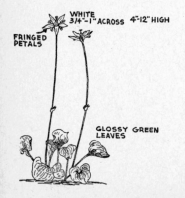

WHITE 3/4"-1" ACROSS

4"-12" HIGH

FRINGED PETALS

GLOSSY GREEN LEAVES

FRINGED GRASS OF PARNASSUS
(*Parnassia fimbriata*)

Grass of Parnassus in no way resembles a grass. Instead a single white flower tops a stem rising from an artistic cluster of glossy green, kidney-shaped leaves. One distinguishing feature is a clasping leaf half way up or more on each stem. The white flower, about 1" across, has 5 white petals veined with yellow or light green. The bottom portion of each petal is fringed artistically on each edge which, together with the odd arrangement of the stamens, makes a most unusual flower. Look for this plant in damp mountain meadows and along alpine streams.

RANGE: Sub-alpine and alpine elevations in Olympics and Cascades. Mt. Rainier, Stevens Pass.

AVALANCHE LILY
(*Erythronium montanum*)

Adders Tongue, Deers Tongue

This beautiful white lily of sub-alpine and alpine meadows often masses in the thousands on the fresh verdant growth bordering retreating snow masses. No other mountain plant creates such a dazzling spectacle nor so completely harmonizes with the ethereal quality of high places.

Often a half-dozen blooms are flaunted from one stem, their whiteness only mellowed by a tinge of gold in the throat. The 6 petal-like flower parts curve back as with most lilies. Leaves are bright green and quite glossy.

RANGE: Blooming from May to August as the snow recedes from high mountains. Cascade Mountains south from near the B.C. boundary. Olympics.

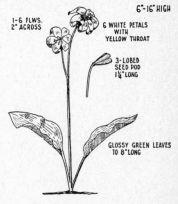

FLOWERS (WHITE)

6"-16" HIGH

1-6 FLWS. 2" ACROSS

6 WHITE PETALS WITH YELLOW THROAT

3-LOBED SEED POD 1¼" LONG

GLOSSY GREEN LEAVES TO 8" LONG

DWARF BRAMBLE
(*Rubus lasiococcus*)

The "raspberry" flower, ½" - ¾" across, with its many stamens, helps to identify this dainty shrub of the raspberry family. Where a root develops from the creeping stems a low plant arises with several distinctive 3 - 5 lobed leaves. These are finely toothed and a pale green beneath. Dwarf bramble should be checked against trailing rubus. See page 66.

The pure white flowers may be seen from May to July close to the edge of receding snows near timberline. Companions are the early blooming snow lilies, buttercups, and white marsh marigolds. The fruit is a small red raspberry, finely hairy and edible.

RANGE: Mostly Sub-Alpine Zone of Olympic and Cascade Mountains.

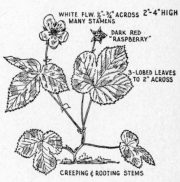

WHITE FLW. ½"-¾" ACROSS 2"-4" HIGH MANY STAMENS

DARK RED "RASPBERRY"

3-LOBED LEAVES TO 2" ACROSS

CREEPING & ROOTING STEMS

BEAR - GRASS
(*Xerophyllum tenax*)

Squaw Grass, Basket Grass

Bears supposedly have a liking for the roots of this distinctive plant. Its dense basal tuft of harsh sword-like leaves are evergreen and very noticeable on slopes at higher elevations. The stout unbranched stem carries sharp spiny leaves.

The magnificent flower head, conspicuous from afar, is a creamy-white plume of tiny whitish flowers with a strong sour odor. As it goes to seed the head elongates to 2' in length. Blooming time is soon after the snow disappears. It is believed that bear-grass only flowers once every several years.

Indians used bear-grass to weave very serviceable clothing and utensils.

RANGE: Middle mountain to sub-alpine elevations in the Cascade Mountains. Sporadic at Coastal elevations. Clallam County, Olympics.

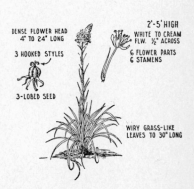

DENSE FLOWER HEAD 4" TO 24" LONG

2'-5' HIGH

WHITE TO CREAM FLW. ½" ACROSS

3 HOOKED STYLES

6 FLOWER PARTS 6 STAMENS

3-LOBED SEED

WIRY GRASS-LIKE LEAVES TO 30" LONG

(123)

WATER-PARSNIP,
WATER-HEMLOCK,
POISON-HEMLOCK

The first two of these poisonous plants grow in marshes or brackish ponds; the latter prefers drier ground. The water-hemlocks in particular are regarded as the quickest acting poisonous plants in North America. A piece of root the size of a walnut might kill a cow in less than 15 minutes. Stems, leaves and root are all poisonous with the greatest concentration being in the thick, fleshy roots. Poison-hemlock was used by the ancient Greeks in putting to death their condemned prisoners. Indians sometimes used it in a mixture to poison their arrows.

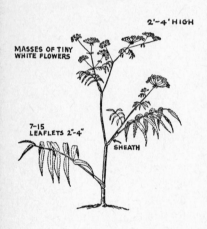

2'-4' HIGH

MASSES OF TINY
WHITE FLOWERS

7-15
LEAFLETS 2"-4"

SHEATH

WATER-PARSNIP
(Sium cicutaefolium)

A common plant of marshes and ponds noticeable in July and August because of its large size and masses of flattish, white flower heads. The "umbrella" flower stems carry very small flowers less than 1/8" across. Leaflets are long and finely toothed and the main leaf stems branch from heavy sheaths. Sometimes a few lower leaves are submerged. These differ from the other leaves in being finely fringed. Seeds are round with raised ribs.

RANGE: Coastal forests and Yellow Pine Zone. Seattle, Tacoma, Spokane, Pullman.

WATER-HEMLOCK
(Cicuta occidentalis)

Although similar in general form to water-parsnip, the leaves branch into side branchlets which may branch again to short stems holding three leaflets. The tapering leaflets may be to 4" long and have coarse teeth. An important point to notice in the water-hemlocks is that the veins on the leaflets run toward the bottom of the teeth notches rather than forward to the points. The flower head is a rounded ball of small white flower clusters. Most of the thick shallow roots when cut open will show horizontal chambers.

RANGE: Eastern Washington. Spokane, Pullman.

OREGON WATER-HEMLOCK (*C. vagans*) puts up a cluster of stout leaf stems. The foliage is generally tinged purple. Ranges across Washington.

POISON HEMLOCK *(Conium maculatum)* sparse in waste places. Shelton, Spokane. An introduced plant which is slowly spreading. Its chief difference from the above is the habitat and very fringed leaflets which give a fern-like appearance.

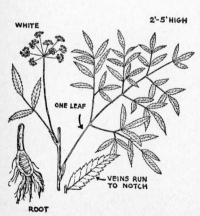

WHITE

2'-5' HIGH

ONE LEAF

VEINS RUN
TO NOTCH

ROOT

COW PARSNIP
(Heracleum lanatum)

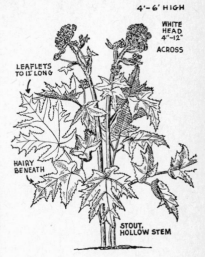

This Hercules of a plant often may reach 6' in height. Its thick coarse stems, large leaflets and wide head of flowers are all in such grand scale that possibly it qualifies for the largest perennial plant in the Province.

It will be seen on moist rich soils from sea level to almost sub-alpine elevations. A common error is that cow parsnip is poisonous. However, cattle will seek it out and the thick flower stems can be used by humans either cooked like carrots or eaten as greens.

The leaves arch from the main stem through a large sheath and hold 3 tremendous leaflets, each of which may be a foot long. At the top of the plant the main stalks divide into an umbrella of short stems each of which branches again into another umbrella framework supporting small, white flowers. The massive slightly rounded flower head may be from 4" - 10" across. After blooming in May at the Coast or several months later in the high mountains, a large number of flattened oval seeds appear, a good identifying feature when only the stalks are standing.

RANGE: Throughout Washington at low and middle elevations in rich, moist soils.

WATER PLANTAIN
(Alisma plantago-aquatica)

Plants growing in marshes are always interesting because they are not observed as often as those on firm ground where most people choose to walk. The water plantain can't claim fame by its branching head of tiny white flowers but its glossy green leaves appear as if belonging in a tropical jungle. They spring from the base of the flower stem and carry a large ovalish leaf at the end of a long thick stem.

Most times the plant is in shallow water or the muckiest of soils such as roadside ditches or low-lying swales.

RANGE: Common in suitable habitat at lower and middle elevations throughout Washington in Coastal Forest and Bunchgrass Zones. Seattle, Tacoma, Ellensburg, Wenatchee, Yakima, Pullman, Waitsburg.

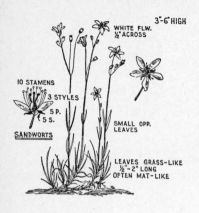

MOUNTAIN SANDWORT
(*Arenaria formosa*)

Rock Sandwort

The wide ranging sandworts are represented by about a dozen species. Nearly all tend to have a tufted or matted base, the leaves, needle-like and those on the stem opposite. Flowers are white with 5 petals, 10 stamens, and 3 styles.

Mountain sandwort is quite common on dry places and rocky ridges near and above timberline. The thin erect stems to 6" high carry dainty starlike blooms about 1/2" across.

RANGE: Exposed dry places mostly at alpine elevations. Olympics and Cascades.

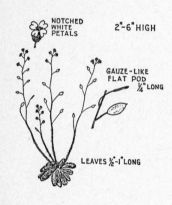

VERNAL WHITLOW GRASS
(*Draba verna*)

Flat Pod

The half-dozen or more whitlow grasses occur from sea level to mountain heights. They have either white or yellow flowers, 4 short petals, 6 stamens, wide sepals, and produce dainty round to narrow flat pods which stick out alternately from each side of the stem. When the two rows of seeds have blown away, flat gauze-like pods are left. Some species have yellow flowers.

Probably the first to greet the spring around March 21st is vernal whitlow grass a dainty wildflower 2" - 4" high. The small leaves 1/2" - 1" long are finely hairy, lobed or toothed.

This is the only one of the many whitlow grasses that has notched petals.

RANGE: Sporadic in Coastal Zone. More common in Sagebrush Zone. Walla Walla.

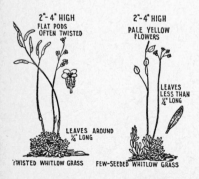

TWISTED WHITLOW GRASS
(*Draba lonchocarpa*)

There are several whitlow grasses quite similar to this but having yellow flowers. The alternate seed pods make a good identifying feature for the flat pods.

A plant of dry rocky places above timberline, it has a compact bunch of tiny narrow leaves about 1/4" long with prominent midribs. Flower stems a few inches high carry a loose head of small white flowers.

RANGE: Rocky places above timberline. Olympics and Cascades.

FEW-SEEDED WHITLOW GRASS (*D. oligosperma*) has small leaves with prominent midribs and covered with star-like hairs. Flowers are light yellow. Alpine Zone of Cascades. Mt. Rainier.

PEPPERPOD
(Platyspernum scapigerum)
(Idahoe scapigera)

During May pepperpod has circular flat pods ,inged with a very fine hoop-like strand. This holds two thin papery films marked with small purplish-brown blotches. These are the enclosed seeds. When the pods are fully ripe one film comes loose and the tiny seeds drop out. A delicate transparent sheath then remains inside the hoop. The unripe pods have a pepper-like flavor attractive to children. Tiny flowers of March and April and quickly withering leaves escape detection.

RANGE: Moist slopes in rocky soils of the Sagebrush and Bunchgrass Zones. Colville, Pullman, Goldendale.

FENDLER WATERLEAF
(Hydrophyllum fendleri)

This low loosely formed plant has a fuzzy ball of whitish flowers, pale green leaves and fleshy stems. The coarsely toothed leaves are divided into a number of leaflets. The 1" - wide cluster of blooms has protruding anthers and stamens. Each flower is about 1/4" across and supported by a hairy calyx.

RANGE: Moist places during May in Yellow Pine and Sub-Alpine Zones.

WHITE CAT'S BREECHES (H. albifrons, H. congestum): This taller waterleaf has larger leaves usually divided into 3 main divisions, the lower two deeply cut, the upper distinctly 3 - lobed. Styles and stamens protrude beyond white petals often spotted with a blue or purple dot. Spring and summer near Sub-Alpine Zone. Olympics, Cascades, and Blue Mountains. Also in Yellow Pine Zone. Okanogan and Klickitat Counties.

SLENDER-STEMMED WATERLEAF (H. tenuipes) resembles the above but has light blue to violet flowers. Shady places in Coastal Forest Zone.

BLACK NIGHTSHADE
(Solanum nigrum)

Many people believe this plant has poisonous properties but the glossy black berries are edible and even cultivated. Black nightshade, a close relative to the tomato, grows to 2' high. The older leaves to 4 1/2" long and 2" wide, generally have irregular shallow teeth. Three to eight small white flowers with protruding anthers are carried in a loose drooping cluster. Plump, glossy black berries are held by a neat greenish calyx.

RANGE: Summer bloomer in dry places in Coastal Forest Zone, also Sagebrush Zone. Tacoma, Yakima and Wawawai.

THREE-FLOWERED NIGHTSHADE (S. triflorum) is a sprawling plant with deeply lobed leaves to 2 1/2" long. Two or three white flowers develop into green berries. Sagebrush Zone.

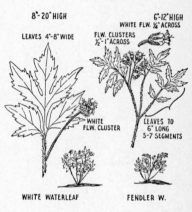

1"- 6" HIGH

FLAT WINGED SEEDS 1/8" ACROSS

FLAT PODS 1/4" ACROSS WITH PURPLISH-BROWN MARKINGS

TINY WHITE FLWS. 1/8" LONG

LEAVES 1/4"-1" LONG ENTIRE OR LOBED

8"- 20" HIGH

LEAVES 4"-8" WIDE

FLW. CLUSTERS 1/2"-1" ACROSS

6"-12" HIGH
WHITE FLW. 1/4" ACROSS

WHITE FLW. CLUSTER

LEAVES TO 6" LONG 5-7 SEGMENTS

WHITE WATERLEAF   FENDLER W.

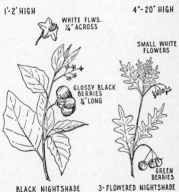

1'-2' HIGH

WHITE FLWS. 1/4" ACROSS

4"- 20" HIGH

SMALL WHITE FLOWERS

GLOSSY BLACK BERRIES 1/4" LONG

GREEN BERRIES

BLACK NIGHTSHADE   3- FLOWERED NIGHTSHADE

(127)

FLOWERS (WHITE)

1"- 4" HIGH

FEATHERY
SEED HEAD

7-8 WHITE TO CREAM
PETALS

MAT OF LEAVES
½"- 1½" LONG
GREY-HAIRY
BENEATH

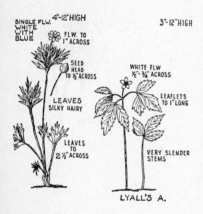

SINGLE FLW. 4"-12" HIGH
WHITE
WITH
BLUE

FLW. TO
1" ACROSS

SEED
HEAD
TO ½" ACROSS

LEAVES
SILKY HAIRY

LEAVES
TO
2 ½" ACROSS

3"- 12" HIGH

WHITE FLW
½"- ¾" ACROSS

LEAFLETS
TO 1" LONG

VERY SLENDER
STEMS

LYALL'S A.

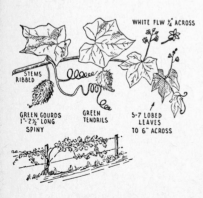

WHITE FLW ¼" ACROSS

STEMS
RIBBED

GREEN GOURDS
1"- 2½" LONG
SPINY

GREEN
TENDRILS

5-7 LOBED
LEAVES
TO 6" ACROSS

WHITE DRYAS
(Dryas octopetala)

Dryas are characterized by the mat-like growth of small crinkled leaves with silvery undersides from a dense layer of hairs. The feathery seed head is another feature. They usually choose gravel bars, rockslides or the poorest of soils.

White dryas often forms extensive mats from which short stems arise carrying white to cream-colored blooms. Note that there are 7 - 8 petals, a rather unusual number for a flower. The leaf margins are marked with rounded teeth.
RANGE: Alpine Zone Cascade Mountains. Mt. Rainier. Not in the Olympics.

DRUMMOND'S ANEMONE
(Anemone drummondii)

The widespread anemones or wind flowers generally have a basal group of toothed or lobed hairy leaves and one or two leaf whorls on the slender stem. The single flowers haven't petals but carry 5 or more petal-like sepals often with a bluish tinge. Stamens are numerous and protrude from a small central cushion. The seed head is a soft feathery or cottony mass. Drummond's anemone sometimes is dwarfed to 2" in height and generally isn't over 8" high.
RANGE: Sub-alpine and alpine zone of Olympics and Cascades.

GLOBE ANEMONE (A. globosa) is a larger edition often to 2' high. Flowers vary from red and purple to white or greenish yellow. Also relatively common in British Columbia and in Oregon. Mountain slopes.

LYALL'S ANEMONE (A. lyallii) is a slender plant with tri-foliate leaves. Shady coastal forests and to sub-alpine elevations in Olympics and Cascades. Also Klickitat County.

WILD CUCUMBER
(Micrampelis oregana)
(Echinoeystis oreganus)

A flaunting climber on fences and shrubbery, wild cucumber each year sends up from a tremendous set of roots a mass of stout stems which might reach a length of 30'. The massed foliage of large roundish leaves with 5 - 7 lobes has a sandpapery touch. Beneath they are marked by prominent raised veins. The small white flowers are of two kinds, one borne singly in the axils of the leaves, the other in loose clusters along a 4" - 6" long stem.

The light green fruit resembles a small cucumber with curved prickles. It is filled with a greenish pulp in which the seeds are imbedded. Flowers start in middle May but both flowers and fruit may be noticed on the same vine in August.
RANGE: Low rich ground in Kings County.

NORTHERN BEDSTRAW
(Galium boreale)

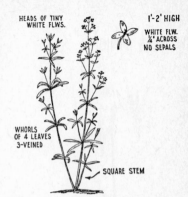

There are more than a half dozen bedstraws in Wash., but all can be quite easily recognized by their square stems and whorls of 4 - 8 leaves at the joints. Actually the two opposite leaf-like bracts give the appearance of a whorl of four.

Flowers carried in branching end clusters range from 1/8" - 1/4" across and have 4 spreading petals. They may be white, pinkish, or greenish. There are no sepals. Often the stems and fruit have short hooked spines which stick to one's clothes.

Northern bedstraw may reach 2' in height and is usually branched at its base into several stems. It may be in bloom from June to September.

RANGE: Dry places in Coastal area. Also moist places in Sagebrush and Bunchgrass Zones.

PALLID EVENING PRIMROSE
(Oenothera pallida)

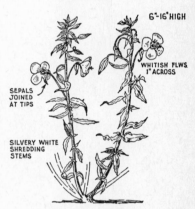

This evening primrose is a gnarled and woody, much branched plant to 16" in height. Sandy or gravelly banks with a direct southern exposure to the parching sun are the customary habitat. The 1" wide flowers are a dirty white color but the buds have a pinkish tinge.. The long sepals are generally twisted and joined at their tips. Blooming time is early summer.

RANGE: Sagebrush Zone. Wenatchee, Chelan, Pasco. Douglas and Klickitat Counties.

WILD CARROT
(Daucus carota)

Queen Anne's Lace

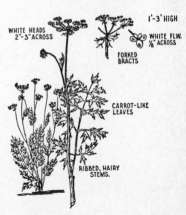

The abundance of this coarse yet dainty plant along roadsides and in waste places coupled with its late blooming time demands the attention.

Growing to 3' high it has a number of stout ribbed stems. The fern-like leaves are finely divided like the domestic carrot. The massed heads of white flowers are 2" - 3" across but the individual 4-petaled bloom is very tiny. The flowers may be seen from July into September and often are the only conspicuous blooms of that particular season.

There may be considerable variation in leaves and size of the plant in these escapes because of hybridization.

RANGE: Dry roadsides and fields of Central and Eastern Washington. Sporadic at Coast.

LITTLE WILD CARROT *(D. pusillus)* is a smaller edition of the above with finer dissected leaves and flower heads hollowed in the center to form a shallow bowl. It blooms in late summer and ranges along the Coastal Zone. Seattle.

(129)

PINK-PURPLE PETALS YELLOW RING

3-10" HIGH

PEACOCK
(*Dodecatheon spp.*)

Shooting Star

Although there are about 10 species in the State the unusual shape of the flower is sufficient to accurately mark a peacock or shooting star. All have thick succulent stems with a group of thin smooth leaves at the base.

Some species may have one or two small flowers branching out near the top, others display a half-dozen or more gaudy blooms. One has white petals and is found in the northern Cascades and Wenatchee Mountains. All the others have pink or purplish petals which streamline out behind like an Indian head-dress. The dark stamens and style cling together to form a spear-like point. Peacocks will be found in bloom from March to May.

RANGE: Low to high elevations throughout Washington.

DESERT SHOOTING STAR (*D. conjugens*) seldom carries more than 3 flowers. Each may grow to 1" in length. Leaves are ovalish with stems about as long as the blade. March to May in Bunchgrass and Yellow Pine Zones. Chelan, Ellensburg, Pullman.

FEW-FLOWERED S. S. (*D. pauciflorum*) has three to eight flowers clustered in colorful array. Note the yellow tube from which the dark purple anthers protrude. The broad paddle-shaped leaves may reach 8" in length. April to July from the Coast to middle mountain elevations. Also Yellow Pine Zone. Yakima, Pullman.

JEFFREY'S S. S. (*D. jeffreyi*) is a plant of moist meadows at sub-alpine elevations. Its large leaves may be wavey edged and extend to about 2/3 the height of the plant. Three to five flowers are the general rule. May to July. Olympics, Cascades and into Idaho.

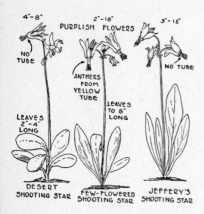

PURPLISH FLOWERS

4"-8"   2"-16"   3"-12"

NO TUBE

ANTHERS FROM YELLOW TUBE

LEAVES TO 8" LONG

NO TUBE

LEAVES 2"-4" LONG

DESERT SHOOTING STAR   FEW-FLOWERED SHOOTING STAR   JEFFERY'S SHOOTING STAR

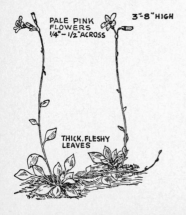

PALE PINK FLOWERS 1/4"-1/2" ACROSS

3-8" HIGH

THICK, FLESHY LEAVES

MONTIA
(*Claytonia parviflora*)

Miner's Lettuce

This plant differs from the other Miner's lettuce (page 106) in having a basal clump of fleshy bright green leaves. The flower is characteristic however, having five thin pale-pink petals. The thin stem imparts a dainty look which, with the blooms, is reminiscent of other spring flowers such as fringe cup and field chickweed also blooming during May and June.

RANGE: Coastal regions and extending eastward through Bunchgrass and Yellow Pine Zones.

SEA BLUSH
(*Valerianella congesta*)

Sea blush is an early spring flower blooming during April and May with blue-eyed Mary, satin flower, stonecrop, camas, peacock and Easter lily. It favors rocky knolls capped by moss.

The stems are squarish and rise between opposite oval leaves which are without stems. Tiny pink flowers are clustered together forming a compact rounded head.

RANGE: Gulf Islands and Coastal region extending along Columbia River to Klickitat County. Other species have slender branching stems and paler flowers. They range east of the Cascades.

THRIFT
(*Statice armeria*)

Sea Lavender

Anyone who grows the garden variety of thrift will be struck by the similarity to the wild species. There is the same compact clump of needle-like leaves about 2" long and stiff flower stems each with its pinkish dome of tiny flowers. After the flower has faded its parchment texture keeps it intact for months leading to some use for thrift in "everlasting" decorations. New shoots keep thrift in bloom for several months in the late spring.

RANGE: Open, grassy bluffs along the sea coast to Alaska. Whidby Island, Olympia, Port Crescent.

NODDING ONION
(*Allium cernuum*)

Nodding onion, which usually stands about a foot high, is easily recognized by its nodding or bent flower head of a dozen or so pink blooms. Six stamens with hair-thin stems protrude far out of the pink cup. Each petal and sepal has one thin vein down its centre line. The blooms will be found from May 15 - July 15. The few "grass" leaves rise from a thin bulb something similar to a green onion. Of the half-dozen wild onions in Wash. this is the most common and widespread.

RANGE: Sub-alpine in Olympics. Cascades on dry places. Bunchgrass Zone of Central Washington.

HOOKER'S ONION (*A. acuminatum*) differs from the above in several ways. If not in bloom the bulb can be examined. It is rounded and has a hexagonal tracing or marking on its outer coat. The few leaves wither by the time the rose-purple flowers are out. The flower head is an erect mass of beautiful, bell-like blooms. It is in bloom in late spring. Coastal region to sub-alpine slopes and Sagebrush Zone to sub-alpine heights east of Cascades.

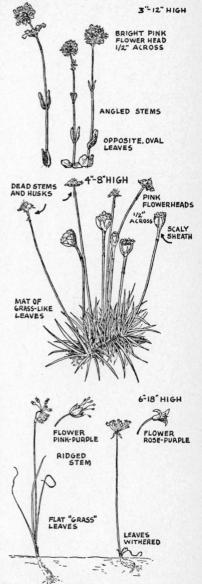

(131)

FLOWERS (PINK)

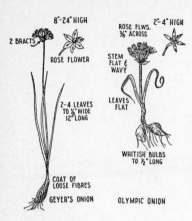

8"-24" HIGH

2 BRACTS

ROSE FLOWER

2-4 LEAVES TO ½" WIDE 12" LONG

COAT OF LOOSE FIBRES

GEYER'S ONION

ROSE FLWS. ⅜" ACROSS

2"-4" HIGH

STEM FLAT & WAVY

LEAVES FLAT

WHITISH BULBS TO ½" LONG

OLYMPIC ONION

3"-20" HIGH

SHARP SEED PODS 1"-1½" LONG

2-10 SMALL, PINK-PURPLE FLWS.

USUALLY MAT OF CARROT-LIKE LEAVES

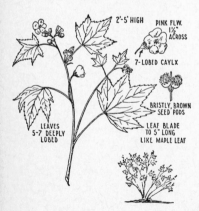

2"-5' HIGH

PINK FLW. 1½" ACROSS

7-LOBED CAYLX

BRISTLY, BROWN SEED PODS

LEAF BLADE TO 5" LONG LIKE MAPLE LEAF

LEAVES 5-7 DEEPLY LOBED

GEYER'S ONION
(*Allium geyeri*)

There are about a dozen species of onions in Washington. An important means of identity is the pattern of the bulb covering. Geyer's onion is the only one with a bulb covered with a weave of loose fibres. Other points are the 2 - 4 narrow leaves and cluster of rose flowers often mixed with pink-tinged bulblets. The two broad bracts under the flower head are usually joined on one edge. Notice that the stamens protrude about three-quarters the length of the petals.

RANGE: From moist ground to rocky exposed places. Bunchgrass Zone. Ellensburg, Coulee City. Spokane, Pullman.

OLYMPIC ONION (*A. crenulatum*) is found only in the Olympic Mountains growing at sub-alpine and alpine elevations. It is very common on rocky exposed places such as Hurricane Ridge.

FILAREE
(*Erodium circutarium*)

Storksbill, Heronsbill

This introduction from Europe has been extending its range on dry open ground for the past 50 years. It grows as a mat of finely cut leaves with flower stems an inch or two high bearing two to ten small bright pink to purplish flowers. Under favorable conditions this relation to the geraniums may reach a foot in height or branch out a foot in length. Commonly seen in bloom from March to May but flowers might be found all summer.

The most distinctive feature is the long sharp seed pods from 1" - 1½" long. These stick up in groups reminding one of a bird's nest full of hungry, long-billed young. Flowers and seed pods may be found at the same time on a plant.

RANGE: Across Washington at lower elevations.

STREAM - BANK GLOBE MALLOW
(*Iliamna rivularis*)
(*Sphaeralcea rivularis*)

This globe mallow is almost shrub-like in size with a common height of four feet. Its large pink blossoms and big leaves remind one of a garden hollyhock. Actually it is related to the wild hollyhocks since both belong to the Mallow Family.

The bushy plant has large maple-shaped leaves with 5 - 7 prominent lobes. The flower with its thin, delicate petals is supported by a cup with seven divisions. The name gives the usual habitat but occasionally the plant strays elsewhere. Blooming time is from June to August.

RANGE: Southern half of Washington in Sagebrush and Bunchgrass Zones and ranging into foothills. Wenatchee, Pullman, Blue Mountains.

PIPSISSEWA
(*Chimaphila umbellata*)

Princes' Pine

Pipsissewa, often associated with pyrola, grows in cool evergreen forests. It is 5" - 10" high with attractive leathery, evergreen, sharply-toothed leaves which cluster around the stem in loose whorls. The 3 - 9 flowers, which bloom in May or June, are bunched near the top of the stem. Waxy petals vary from white to pink.

RANGE: Throughout Washington in cool, damp, evergreen forests. Mostly at middle mountain elevations.

MENZIES' PIPSISSEWA (*C. menziesii*) is a smaller species with fewer leaves, 1 - 3 flowers, and growing to 6" high. Middle mountain elevations.

PYROLA
(*Pyrola spp.*)

Wintergreen

There are at least 7 or 8 species in Washington. Two of these may be without leaves but in general, pyrola has distinctive thick evergreen leaves in basal clusters.

Plants may be from a few inches in height to over a foot high. The flowers, arranged singly along the stem, droop down and have thick waxy petals varying from greenish white to red. Every flower has a long curved beak protruding from it. Even the seed carries this distinctive beak.

RANGE: General across the State but most abundant at mountain elevations.

SINGLE DELIGHT OR ONE-FLOWERED PYROLA (*Moneses uniflora*) has leaves like the pyrolas but is only 2" - 4" high. The single saucer-shaped, whitish or pinkish flower has a forked beak. Blooms June to August. Scattered in Coastal region but most common at middle elevations of Cascades.

BLEEDING HEART
(*Dicentra formosa*)

Its delicately fringed leaves sweep upward and almost hide the drooping row of pinkish "hearts." Each flower is a symmetrical jewel formed by the petals being held together near their tip. Matching their timid look at the world is the faint fragrant perfume. It blooms from May to June.

RANGE: Rich shady woods from sea level to middle mountain elevations west of the Cascade Mountains. Spotty east of Cascades. *D. uniflora* growing sparsely near Mt. Adams has only one or two flowers.

DUTCHMAN'S BREECHES (*D. Cucullaria*) has similar foliage but seldom reaches a foot high. Nodding flowers have a yellow tip. Seeds shiny black. Sagebrush Zone of southeast Washington. Almota. Waitsburg.

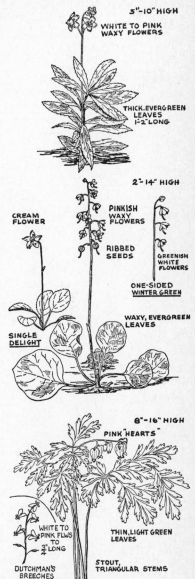

5"-10" HIGH

WHITE TO PINK WAXY FLOWERS

THICK, EVERGREEN LEAVES 1-2" LONG

2"-14" HIGH

CREAM FLOWER

PINKISH WAXY FLOWERS

RIBBED SEEDS

GREENISH WHITE FLOWERS

ONE-SIDED WINTERGREEN

WAXY, EVERGREEN LEAVES

SINGLE DELIGHT

8"-16" HIGH

PINK "HEARTS"

THIN, LIGHT GREEN LEAVES

WHITE TO PINK FLWS TO 3/4" LONG

DUTCHMAN'S BREECHES

STOUT, TRIANGULAR STEMS

TINY PINK
FLWS ⅛"
ACROSS

2'-10'HIGH

LEAVES
¼"-1" LONG
ROLLED OVER

DARK BROWN
SHRUBBY STEMS

BEACH KNOTWEED
(*Polygonum paronychia*)

This little perennial has tough woody stems and narrow curled-over leaves. The clusters of small pinkish flowers at the twig ends aren't imposing but interest in this plant arises from its ability to live on exposed beaches and wind-blown sand dunes. The flower has 5 petals each with a dark center line, 8 stamens, and a 3-cleft style. It blooms during mid- and late summer months.

Leaves are dark green, have strongly rolled-over edges and a prominent mid-rib beneath.

RANGE: Sandy beaches and dunes along Coast and on Gulf Islands.

6"-16" HIGH
BRIGHT PINK FLW.
1½"-2" ACROSS

SEPALS JOINED

DULL GREEN LEAVES
1"-2" LONG

CLARKIA
(*Clarkia pulchella*)

This flower might qualify for the oddest looking bloom in the State. At first glance it appears as if the flowers have been torn to ribbons but actually there are 4 deeply lobed petals of a bright pink-purplish hue. Notice how the flower stems are swollen and the sepals joined together at their tips. The plant is fairly uniform in height ranging from 6" - 12". Dull green leaves 1" - 2" long almost pass unnoticed compared to the attraction of this unmistakable plant. It gets its name from William Clarke of the famed Lewis and Clarke Expedition into the far Northwest.

RANGE: Bunchgrass and Sagebrush Zones. Gifford Ferry, Yakima, Pullman, Blue Mountains.

1'-2' HIGH

BRISTLY
PINK
FLOWERS

KNAPWEED
(*Centaurea spp.*)

The knapweeds, particularly those with rose or purplish flowers, will often be mistaken for thistles. However, the leaves which range from thin narrow ones to wide and serrated are not spiny... The bulb or involucre beneath the tousled flower is formed of triangular scales, in some species satiny smooth, and in others with fine bristles. The showy flowers may be yellow, blue, violet, or white and range in size from small blooms ½" across to others close to 2". Notice how they are usually at the tips of the many branched plant. Seed heads are a white fluffy mass like thistles at seed. These plants bloom from mid summer to early fall.

RANGE: Scattered throughout Eastern Washington.

BATCHELOR'S BUTTON (*C. cyanus*) is plentiful in some areas as an escaped garden flower. Although most often blue it does vary to white, purple or red. Don't confuse this with Blue Sailors. See page 161. Batchelor's Button has narrow leaves—mostly not toothed—and is not as coarse a plant. Spokane County. Pullman, Dayton.

COLLOMIA
(Collomia grandiflora)

There are several species of collomias. All are annuals with rather small trumpet-like flowers in dense terminal clusters. The gilias are very close relatives.

This collomia is the showiest of the group with very unusual salmon- or orange-colored flowers often fading to white. Flowers form a cluster of up-pointing trumpets in an overlapping leafy base somewhat resembling half of a miniature cabbage. The calyx is rough and sticky. Blooming time is June and July.

Plants are usually unbranched and grow singly and well scattered in dry exposed places.

RANGE: Very scattered at low elevations along Coast. Common in Sagebrush and Bunchgrass Zone.

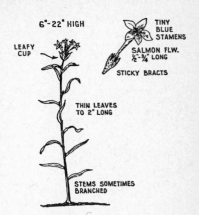

THIN-LEAVED ORTHOCARPUS
(Orthocarpus tenuifolius)

The genus *Orthocarpus* with its head of colored bracts bears a close resemblance to the paintbrushes, with shades of yellow, pink, red, and purple. Behind the bracts tiny trumpet-shaped flowers are almost hidden from sight. Typically they have an erect or curving upper lip and a lower one with three divisions.

In this species the hairy leaves are divided into three narrow fingers replaced near the top by delicately tinged pink bracts. Behind these may be seen flowers ½" - ¾" long, yellow and purplish in color, and with a hooked nose or beak. Blooming time is June and July.

RANGE: Bunchgrass Zone. Okanogan, Douglas, Spokane Counties, etc.

PINK OWL'S CLOVER (*O. bracteosus*) has a head of triangular bracts shaded a dull purple. The few flowers are a reddish purple color. Seattle. Western Klickitat County.

YELLOW ORTHOCARPUS (*O. luteus*) is a thin-stemmed plant to 16" high. Flowers are yellow and about ¼" long. Bracts are greenish and divided into 3 - 5 pointed lobes. Blooms July and August. Bunchgrass and Sagebrush Zones.

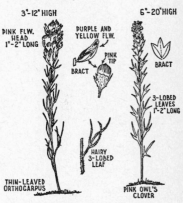

STRAWBERRY BLITE
(Chenopodium capitatum)

This plant with the bright red "strawberries" stuck to its stem belongs to the Goosefoot Family —a fanciful resemblance relating to the shape of the large triangular leaves. It may grow upright to 2' high or be sprawling.

The fruit forms in August and September after inconspicuous small greenish flowers. A red dye was made by the Indians from the "strawberries" which are edible raw or cooked.

RANGE: Grows best on upturned ground. Sporadic in Bunchgrass Zone. Spokane, Pullman.

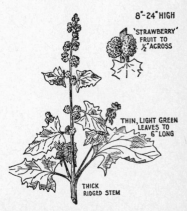

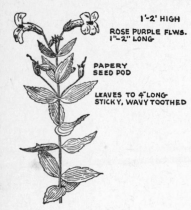

1'-2' HIGH
ROSE PURPLE FLWS.
1"-2" LONG

PAPERY
SEED POD

LEAVES TO 4"LONG
STICKY, WAVY TOOTHED

RED MONKEY FLOWER
(Mimulus lewisii)

Lewis Monkey Flower

This red mimulus often displays a spectacular mass of color many feet across. It is quite common in alpine terrain along wet banks or stream edges. The stems cluster together thickly and hold opposite, purplish-red flowers from 1" - 2" long. These "snapdragon" flowers have five petals of which two turn up and the other three down. The throat has a touch of yellow in it and may be quite hairy. A succession of new buds keeps it a profusion of bloom during July and August. The leaves are opposite and have parallel ribs which add to their beauty.

RANGE: Sub-alpine slopes of Olympics. Cascade and Blue Mountains.

STAR FLOWER
(Trientalis latifolia)

Here is a forest sprite that is fashioned in manner both neat and delicate. The simple slender stem bears a symmetrical whorl of thin oval leaves each from 1" - 3" long. These are glossy green in color and number from 4 - 7. From the centre of the leaf whorl there arises 1 - 4 thin graceful stems each carrying a single star-like flower of charming simplicity. Sometimes it is pure white, again with a pinkish tinge. Look for star flower in shady moist forests from May into June.

RANGE: Coastal forest region and at middle elevations of Cascade and Blue Mountains.

UPLAND STAR FLOWER (*T. arctica*) is much smaller than the above being only a few inches high. It grows on sphagnum moss or boggy soils and has a white waxy flower about $\frac{1}{2}$" across which is out in June to July. The range is the Coastal forest region and the Blue Mountains.

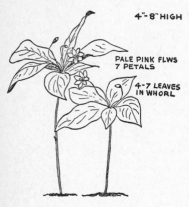

4"-8" HIGH

PALE PINK FLWS
7 PETALS

4-7 LEAVES
IN WHORL

WATER KNOTWEED
(Polygonum amphibium)

Water Buckwheat

On occasion water knotweed grows so thickly that the surface of the water is given a pinkish blush from the short rosy spikes of flowers. Shallow lake edges or ponds are home to this aquatic plant which roots in the mud and raises to the surface stems up to 20' long. Often the leathery oblong leaves aren't noticed for they usually lie flat on the water. Look for the rose-pink spikes during July and August. They can be seen from afar. Water knotweed is a plant everyone should know because of its unusual aquatic nature and attractive bloom.

RANGE: Coastal forests and Yellow Pine Zone. Seattle, Okanogan County, Pullman.

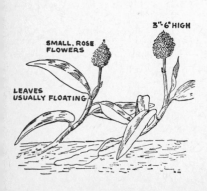

3"-6" HIGH

SMALL, ROSE
FLOWERS

LEAVES
USUALLY FLOATING

COLUMBINE
(*Aquilegia formosa*)

Sitka Columbine — Western Columbine

Among the amazing floral works of Nature, columbine surely leads the way. The word columbine, which refers to a dove, is most apt for the five scarlet petals that arch backward do have a fancied resemblance to five perched doves. The "head" is a honey gland which can only be reached by humming birds or long-tongued butterflies. Moist, partly shaded roadsides and glades are sought. In alpine meadows vast areas often are covered almost completely with this prolific bloomer. Flowers show from May to August.

RANGE: Coastal region of Cascade Mountains to 5,500'. Yellow Pine Zone of Central Washington. Blue Mountains. Olympics.

YELLOW COLUMBINE (*A. flavescens*) is more rare than the above. The flowers are almost completely yellow. At middle to high elevations in Cascade Mountains. Mt. Baldy, Wenatchee Mountains.

WILD TIGER LILY
(*Lilium parviflorum*)

The wild tiger lily is very suggestive of the cultivated plant. Sometimes there are from 6-9 drooping blooms. The long anthers stand out from the flower. Since wild tiger lily grows from low to high altitudes the blooming season may range from June to August. Most of the narrow leaves form whorls up and down the stem. The plant grows from a large scaly white bulb that is edible when cooked.

RANGE: Coastal forest region and extending across Cascades into edge of Yellow Pine Zone.

BROWNS PEONY
(*Paeonia brownii*)

This peony is the sole native species of North America. Its dull brownish-red flowers and habit of growing as scattered individuals keep it relatively obscure. The heavy flower, about 1" across, appears to have a double row of petals. Actually the outer row are greenish to purplish sepals and the slightly larger inner sheaf is formed of 5-10 dull brownish-red petals. The center of the flower has an irregular fleshy bulb on which the stamens are set.

Leaves are fleshy with a waxy feel. Soon after blooming in April or May the whole plant droops to the ground.

RANGE: East of the Cascades. Grassy slopes of Yellow Pine Zone to Sub-alpine Zone. Spokane, Leavenworth.

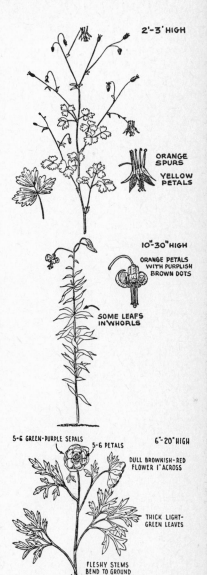

2'-3' HIGH

ORANGE SPURS

YELLOW PETALS

10"-30" HIGH

ORANGE PETALS WITH PURPLISH BROWN DOTS

SOME LEAFS IN WHORLS

5-6 GREEN-PURPLE SEPALS

5-6 PETALS

6"-20" HIGH

DULL BROWNISH-RED FLOWER 1" ACROSS

THICK LIGHT-GREEN LEAVES

FLESHY STEMS BEND TO GROUND AFTER BLOOMING

INDIAN PAINTBRUSH
(Castilleja spp.)

Painted Cup

Many different species grow in Washington with colors ranging through shades of yellow, orange, pink and crimson. The tiny flowers are hidden by crimson, leaf-like bracts which give the plant the look as if having been dipped in a pot of bright paint. Two of the most common are given below:
C. angustifolia is from 6"-12" high with lower leaves very noticeably lobed. Throughout Washington at lower elevations.
C. miniata may be 2' high and has narrow, sharp-pointed leaves. It favors moist places and is most abundant at high elevations.

YELLOW PAINTBRUSH may be one of several species growing in open places above timberline.

MAGENTA PAINTBRUSH (*C. oreopola*) has a beautiful purplish tinge. Alpine meadows of Olympics and Cascades.

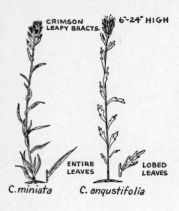

CRIMSON LEAFY BRACTS.
6"-24" HIGH
ENTIRE LEAVES
LOBED LEAVES
C.miniata   *C. angustifolia*

SCARLET GILIA
(Gilia aggregata)

The vividness of the scarlet trumpets is beyond belief and many persons think they have found something of great rarity when first seeing it. Actually it is quite common in certain ranges. The thin stems are usually quite straight with a number of slender branches near the top. The leaves are narrow, drab and hardly noticed. Thin trumpets about 1" long flare into 5 petals with small white marks dabbed on the red. The blooming season is from May 15 - July 15.

RANGE: East of Cascades from Sagebrush Zone to 6,000' on southern exposures. Blue Mountains.

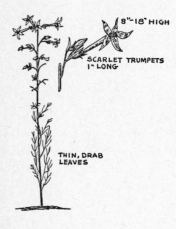

8"-18" HIGH
SCARLET TRUMPETS 1" LONG
THIN, DRAB LEAVES

SPREADING PHLOX
(Phlox diffusa)

Carpet Pink

The green cushions of short thin leaves decorated with small pink blossoms show from June to August. The flowers are less than 1/2" across and sit close to the leaves.

RANGE: Open rocky places in high mountain forests to alpine heights. Olympics and Cascades.

DOUGLAS PHLOX (*P. douglasii*) forms a low mat like the above. The many flowers may be white, pink or mauve and bloom in May. Dry exposed places on easterly slopes of Cascades. Two other species, *P. rigida* and *P. canescens* (*hopdi*) are also mat-like and very similar.

MOSS CAMPION (*Silene acaulis*) closely resembles the above species. It forms a more compressed mat and ranges at alpine heights in the Cascades.

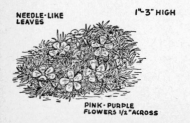

NEEDLE-LIKE LEAVES
1"-3" HIGH
PINK-PURPLE FLOWERS 1/2"ACROSS

PHLOX
(Phlox longifolia)

3"-10" HIGH

PINK
FLOWERS

THIN LEAVES
3/4"-2" LONG

Phlox is one of the welcome spring wildflowers of the Dry Interior. It grows on the lower mountain slopes where yellow bells and spring sunflowers also are found earlier in the season. Usually the plant forms a low rounded tuft covered with a mass of small pink or lavender flowers.

Leaves are long and thin. When crushed they emit a pungent odor. After blooming from May into June the plant becomes quite inconspicuous amongst the range plants.

RANGE: Dry places east of Cascades. Sagebrush and Bunchgrass Zones mostly.

P. viscida is similar but with hairy, sticky, toothed leaves. Bunchgrass Zone of south central Washington and Blue Mountains.

BITTERROOT
(Lewisia rediviva)

Rock Rose

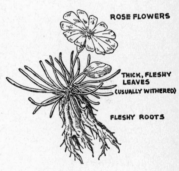

1"-3" HIGH

ROSE FLOWERS

THICK, FLESHY
LEAVES
(USUALLY WITHERED)

FLESHY ROOTS

Bitterroot is an abundant spring bloom on the most exposed places throughout the dry Interior. It suddenly appears in May as if by magic and disappears in the same fashion. The rose-pink flowers hug close to the ground, their 10 - 15 petals spread wide in the sunshine. By the time the flowers appear the tufts of fleshy leaves have dried up. The root is thick and fleshy and was used in large quantities by the Indians. When the roots are boiled they swell up and become jelly-like. An early explorer says that a sack of roots would buy a good horse. The bitterroot is the state flower of Montana.

RANGE: On rocky places through the Sagebrush and Bunchgrass Zones. Ellensburg, Spokane, Wenatchee.

ROSY PUSSYTOES
(Antennaria rosea)

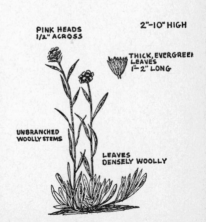

PINK HEADS
1/2" ACROSS

2"-10" HIGH

THICK, EVERGREEN
LEAVES
1"-2" LONG

UNBRANCHED
WOOLLY STEMS

LEAVES
DENSELY WOOLLY

Most of the pussytoes are white. See page 116. All have the whitish matted stems and leaves characteristic of plants that live in bright sunshine and withstand drought. The fanciful name comes from the resemblance of the soft roundish heads to the hairy toes of a cat. Pink pussytoes sometimes is dwarfed to a few inches in height but otherwise may reach to 8". The alternative leaves are very narrow and almost white with a soft wool. They form a thick mat at the base. The flowers bunch in a rounded head of rosy balls which get their color from the outer papery bracts. If the plant is picked it will retain its natural color for years.

RANGE: East slopes of Cascades into Bunchgrass and Yellow Pine Zones.

(139)

FLOWERS (RED)

5 PETALS
5-PARTED CALYX

8"-18" HIGH

FLOWERS ¾" ACROSS
ORANGE TO BRICK-RED

LEAVES PALE GREEN
MEALY, TO 2" LONG

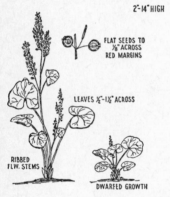

2"-14" HIGH

FLAT SEEDS TO ⅛" ACROSS
RED MARGINS

LEAVES ½"-1½" ACROSS

RIBBED FLW. STEMS

DWARFED GROWTH

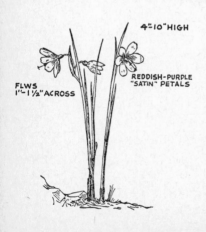

4"-10" HIGH

REDDISH-PURPLE "SATIN" PETALS

FLWS 1"-1½" ACROSS

WHITE-LEAVED GLOBE MALLOW
(*Sphaeralcea munroana*)

Munroe's Desert Mallow

This flower grows in arid places with sagebrush as a common companion and has a bloom of an unusual orange or brick-red color. Other features of significance are the very pale green leaves and stem, and rather loose form of several branching fibrous stems. The leaves have the characteristic mealy texture and lobing of the mallows. They have 3 - 5 lobes and reach 2" in length with leaf stems almost as long.

Flowers and buds form showy clusters in the leaf axils. The five colorful petals are held by a 5 - parted calyx and there are numerous stamens. Blooming time varies from May in the extreme south-east to late summer in more northern regions.
RANGE: Sagebrush Zone throughout Washington. Coulee City, Yakima, Wenatchee, El Paso.

MOUNTAIN SORREL
(*Oxyria digyna*)

Like the closely related sorrels (*Rumex spp.*) the leaves of mountain sorrel have a bitter acid taste. Some plants on very poor situations may only reach 2" in height and have leaves hardly larger than ½" across. Generally it is from 4" - 14" high with about six thin rounded basal leaves from ½" - 1½" wide.

The small, green flowers are inconspicuous and unattractive but, as is often the case, give rise to distinctive seed masses. Each seed is flat, circular, and about ⅛" across. The margin or wing is a pale red imparting a blush to the entire seed mass. Notice the extremely fine stems carrying each seed.
RANGE: Blooming July to September near or above timberline. Olympics, Cascades.

SATIN FLOWER
(*Sisyrinchium grandiflorum*)

Grass Widows

The northern Coast region and adjacent islands enjoy a climate that produces an abundance of spring wild flowers. Camas, stonecrop, saxifrage, Easter lily, violets, trillium, and peacocks are some of the more common and no doubt satin flower should be included. Almost every rocky knoll with its springy carpet of fresh moss is further enlivened in April by clumps of beautiful satin flower. From a spray of long thin leaves that look like stout grass blades there arises a stem or two bearing several reddish-purple flowers with unusual satin-like petals. A single flower may be from 1" - 1½" across and when massed they are particularly attractive. Unlike most flowers they have a very short life and start to wither after a day or two of full bloom. See page 160 for other species.
RANGE: Gulf Islands and north Coastal region. Also Yellow Pine Zone, Yakima, Pullman, Spokane.

(140)

HAIRY CAT'S EAR
(*Hypochaeris radicata*)

There is a close resemblance to a dandelion in the form and color of this flower. However, thin wiry green stems, often branched, hold it aloft rather than thick milky ones.

The scalloped and hairy leaves spread in a fanciful rosette pattern. Hairy cat's ear has an extended blooming season lasting from mid-summer to mid-September. Its dandelion-like characteristics are followed through by a white ball of downy seeds. A troublesome plant in lawns.

RANGE: Common in Coastal areas. Seattle.

SMOOTH CAT'S EAR (*H. glabra*) is a smaller plant to 12" high. The flowers are less than ¾" across and the leaves aren't hairy. It is found along the Coastal area into California.

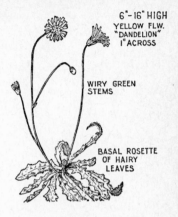

6"-16" HIGH
YELLOW FLW.
"DANDELION"
1" ACROSS

WIRY GREEN STEMS

BASAL ROSETTE OF HAIRY LEAVES

AGOSERIS
(*Agoseris spp.*)

Mountain Dandelion

The near-dozen agoseris all display great variety in the leaves. Characteristics of the group include dandelion-like flowers, a milky juice and a white fluffy seed head. In dandelions the bracts are in one main row with an outer shorter row being bent back. Agoseris have several rows of bracts in a "shingle" effect.

SLENDER AGOSERIS (*A. gracilens*) grows to 2' high and has bright yellow flowers with a dull reddish tinge on the under parts. Mostly Sub-alpine Zone of mountain systems across Wash.

ORANGE-FLOWERED AGOSERIS (*A. aurantiaca*): Usually less than 1' high with a deep orange-colored flower. Cascade Mountains and Olympics. Sub-alpine to alpine heights.

SMOOTH AGOSERIS (*A. glauca*): Flowers may reach 2" across and are pale yellow with a purplish tinge beneath. Blooms July to August. Fairly dry ground east of the Cascades. Usually Bunch-grass Zone. Ellensburg, Spokane, Pullman.

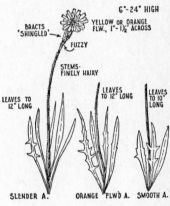

6"-24" HIGH
YELLOW OR ORANGE
FLW., 1"-1½" ACROSS

BRACTS 'SHINGLED'
FUZZY
STEMS - FINELY HAIRY

LEAVES TO 12" LONG
LEAVES TO 12" LONG
LEAVES TO 10" LONG

SLENDER A.   ORANGE FLW'D A.   SMOOTH A.

COMMON ST. JOHNSWORT
(*Hypericum perforatum*)

An European introduction, St. Johnswort is becoming a serious weed. There is a supposition that this plant always bloomed on June 24, St. John the Baptist's Day. It is moderately poisonous but only to white-colored animals.

The several different species all have yellow flowers with an abundance of protruding yellow stamens. In this case the stamens form clusters. The petals are faintly black-dotted on the margins as are the leaves. June into August.

RANGE: At low elevations across Washington. Often along roadsides.

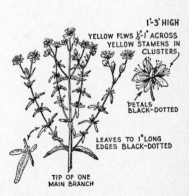

1½-3' HIGH
YELLOW FLWS ½"-1" ACROSS
YELLOW STAMENS IN CLUSTERS

PETALS BLACK-DOTTED

LEAVES TO 1" LONG
EDGES BLACK-DOTTED

TIP OF ONE MAIN BRANCH

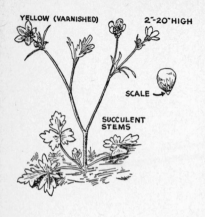

YELLOW (VARNISHED)   2"-20"HIGH

SCALE

SUCCULENT STEMS

WESTERN BUTTERCUP
(*Ranunculus occidentalis*)

Of course everyone recognizes a buttercup or do they? There are about 20 species in Washington excluding those known as watercrowfoots which have white petals and no basal scale. See page 150. A feature of the buttercups is the varnished golden petals with a little scale at the base of each petal. The leaves vary in shape very noticeably. In some species they are lobed while others display leaves finely dissected. Potentilla's have compound leaves and avens have 5 green sepals with 5 bractlets between. Buttercups are found in a wide variety of habitat and blooming from March to July. Some choose wet places, others open dry fields. They may be only an inch or two high or on stems that lift them 20" into the air.

RANGE: Widespread at low and middle elevations. Some species confined to certain regions.

SNOW BUTTERCUP (*R. eschscholtzii*): This flower of brightest gold bejewels the fresh greenery around the edges of snowbanks. The several lower leaves are fancifully lobed but another group of narrow leaves make a circlet halfway up the stem. This buttercup is perhaps the most common one above timberline and will be found in bloom from early to late summer as the snow recedes. Common on mountains throughout.

CREEPING BUTTERCUP (*R. repens*): The creeping stems which root here and there account for masses of this buttercup in wettish situations. The stem and leaves are slightly hairy. Leaves are divided into 3 separate leaflets or merely 3-parted. The flower is a bright golden yellow. Lower elevations west of Cascades.

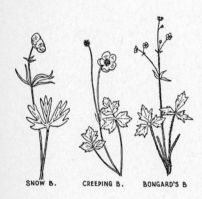

SNOW B.   CREEPING B.   BONGARD'S B

BONGARD'S BUTTERCUP (*R. bongardi*): The small pale yellow flowers not more than ¾" across and the deeply 3-lobed leaves, again 3-lobed, distinguish this buttercup. Usually the 1' - 2' high stems and leaves are hairy. It ranges across the State in shady, moist forests of lower elevations.

SPRING GOLD
(*Lomatium utriculatum*)
Hog-fennel

The heads of tightly packed small flowers are a brilliant yellow nicely set off by the dark green carrot-like leaves. In early spring the plant usually forms a low, rounded tuft but later in the season the flower gains height and the flower stems rise into the air showing the umbrella framework holding the blooms. Mossy rocky places are where to look for spring gold during April and May.

For other species see page 143.

RANGE: Gulf Islands and dry places in Coast Forest Zone. Orcas Island, Tacoma, Olympic Mountains.

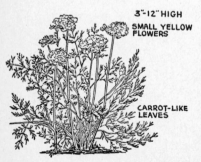

3"-12"HIGH

SMALL YELLOW FLOWERS

CARROT-LIKE LEAVES

NARROW-LEAVED PARSLEY
(Lomatium triternatum)

Nineleaf Biscuitroot

There are a half-dozen or more lomatiums. Most species like dry exposed places and are early bloomers. Leaves and flower stems spring from the ground for there is little or no true stem. Leaf stems are broadened at the base and divided into segments. Some resemble parsley leaves, others fern leaves, and two species still differ as shown. Flowers may be white, yellow, or purple, and have no or hardly visible sepals. Note the absence of bracts at the main flower hub, but see how they are present below each of the flower heads. Seeds are smooth and flat with thin side wings.

Narrow-leaved parsley may reach 2' in height and blooms from April to July. The root is edible raw or cooked or ground into flour.

RANGE: Common in Sagebrush and Bunchgrass Zones.

INDIAN CONSUMPTION PLANT *(L. nudicaule).* Note the shape of its leaves and the stem swelling at the main flower hub. It blooms from April to July. Indians used the ground-up seeds as a medicine for consumptive diseases. Dry places along Coastal area and into mountains.

WOOLLY SUNFLOWER
(Eriophyllum lanatum)

This bright little sunflower is supported on slender hairy stems which rise from a twisted mat of olive-green leaves. The leaves are very woolly beneath and give the flower its common name. Those on the stem are 3-7 lobed while the lower ones are entire.

The flower, which is 1" - 1½" across, has 9 - 11 broad golden-yellow petals and a beady yellow centre. Like most sunflowers it loves bright sunshine and is found on dry exposed places.

RANGE: Dry places Coastal Forest Zones. Subalpine in Olympics. In Sagebrush and Bunchgrass Zones of Eastern Washington.

GOLDEN FLEABANE
(Erigeron aureus)

This cheery little midget sunflower greets the hiker in the high mountains. Only a few inches tall, it adorns rocky ridges and gravelly pockets. The dull green leaves are basal except for a small one on the stem. This plant blooms during the late summer.

RANGE: Alpine terrain of the Cascade Mountains. Mt. Rainier, Steven's Pass.

LYALL'S APLOPAPPUS *(Aplopappus lyallii)* is liable to be confused with golden fleabane. However it has leaves well up on the stem and both leaves and stem are sticky and hairy. Rocky soils at high elevations in Olympic and Cascade Mountains.

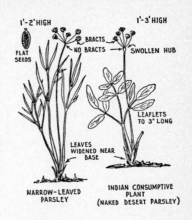

1'-2' HIGH — 1'-3' HIGH — BRACTS — NO BRACTS — SWOLLEN HUB — FLAT SEEDS — LEAFLETS TO 3" LONG — LEAVES WIDENED NEAR BASE

NARROW-LEAVED PARSLEY

INDIAN CONSUMPTIVE PLANT (NAKED DESERT PARSLEY)

YELLOW 1"-1½" ACROSS — 4"-12" HIGH

WOOLLY OLIVE-GREEN LEAVES 3-7 LOBED

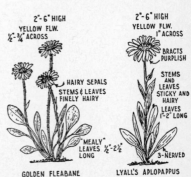

2"-6" HIGH YELLOW FLW. ½-¾" ACROSS — 2"-6" HIGH YELLOW FLW. 1" ACROSS — HAIRY SEPALS STEMS & LEAVES FINELY HAIRY — BRACTS PURPLISH — STEMS AND LEAVES STICKY AND HAIRY — LEAVES 1-2" LONG — "MEALY" LEAVES ½-2½ LONG — 3-NERVED

GOLDEN FLEABANE

LYALL'S APLOPAPPUS

FLOWERS (YELLOW)

YELLOW FLW.
¾" ACROSS
6 RAGGED PETALS

3"-6"HIGH

1-2 STEM LEAVES

LEAVES ABOUT ¼" LONG
OLIVE GREEN

WOODY STEMS
& ROOTS

NARROW-LEAVED APLOPAPPUS
(Aplopappus stenophyllus)

This pretty flower, less than 1" across, looks like a miniature edition of a sunflower from its 6 large yellow petals and spongy yellow center with protruding yellow tubes. Being only from 3" - 6" high its mat-like growth of narrow pointed leaves appears quite in keeping. These are about ¼" long, dark olive-green and finely hairy. One or two leaves often adorn the upper part of the flower stem. The base of the plant is woody and branches from a long stringy root. This aplopappus blooms in May on dry rocky ground and has as common companions thyme-leaved eriogonum, daggerpod, and sagebrush violet.

For an alpine species see page 143.

RANGE: Sagebrush and Bunchgrass Zones bordering Cascade Mountains. Wenatchee, Ellensburg, Yakima.

GOLD STAR
(Crocidium multicaule)

Gold Fields

Gold Star or Gold Fields during April and May suffuse many a field with a golden hue. It makes up for its lack of stature by growing in extensive patches with a profusion of flowering stems. These are woolly when young with the wool often persisting in the axils of the leaves.

The small alternate leaves have a few carelessly spaced teeth while several broader leaves grow at the base of the stems. The flower is about ½" across and yellow throughout. The 12 or so tapering petals are slightly pleated and emit a faint perfume.

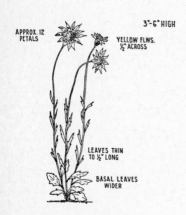

APPROX. 12
PETALS

3"-6"HIGH

YELLOW FLWS.
½" ACROSS

LEAVES THIN
TO ½" LONG

BASAL LEAVES
WIDER

RANGE: Common throughout the Bunchgrass Zone along Highway 8. Vicinity Ellensburg, Blue Mountains, Columbia River through Central Washington, Whidby and Orcas Islands.

MUSK FLOWER
(Mimulus moschatus)

This plant is the least attractive of the numerous mimulus or monkey-flowers. Its weak drooping stems are sticky and hairy as well as often being slimy. The reputed musky odor varies considerably in strength.

The yellow flowers are two-lipped; the upper two-lobed, the lower three-lobed. The hairy throat is very narrow and marked with dark lines or spots. It blooms from May to late July.

RANGE: Ditches and marshes of Coast forests and to middle elevations in the Olympics, Cascade and Blue Mountains. Also in Yellow Pine Forest Zone.

CLUSTERED OR ALPINE MONKEY FLOWER *(Mimulus caespitosus)* is one of the loveliest flowers of sub-alpine and alpine meadows. It flourishes along cold streams often forming mats of bright gold.

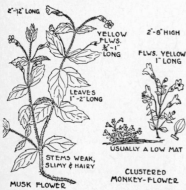

2"-12" LONG

YELLOW
FLWS.
¾"-1"
LONG

2"-8"HIGH

FLWS. YELLOW
1" LONG

LEAVES
1"-2"LONG

STEMS WEAK,
SLIMY & HAIRY

MUSK FLOWER

USUALLY A LOW MAT

CLUSTERED
MONKEY-FLOWER

(144)

YELLOW VIOLETS
(Viola spp.)

Besides the three yellow violets below there are other species having white, pale mauve or deep blue flowers.

TRAILING YELLOW VIOLETS (*V. sempervirens*): This slender creeper produces a mat-like growth, attractive because of the evergreen, heart-shaped leaves. The lower petals are delicately veined with brown. Mostly Coastal Forest Zone.

JOHNNY-JUMP-UP (*V. nuttallii*) forms a tuft of beautiful upright leaves. They are short-stemmed and usually hairy. The flower is faintly marked with purple veins. Dry grassy places east of Cascades. Sagebrush and Bunchgrass Zones.

YELLOW VIOLET (*V. glabella*) is distinguished by toothed leaves of which 2 or 3 branch out near the top of the stems. It grows to 10" in height. The single large flowers have brownish veins. Common across the State.

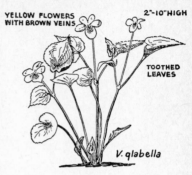

YELLOW FLOWERS WITH BROWN VEINS
2"-10"HIGH
TOOTHED LEAVES
V. glabella

STONECROP
(Sedum spp.)

During May and June rocky bluffs are enlivened by dabs and fringes of brightest yellow. Stonecrop with its irregular head of star-like flowers and bursting buds is strictly a rock plant at the Coast. Probably the most noticeable feature is the rough rosettes of thick fleshy leaves which cling tightly to the thin moss layer on the rocks. The thick leaves, acting like the cactus, store enough water to tide the hardy flower over dry periods.

RANGE: Various species are found throughout Washington with the plant ranging in altitude to sub-alpine slopes.

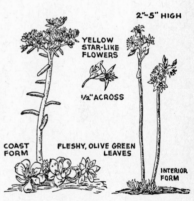

YELLOW STAR-LIKE FLOWERS
2"-5" HIGH
½" ACROSS
COAST FORM
FLESHY, OLIVE GREEN LEAVES
INTERIOR FORM

YELLOW MONKEY FLOWER
(Mimulus langsdorfii)

Yellow mimulus grows from sea level to alpine heights. The clear yellow "snapdragon" flower is about ¾" long with brown or crimson dots in a bearded throat. The petals drop almost immediately after it is picked. The stem is angled and very succulent as are the opposite leaves, thus leading to its use in salads. The blooming period is from May to August.

RANGE: Wet places across the State. Tacoma, Ellensburg, Coulee City, Wawawai.

BABY MONKEY FLOWER (*M. alsinoides*) only grows a few inches high. The curious little yellow face is spotted with one or two purplish dots on the lower lip. Most flowers bloom in April. Gulf Islands. Scattered in Coastal forests and Cascades.

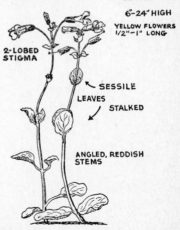

6"-24" HIGH
YELLOW FLOWERS ½"-1" LONG
2-LOBED STIGMA
SESSILE LEAVES
STALKED
ANGLED, REDDISH STEMS

FLOWERS (YELLOW)

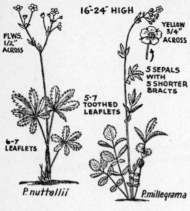

P. nuttallii

16"-24" HIGH

YELLOW 3/4" ACROSS

FLWS. 1/2" ACROSS

5 SEPALS WITH 5 SHORTER BRACTS

5-7 TOOTHED LEAFLETS

6-7 LEAFLETS

P.millegrama

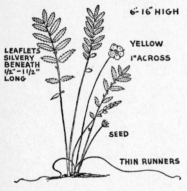

6"-16" HIGH

LEAFLETS SILVERY BENEATH 1/2"-1 1/2" LONG

YELLOW 1" ACROSS

SEED

THIN RUNNERS

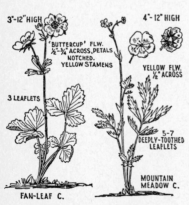

3"-12" HIGH

'BUTTERCUP' FLW. 1/2"-3/4" ACROSS, PETALS NOTCHED. YELLOW STAMENS.

3 LEAFLETS

FAN-LEAF C.

4"-12" HIGH

YELLOW FLW. 1/2" ACROSS

5-7 DEEPLY-TOOTHED LEAFLETS

MOUNTAIN MEADOW C.

CINQUEFOILS
(Potentilla spp.)

Fivefinger — Potentilla

A common name, fivefinger, is descriptive of leaves of species which have five leaflets. There are over a dozen in Washington but all have the same shiny buttercup flower. Only one is purple colored. Five green sepals show their tips around the flower. Five shorter bracts alternate with these and by this arrangement it is possible to make sure of the cinquefoils. The leaves differ widely, some being finger-like, the others with leaflets opposite one another.

P. milligrana is a rangeland plant of South Central Washington. Sporadic west of Cascades. The height is from 12" - 24". Blooming period July.

NUTTALL CINQUEFOIL (*P. nuttallii*) has 5 finger-like leaflets each 2" - 3" long. The leaves are hairy on both sides. Bunchgrass Zone.

P. gracilis similar to the above is distinguished by densely hairy stems and leaflets. Gulf Islands, Olympics, Coastal forests.

MARSH CINQUEFOIL (*P. palustris*) has purple flowers. The stout stems are almost flat on the ground but the tips turn up. Margin of bogs and lakes in Coastal forests and in Yellow Pine Zone of Northeastern Washington.

SILVERWEED (*P. Anserina*) has single flowers on a long stem. The leaflets are fringe-like, green above but strikingly silvery beneath. Saline meadows and marshes along Coast and in the Sagebrush Zone of the "Scablands".

FAN-LEAF CINQUEFOIL
(Potentilla flabellifolia)

This very common flower of alpine meadows might be mistaken for a buttercup unless the notched petals and green sepals are noticed. The flower is more than 1/2" across and adorned by a cluster of a dozen yellow stamens. Usually several flowers branch from the main stem.

The leaves are reminiscent of a strawberry plant, being formed by 3 leaflets, wedge-shaped at the base and coarsely toothed above. Fan-leaf cinquefoil blooms during the summer while most alpine flowers are at their height of color.

RANGE: Sub-alpine and Alpine Zone of Olympics and Cascades. Mt. Rainier, Stevens Pass.

MOUNTAIN MEADOW CINQUEFOIL (*P. diversifolia*) (*P. dissecta*) grows to 12" high and is sparsely hairy. Long-stemmed leaves carry 5 - 7 deeply toothed leaflets. Moist situations near and below timberline in Cascades and Olympics. Mt. Angeles, Goat Mountains.

(146)

GROUNDSELS AND RAGWORTS
(Senecio spp.)

These include a large number of plants with smallish yellow to orange flowers, alternate leaves and bracts in one row.
WESTERN GOLDEN RAGWORT (*S. pseudaureus*) has flat-topped heads of numerous yellow flowers and brownish centres. Note the two types of leaves. East slopes of Cascades. Middle elevations.
GIANT RAGWORT (*S. triangularis*) is 2' - 3' high, leafy to the top and crowned with flat-topped heads of small yellow flowers. It is a plant of high mountains and blooms in late summer. Olympics, Cascades, Blue, and other mountains from middle to sub-alpine elevations.
COMMON GROUNDSEL (*S. vulgaris*) is a common weed less than 2' high and with branching stems. The bracts have a shorter row around the base and these are black tipped. Scattered in Coastal Forest Zone.

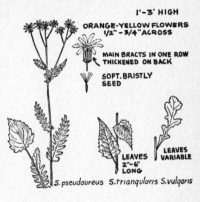

1'-3' HIGH
ORANGE-YELLOW FLOWERS
1/2" - 3/4" ACROSS
MAIN BRACTS IN ONE ROW THICKENED ON BACK
SOFT, BRISTLY SEED
LEAVES 2"-6" LONG
LEAVES VARIABLE
S. pseudaureus S. triangularis S. vulgaris

COLUMBIA BUTTERWEED
(Senecio columbianus)

This senecio is a small plant usually about 16" high. Leaves near the base are mostly round-tipped while the ones just above are sharp-pointed and reduce in size as they climb the stem.
The jumble of butter-colored flowers may be loosely or tightly clustered. Bracts are in one main row and over half the length of the flower head. Each bract has a triangular black tip.
RANGE: Late summer on dry ground of Sagebrush, Bunchgrass, and Yellow Pine Zone. Blue Mtns.
SAWTOOTH BUTTERWEED (*S. serra*) grows to 5' high with small yellow flowers in flat-topped clusters during July and August. Leaves to 4" long are green and sharply saw-toothed. A few lower leaves may be quite egg-shaped. Arid sagebrush plains upward to high mountain forests.

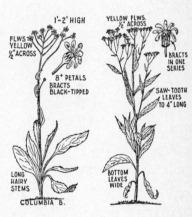

1'-2' HIGH
FLWS YELLOW 1/2" ACROSS
8+ PETALS
BRACTS BLACK-TIPPED
LONG HAIRY STEMS
COLUMBIA B.
YELLOW FLWS. 1/2" ACROSS
BRACTS IN ONE SERIES
SAW-TOOTH LEAVES TO 4" LONG
BOTTOM LEAVES WIDE

SLENDER HAWKWEED
(Hieracium gracile)

Other flowers such as the groundsels (*Senecio spp.*) and hawksbeard (*Crepis spp.*) also have yellow blooms turning to untidy seed heads. In hawkweeds the cup that holds the flower has one main row of flat, sharp-pointed bracts. In this species the cups are black and hairy. Flowers are pale yellow, about 1" across. The light green leaves form a rough rosette. July and August.
RANGE: High mountains throughout Washington.
HAIRY HAWKWEED (*H. scouleri*) has 2-3 rows of bracts covered with long hairs. This hairyness is continued on leaves and stem. Range country, Bunchgrass Zone of Eastern Washington.
WHITE HAWKWEED (*H. albiflorum*) has a dozen or more white flowers. The height is from 2' - 3'. Leaves and lower stem are hairy. Across Washington. Coastal region and Cascades. Yellow Pine Zone and middle mountain elevations.

8"-14" HIGH
PALE YELLOW FLOWERS WITH BLACK COLLAR ABOUT 1/2" ACROSS
BLACK HAIRS
ONE MAIN ROW OF BLACK HAIRY BRACTS TO 1/2" LONG
SLENDER STEMS
LEAVES LONG-STEMMED

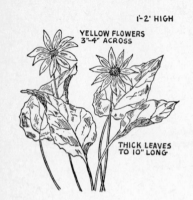

1'-2' HIGH

YELLOW FLOWERS
3"-4" ACROSS

THICK LEAVES
TO 10" LONG

SPRING SUNFLOWERS
(Balsamorhiza sagittata)

Balsam-Root

During May, acre upon acre of open mountain slopes in the Central and Eastern Interior are covered with bunches of these bright yellow flowers. A dozen or so large flowers may rise from each bunch of big olive-green leaves and the individual clumps may almost touch. These dry up during the hot summer and the twists of parched leaves remain as poor evidence of their former glory.

Indians ate the rich oily seeds either raw or mixed with deer fat and boiled by means of hot stones. The roots were eaten raw or roasted with much care and ceremony in large pits.

RANGE: Abundant from Sagebrush and Bunchgrass Zones into the Yellow Pine Zone. Wenatchee, Spokane.

NORTHWEST BALSAMROOT
(Balsamorhiza deltoidea)

The 8 or so balsamroots in Washington have showy yellow 'sunflowers', large basal leaves with few or none on the stems, and a flower cup of several rows of bracts. Generally there is a single bloom to a stem but in this species and *B. careyana* there may be several. This plant differs from spring sunflower in having smooth green leaves rather than olive grey.

RANGE: Dry ground mostly west of Cascades. Tacoma, Vancouver, Yakima.

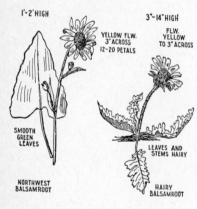

1'-2' HIGH

YELLOW FLW.
3" ACROSS
12-20 PETALS

SMOOTH
GREEN
LEAVES

NORTHWEST
BALSAMROOT

3"-14" HIGH

FLW.
YELLOW
TO 3" ACROSS

LEAVES AND
STEMS HAIRY

HAIRY
BALSAMROOT

HAIRY BALSAMROOT (*B. hirsuta*) is usually less than a foot high and has twisted basal leaves. The flower is about 3" across and blooms during May. Dry ground east of Cascades. Wenatchee, Blue Mountains.

ROSY BALSAMROOT (*B. rosea*) resembles the above but has pinkish to pale purple ray petals. Exposed ridges in arid regions. Vicinity Touchet and Wallula.

HOOKER BALSAMROOT
(Balsamorhiza hookera)

This balsamroot differs from the more common ones in having its hairy grayish-green leaves cut into segments. The plant averages a foot in height and carries one bloom per stem. The yellow petals surround a deep golden center to make a beautiful bloom around 2" across. Leaves often lie close to the ground. There are none on the stems, a distinguishing feature from the mule-ears or wyethia species. See page 149. The leafy bracts underneath the flower head are in an overlapping pattern of 3 rows. Balsamroots reach their peak of brilliance in May.

RANGE: Dry open flats and hillsides in the Sagebrush, Bunchgrass and Yellow Pine Zones.

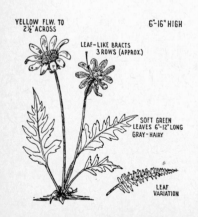

YELLOW FLW. TO
2½" ACROSS

LEAF-LIKE BRACTS
3 ROWS (APPROX.)

SOFT GREEN
LEAVES 6"-12" LONG
GRAY-HAIRY

6"-16" HIGH

LEAF
VARIATION

SMOOTH DWARF SUNFLOWER
(Wyethia amplexicaulis)

Mule-ears, Pik

This showy yellow flower like the balsamroots, has smooth, glossy leaves shaped like a mule's ears and also stem leaves. Flower stems each carry a cluster of blooms during May or June. The heavily veined leaves may be toothed and appear varnished from the secretion of resinous glands.

The genus *Wyethia* is named after Nathaniel Wyeth, an adventurous explorer who crossed the continent to Oregon in 1834.

RANGE: Low meadows and slopes of the Sagebrush and Bunchgrass Zones.

COMPASS PLANT *(W. angustifolia)* variously called Wyethia and Narrow-leaved Sunflower differs by its range, narrow dullish leaves, and one flower to a stem. An unfounded belief says that the leaves always point north and south. Sporadic west of Cascades in dry open places. West Klickitat County.

FLOWERS (YELLOW)

12"-36" HIGH

YELLOW "SUNFLOWER" TO "3" ACROSS

LEAVES WITHOUT STEMS 3 VEINED

STEM WHITE-HAIRY

LEAVES WITH STEMS

COMMON SUNFLOWER
(Helianthus annus)

Usually people quite correctly connect this large sunflower to the cultivated varieties which often escape along roadsides. However these generally have larger and fewer flowers to a plant.

Common sunflower is coarse and branching with a height of from 2'-6'. Its heavy stem is very rough and sometimes sticky. Lower leaves are heart-shaped and alternate. The showy flower with its dark reddish-brown center varies from 3"-5" across. Its seeds are edible.

RANGE: Blooming August and September in the Sagebrush and Bunchgrass Zones. Wenatchee, Coulee City, Almota.

2'-6' HIGH

SUNFLOWER 3"-5" ACROSS

LEAVES LARGE AND COARSE

HELIANTHELLA
(Helianthella douglassi)

This is another of the sunflower-like plants so abundant in Washington. Among these may be included the balsamroots, brown-eyed Susan, compass plant and smooth dwarf sunflower. The shapes of the leaves are good distinguishing points. In this 1'-3' high cluster of stems the leaves are noticeably three-veined. Those near the bottom have stems and are mostly opposite. Those near the top may be alternate and do not have stems.

The flower center is about 1" across, and dark brown. Bright yellow ray petals also measure about 1" in length and have several distinct veins.

RANGE: In bloom June and July in Sagebrush, Bunchgrass and Yellow Pine Zones. Ellensburg, Wenatchee, Pullman.

BRACTS SMOOTH IN 2-3 ROWS

10"-24" HIGH

YELLOW "SUNFLOWER" TO 3" ACROSS

LEAVES TO 6" LONG

DARK GREEN VEINY LEAVES TO 14" LONG & 4" WIDE VARNISHED LOOK

(149)

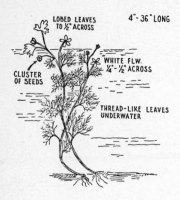

LOBED LEAVES
TO ½" ACROSS

4"- 36" LONG

WHITE FLW.
¼"- ½" ACROSS

CLUSTER
OF SEEDS

THREAD-LIKE LEAVES
UNDERWATER

WATERCROWFOOT BUTTERCUP
(*Ranunculus aquatilis*)

This unusual buttercup lives completely under water except for its flower and seed head and the occasional 3-lobed floating leaf.

Its stems, to 3' long, find a home in warm rivers, lakes, or very stagnant pools. Here it often forms thick masses of submerged entwining stems and thread-like leaves. These are soft and appear to collapse when removed from the water. The white flowers have no scale on the base of the petals which sometimes are yellowish. The large seeds form a bulky cluster.

RANGE: In bloom April to August across Washington and up to mountain forest elevations.

R. circinatus differs in not having any floating broad leaves nor does its foliage collapse upon taking it from the water. Range as above.

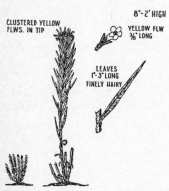

CLUSTERED YELLOW
FLWS. IN TIP

8"- 2' HIGH

YELLOW FLW
⅜" LONG

LEAVES
1"- 3" LONG
FINELY HAIRY

LEMONWEED
(*Lithospernum ruderale*)
(*Lithospernum pilosum*)

Western Gromwell

In open country from May to July watch for an outstanding bushy green plant 1'-2' high having a rough hairy appearance. Upon investigation the small pale yellow funnel-like flowers will be seen almost hidden among the small leaves at the tips of the stems.

The general bushy appearance is brought about by the very leafy stems. Leaves are alternate but bunch together toward the top until becoming tightly packed. Those at the tip of the flower head protrude beyond the small flowers.

RANGE: Open slopes in the Sagebrush and Bunchgrass Zones with intrusions into open woods.

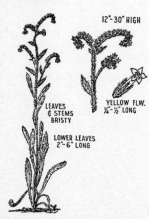

12"- 30" HIGH

LEAVES
& STEMS
BRISTLY

YELLOW FLW.
¼"- ½" LONG

LOWER LEAVES
2"- 6" LONG

RIGID FIDDLENECK
(*Amsinchia retrorsa*)

Other names are amsinchia and tarweed for this group of a half dozen species confined largely to dry terrain east of the Cascades. They are recognized by their bristly leaves and stems and the long flowering head twisted in a curl like the neck of a violin. Flowers are funnel-like and range from yellow to orange in color. The 5 stamens usually are hidden in the throat.

Bristly husks along the outer edge of the curved stem carry horny seeds or nutlets shaped like a broad arrowhead. Rigid fiddleneck may be found in bloom from early spring to late summer because new flowers keep forming along the 'fiddle neck'.

RANGE: Open ground or fields with preference for some moisture. Mostly in the Sagebrush and Bunchgrass Zones.

YELLOW BELL
(*Fritillaria pudica*)

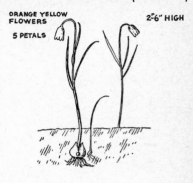

ORANGE YELLOW FLOWERS

5 PETALS

2"-6" HIGH

Mission Bell — Yellow Fritillary

The slopes and benches of the bare, arid valleys are liberally sprinkled with this shy little yellow bell from April into May. It seldom grows over 4" high and has one nodding fragrant orange to yellow flower about 1/2" long. The 2 or 3 long narrow leaves are olive-green in color and start well up on the flower stem. The tiny white bulb giving rise to the flower is about 1" beneath the ground. Like the Easter lily at the Coast it suffers from thoughtless over-picking.

RANGE: Ranging from the Sagebrush and Bunch-grass to the Yellow Pine Forest Zone. White Salmon, Pullman, Spokane.

CACTUS
(*Opuntia fragilis*)

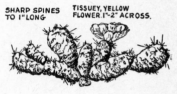

1"-3" HIGH

SHARP SPINES TO 1" LONG

TISSUEY, YELLOW FLOWER. 1"-2" ACROSS.

The spiny clumps of wrinkled fleshy cactus are a characteristic plant of the arid sagebrush range-lands. The beautiful yellow tissuey blossoms give the otherwise drab cactus a brief period of glory from June into July. The whole spiny mass is often covered with these bright blooms. The thick, spongy stem carries on the function of leaves and is designed for storing precious water. Spines protect the succulent stems from animals.

RANGE: Common in Southern B.C. and extending rather sparsely through Sagebrush Zone along Okanogan River possibly as far as Wenatchee. Rare on Gulf Islands.

MANY-SPINED PRICKLY PEAR
(*Opuntia polycantha*)

4"-10" HIGH

TISSUEY FLWS. YELLOW (OR PURPLISH)

4-11 SPINES TO CLUSTER

FLATTISH SEGMENTS TO 4" LONG

SPINY MATS TO 2' ACROSS

This is the largest of the three 'cactus' growing in Washington. A ragged mass of this long-spined cactus is about as dangerous to the unwary person as a rattlesnake. Needle-sharp spines may be 2" in length and have a terrific holding quality when stuck in flesh or shoes. Clumps of spines are just less than 1/2" apart and rise from small rounded knobs known as areoles.

The beautiful tissue-like flower is usually yellow although purplish-tinged ones do occur. Blooming time is June and July—a phenomena in color that all too few people see.

RANGE: Sagebrush Zone occurring along Snake River from Clarkston westward to Columbia River. Yakima River Valley.

(151)

FLOWERS (YELLOW)

10"-20" HIGH   PALE YELLOW FLWS.

8"-16" HIGH

WHORL OF NARROW BRACTS

WHITE TO YELLOW FLOWERS

LEAVES 3"-6" WHITE WOOLLY

LEAVES WOOLLY BENEATH GREEN ABOVE 3"-8" LONG

HEART-LEAVED ERIOGONUM   SNOW ERIOGONUM

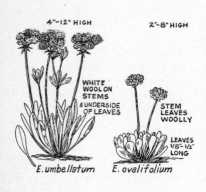

4"-12" HIGH

2"-8" HIGH

WHITE WOOL ON STEMS & UNDERSIDE OF LEAVES

STEM LEAVES WOOLLY

LEAVES 1/8"-1/2" LONG

E. umbellatum   E. ovalifolium

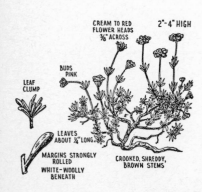

CREAM TO RED FLOWER HEADS 3/8" ACROSS

2"-4" HIGH

BUDS PINK

LEAF CLUMP

LEAVES ABOUT 1/4" LONG

MARGINS STRONGLY ROLLED WHITE-WOOLLY BENEATH

CROOKED, SHREDDY, BROWN STEMS

HEART-LEAVED ERIOGONUM
(Eriogonum compositum)

In this eriogonum the shape and color of the leaves are fairly reliable identification features. It has a loosely branched form often with a mat-like growth of stems and leaves. The leaves are a distinct broad dagger or arrow-head shape with stems up to twice the length of the blade. They are white-hairy beneath but a pale green above.

The thick flower stem is hollow and near the top branches into 4-10 arms or spokes marked by a whorl of narrow bracts. Flowers, held in their hairy cups, are pale yellow to creamy and form a large showy head.

RANGE: May to July in poor soils of the Sagebrush and Bunchgrass Zones. Dry places in Columbia Gorge.

SULPHUR ERIOGONUM
(Eriogonum umbellatum)

There are about 2 dozen species of eriogonum in Washington, some with a number of varieties. Leaves are not toothed but often hairy at least on the undersurface. The white to yellow flowers are very small and project in clusters from a toothed cup or involucre. There are no petals but the 6-parted calyx does resemble them. Nine stamens provide a further identifying feature. Sulphur eriogonum has an intense orange-yellow shade often with dabs of crimson in the late fall. Leaves at the stem nodes give it a two-layer effect.

RANGE: East slopes of Cascade Mountains and eastward on dry ground to sub-alpine elevations.

CUSHION ERIOGONUM (E. ovalifolium) has a compact mass of small oval leaves less than 1/2" long. Flowers are soft yellow sometimes touched with red. Alpine slopes of Olympics and Cascades. Mt. Rainier.

THYME-LEAVED ERIOGONUM
(Eriogonum thymoides)

This picturesque shrubby little plant is a low much-branched shrub with woody shredding stems and tiny leaves clustered at the end of the twigs. The leaves, averaging about 1/4" in length, are so strongly curled over at the edges that a channel is formed on the underside through which a mat of woolly white hair shows.

Flower stems a few inches high have a whorl of approximately 7 small leaves about half way up. The single flower cup or involucre holds a number of very small yellow to red hairy flowers making a varied colored cluster about 1/2" across.

RANGE: April and May on dry soils of Sagebrush Zone from Spokane River southward. Especially common in Eastern Washington.

DEATH CAMAS
(*Zigadenus venenosus*)

Death camas bears a resemblance to camas through its long grass-like leaves and main stem with a spike of flowers at the tip. When not in flower the two plants have a close resemblance. The several long thin leaves have a deep groove which forms a keel on the opposite side. The creamy colored flowers are less than 1/2" across and have 3 sepals and 3 petals which simply appear as 6 petals. The dark-coated bulb, shaped like an onion, is very poisonous. Young leaves can be fatal to grazing stock.

Death camas may be found wherever camas grows. It blooms from April 15 to June but later in the Interior.

RANGE: Gulf Islands, dry places in Coastal Forest and Bunchgrass Zone. Pullman, Spokane.

OYSTER PLANT
(*Tragopogon major*)

Salsify — Goat's Beard

This weedy plant, widely cultivated throughout Europe and North America, is generally called salsify. The thick root is edible in early spring or late fall or the young stem and leaves may be eaten as a cooked vegetable.

A stout flower stem carries a bright yellow dandelion-like flower about 2" across. The seed head that follows is similar in shape and form to that of a dandelion but may be 3" wide. Several long alternate grass-like leaves clasp the stem near the base. This species has a thickened flower stem near its top and thus may be distinguished from *T. pratensis*. *T. porrifolius* has purple flowers and grows in the Bunchgrass Zone.

RANGE: *T. dubius* and *T. pratensis* are sporadic along roadsides of Eastern Washington.

WESTERN WALLFLOWER
(*Erysium occidentale*)

Of the four or five wallflowers in Washington the two illustrated are the showiest. Flowers are yellow to orange and quite distinctive among other blooms during late spring and early summer. The broad petals taper to very narrow bases. There are 6 stamens and as the flower goes to seed the pistil protrudes further and further. Eventually a long pod holding one row of seeds is formed.

RANGE: Generally in Sagebrush Zone from Yakima southward.

ROUGH WALLFLOWER (*E. asperum*) has slightly smaller flowers and leaves with wavy margins. Sagebrush Zone of Central Washington and along the lower mountain slopes of the Cascades. Common in Sub-alpine Zone of Olympic Mountains.

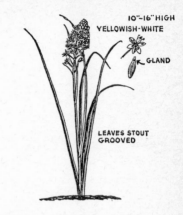

10"-16" HIGH
YELLOWISH-WHITE

GLAND

LEAVES STOUT
GROOVED

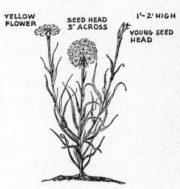

YELLOW FLOWER

SEED HEAD 3" ACROSS

1'- 2' HIGH
YOUNG SEED HEAD

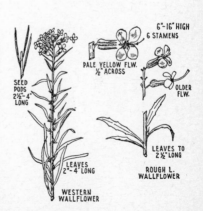

SEED PODS 2½"-4" LONG

PALE YELLOW FLW. ½" ACROSS

6"- 16" HIGH
6 STAMENS

OLDER FLW.

LEAVES 2"- 4" LONG

WESTERN WALLFLOWER

LEAVES TO 2½" LONG

ROUGH L. WALLFLOWER

FLOWERS (YELLOW)

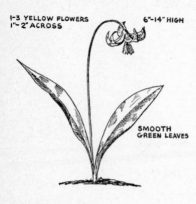

1-3 YELLOW FLOWERS
1"-2" ACROSS

6"-14" HIGH

SMOOTH
GREEN LEAVES

SNOW LILY
(Erythronium grandiflorum)

Glacier Lily—Fawn Lily

This bright flower of the purest yellow has two glossy green leaves contrasting with the one to three flowers with their six long recurved petals. Like the avalanche lily and western anemone it blooms soon after the snow has left the ground.

RANGE: Seldom below 4,000' and mostly in Subalpine Zone. Olympics, Mt. Adams, Mt. Rainier, Wenatchee and Blue Mountains. In Northeastern Washington from Bunchgrass Zone upwards.

WOOD BETONY
(Pedicularis bracteosa)

Northern Fernleaf

Wood betony, a plant of the high mountains, has an unusual spike of flowers. These hook-beaked oddities are pale yellow in color but occasionally with a pinkish tinge. They present a series of quaint little faces one peeping over top of the other. This arrangement and a twisting beak is characteristic of the louseworts or *Pedicularis spp.* The leaves are finely divided.

RANGE: Moist sub-alpine slopes throughout Washington.

CONTORTED LOUSEWORT (*P. contorta*) has soft yellow flowers about ½" long and with a remarkably twisted beak. The plant is from 8" - 15" high. Alpine heights in Olympics, Cascades and Blue Mountains. Yellow Pine Zone of Northeastern Washington.

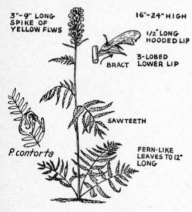

3"-9" LONG
SPIKE OF
YELLOW FLWS

16"-24" HIGH

½" LONG
HOODED LIP

BRACT

3-LOBED
LOWER LIP

SAWTEETH

FERN-LIKE
LEAVES TO 12"
LONG

P. contorta

SICKLETOP LOUSEWORT (*P. racemosa*) has white or pink flowers with a beak that curves inward. Foliage purplish. Middle to sub-alpine elevations in Cascades. Also Yellow Pine Zone and upwards.

ELEPHANT HEAD (*P. groenlandica*) has purplish or reddish flowers with a long, upcurved beak. See page 177.

GUMWEED
(Grindelia spp.)

Several gumweeds are found in Washington. Most plants are bushy with a bright yellow flower on a rough, sticky bur. This bur has 5 or 6 rows of gummy bracts which curl outward at their tips. *G. squarrosa* is scattered along roadsides in Eastern Washington. *G. nana* grows in the Bunchgrass Zone. Spangle, Pullman. *G. oregana* has basal leaves 2" - 8" long and is found on high beaches along the sea coast.

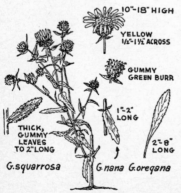

10"-18" HIGH

YELLOW
½"-1½" ACROSS

GUMMY
GREEN BURR

THICK,
GUMMY
LEAVES
TO 2" LONG

1"-2"
LONG

2"-8"
LONG

G. squarrosa

G. nana *G. oregana*

(154)

BROAD-LEAF ARNICA
(*Arnica latifolia*)

The straight stem to 2' high is unbranched and carries flowers about 2" across. The large oval coarsely toothed leaves branch opposite from one another, the lower ones having short stems. The showy flowers have a light brown center. Medicinal arnica for cuts and bruises is from an European species.

RANGE: Most abundant at sub-alpine heights. Olympics, Cascades and Blue Mountains.

HEART-LEAF ARNICA (*A. cordifolia*) grows at lower elevations but often in moist forested mountains. It is only 10" - 18" in height but has a slightly larger flower than broad-leaf arnica and often 3 to a stem. The large, heart-shaped leaves grow near the ground and have long stems. Abundant at middle elevations and also Yellow Pine Zone. Spokane, Wenatchee.

A. fulgens differs in having long thin leaves. Bunchgrass Zone. Waitsburg, Spokane, Republic.

10"- 18" HIGH
YELLOW FLOWERS 1 1/2" ACROSS
PLEATED PETALS
FINE HAIRS
12"-24" HIGH
SILKY HEAD
"HEART" LEAVES
SHORT LEAF STEMS

A. cordifolia   A. fulgens   A. latifolia

GOLDEN ASTER
(*Chrysopsis hispida*)

Here is a plant with flowers much like an aster except it has yellow rather than purple or violet rays and an overall greyish color of stems and leaves. This peculiar tinge results from fine matted hairs, a protection from the intense exposure and drought. The fibrous roots penetrate many feet into the soil. The blooming period is midsummer.

RANGE: Exposed places in Sagebrush and Bunchgrass Zones. Mostly Eastern and Northeastern Washington.

C. villosa is more hairy and shaggy than the above. Mostly in Sagebrush Zone but also sparsely in Gulf Islands.

6"-16" HIGH
YELLOW PETALS AND CENTER 1 1/2"-2" ACROSS
LEAVES, STEMS VERY WOOLLY

BROWN-EYED SUSAN
(*Gaillardia aristata*)

Gaillardia

When most of the early flowers have disappeared and the sidehills and fields are taking on the dehydrated look of summer in the Interior then brown-eyed Susan appears to charm the eye. To most people it is a bright little yellow sunflower with a reddish brown center. The drab rough leaves are not very noticeable so the flower reposes without detraction at the top of a long erect stem. The bloom is from 1 1/2" - 2" across and the yellow ray flowers are deeply notched at their tips. Dry open fields during June and July.

RANGE: East of Cascades in Sagebrush and Bunchgrass Zones.

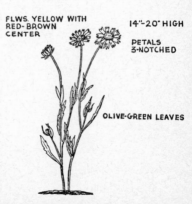

FLWS. YELLOW WITH RED-BROWN CENTER
14"-20" HIGH
PETALS 3-NOTCHED
OLIVE-GREEN LEAVES

FLOWERS (YELLOW)

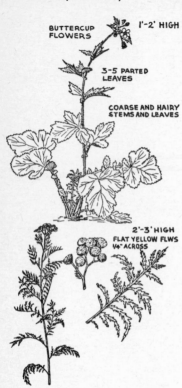

BUTTERCUP FLOWERS — 1'-2' HIGH

3-5 PARTED LEAVES

COARSE AND HAIRY STEMS AND LEAVES

2'-3' HIGH
FLAT YELLOW FLWS
1/4" ACROSS

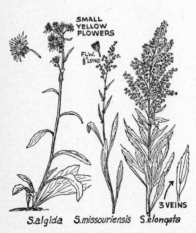

SMALL YELLOW FLOWERS

FLW. 1/8 LONG

3 VEINS

S.algida   S.missouriensis   S.elongata

LARGE-LEAVED AVENS
(Geum macrophyllum)

Large-leaved avens produces a bright yellow buttercup-like flower. Otherwise the plant is coarse and hairy with large ragged leaves. The leaves growing from the base are about 6" - 9" long with small toothed leaflets on either side and a large terminal one. Leaves off the stem are rounded with 3 - 5 lobes.

Avens generally have 5 green sepals with 5 small bractlets between.

The flowers, either singly or in a few-flowered cluster, grow at the tip of the branches and will be seen in bloom during May at the Coast. The flower develops into a round burr with hooked prickles.

RANGE: Most common in Coastal Forest Zone but also in wet places of Yellow Pine Zone.

TANSY
(Tanacetum vulgare)

Usually between 2' and 3' high, it becomes very prominent when the compact clusters of flattish yellow flowers burst into full bloom. Each bloom is only 1/4" across but the bunched grouping is very effective above the thick mass of dark green carrotty leaves. The flowers are out during the latter part of August and the first half of September. This plant is a European weed but was once cultivated as a garden flower.

RANGE: Very scattered along Coast and abundant locally in Bunchgrass Zone.

GOLDENROD
(Solidago elongata)

A widespread belief that pollen from goldenrod caused hay fever has been proven wrong. The 100 or so species in North America contain some exceptionally beautiful flowers.

The common goldenrod often forms masses of golden bloom during midsummer where there is rich moist soil for its roots. The pyramid of small yellow flowers was used once as a source of yellow dye and a bright dye it must have made.

RANGE: Coastal Zone and wet places in Bunchgrass Zone.

NORTHERN GOLDENROD (S. algida), a high mountain plant, is usually less than a foot in height. It carries a tousled head of rather large yellow flowers. The stem is often bent near the base. Leaves are toothed on the top half. Subalpine and alpine in Olympics and Cascades.

MISSOURI GOLDENROD (S. missouriensis) is a slender plant to 2' high. The flower head is open from drooping branches. Leaves are thick, narrow and often have 'ears' at their base. Bunchgrass Zone.

(156)

MOCCASIN FLOWER
(*Cypripedium parviflorum*)

Small Lady's Slipper — Yellow Lady's Slipper

The pouch-like yellow flower of satiny texture can be very well likened to a dainty moccasin. Enhancing its beauty are the claret-purple streaks and markings which are found on the lining. A bizarre touch is added by the long twisted sepals. The leaves are rich green and artistically arranged. The moccasin flower is comparatively scarce in Wash. Usually moist shady sites or high mountain stream banks provide a suitable setting. It blooms from June to July. See page 120 for others.

RANGE: Wet places in Yellow Pine Zone. Spokane County, Mt. Stuart, Wenatchee Mountains, Mt. Carlton, Spokane, Pullman, Blue Mountains.

10"-20" HIGH

YELLOW 'MOCCASIN' CLARET STREAKS

LEAVES 2"-6" LONG

SKUNK CABBAGE
(*Lysichiton kamtschatcense*)

Skunk cabbage is most noticeable in March and April before the shrubs have come into leaf. Then almost every swampy or mucky place is dotted with soft yellow sheaths which give off a sickish sweet smell. The thick fleshy club inside the sheath carries a large number of small green flowers. Later the club will show a cluster of bright red berries. The leaves probably are the largest of any native plant. Some may grow to 3' in length and be a foot wide. If crushed the plant gives off a pungent odor thus leading to its common name.

RANGE: Generally under or near cedar trees. Coastal forests and Cascade Mountains to 4,000'. Swampy ground in Northeastern Washington.

6"-24" HIGH

YELLOW CAPE

LEAVES TO 3' LONG

GREENISH FLOWERS

YELLOW POND LILY
(*Nymphaea polysepala*)

The large scaly roots of this native plant are anchored firmly in the mud. From them long stems reach upward to the lake surface. The yellowish-green flowers are cup-like and have a knob in their center. This is formed of petals and the other plant organs. The blooms will be seen from May through the summer. The seeds were gathered once by the Indians and ground into flour. The large flat leaves, either ovalish or heart-shaped, float on the water and provide convenient docking facilities for dragon flies and frogs.

RANGE: Sparse in Coastal region but more common in Bunchgrass Zone of Northeastern Washington.

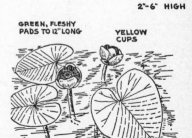

2"-6" HIGH

GREEN, FLESHY PADS TO 12" LONG

YELLOW CUPS

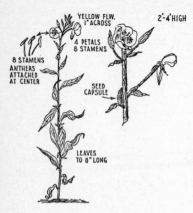

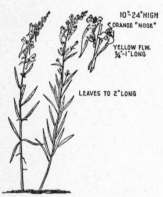

EVENING PRIMROSE
(Oenothera biennis)

Watch for possible confusion between the evening primroses and godetias. The stamens of the evening primrose hold the anthers at the center while in the godetias they are attached at one end. Most godetias are pink in contrast to the yellows and whites of the evening primroses.

Plants are generally so widely scattered that they are missed unless a person looks closely for them although the stout and occasionally branched stem may reach 4' in height.

The satin-like flowers are an exquisite soft yellow color and about 1" across. They are at their best on a cloudy day or in the early morning or evening. See how the flower stem swells at its base and eventually withers away to leave an upright 4-sided seed capsule. Leaves are numerous and to 8" long. The lower ones usually have "wings" near their base.

RANGE: Sagebrush and Bunchgrass Zones of Eastern Washington. Mostly west of the Cascades but also sporadic at Coast.

BUTTER AND EGGS
(Linaria vulgaris)

There's no chance of mistaking butter and eggs for anything else. The intricate yellow flower with its orange "nose" is a close match to the yellow of butter and orange of an egg yolk. The blooms are in rich profusion on the top of an erect stalk to 2' high. The inch-long flowers have a graceful yellow spur and two lips, the upper being two-lobed and the lower three-lobed and pouch shaped. The "egg" color comes from an orange swelling almost closing the throat. Leaves are narrow and up to 2" long. Although they are regarded as being alternate there are times when they appear opposite.

RANGE: A naturalized European weed now widely spread on exposed places at lower elevations across the State.

YELLOW WILLOW HERB
(Epilobium luteum)

Its luxuriant growth along mountain streams is similar in habitat and form to red mimulus. Stems are erect and to 2' high. Leaves are to 3" long, heavily veined, sharply toothed, and generally in opposite pairs.

The modest flowers are held erect on long stems near the top of the plant. They are pale yellow and ½" - ¾" long. The 4 folded petals suggest a closed flower. Four long narrow sepals support the reticent bloom. Depending on elevation the blooming period varies from early to late summer.

RANGE: Moist meadows and stream edges from middle mountain to high elevations. Cascade and Olympic Mountains ranging northward to Alaska.

GREAT MULLEIN
(*Verbascum thapsus*)

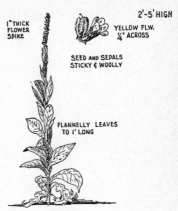

FLOWERS (YELLOW)

2'-5' HIGH

1" THICK FLOWER SPIKE

YELLOW FLW. ¼" ACROSS

SEED AND SEPALS STICKY & WOOLLY

FLANNELLY LEAVES TO 1' LONG

The tall thick stem of the great mullein and its large flannelly leaves quickly attract the attention. The stem often reaches 5' in height and is sometimes branched near the top into several upright arms. Dead stalks often stand all winter. Leaves are up to a foot long and have a coarse blotting paper texture with a covering of fine woolly hairs. They are rather repelling to the touch. Leaf bases form long ribs running down the stalk.

Tiny yellow flowers bursting out here and there on the flowering spike have a pleasant smell and the formation of new buds at the top keeps the great mullein in ragged bloom for several months from mid-summer onward.

RANGE: Scattered in poor ground in Coastal region. Widespread on poor land east of Cascades.

FALSE ASPHODEL
(*Tofieldia intermedia*)

Western Tofieldia

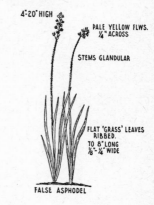

4"-20" HIGH

PALE YELLOW FLWS. ¼" ACROSS

STEMS GLANDULAR

FLAT 'GRASS' LEAVES RIBBED. TO 8" LONG ⅛"-¼" WIDE

FALSE ASPHODEL

A close watch during July and August along the lush growth bordering streams, swamps, or meadows often reveals the small yellowish flower head of the false asphodel, although the finely ribbed grass-like leaves are usually lost from sight. The unbranched flower stem has a slightly dirty look and sticky touch. The small pale-yellowish flowers about ¼" across form a loose cluster. The stamens are darkish and provide a dainty touch.

RANGE: Mostly wet places in sub-alpine and alpine elevations of Olympic and Cascade Mountains.

OVAL - LEAF ALUMROOT
(*Heuchera ovalifolia*)

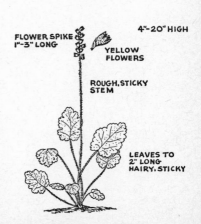

FLOWER SPIKE 1"-3" LONG

4"-20" HIGH

YELLOW FLOWERS

ROUGH, STICKY STEM

LEAVES TO 2" LONG HAIRY, STICKY

Alumroots with white flowers are on page 115.

This hardy plant grows on rock slides and the poorest of soils producing its leaves and flowers before the extreme heat of midsummer. The oval leaves with their irregular lobes grow at the bottom of the stem and are thick, sticky and hairy. Small yellowish flowers form a cluster along the upper part of the slender hairy stems. They bloom in early June to July at higher elevations.

RANGE: East slopes of Cascades and Central Washington.

H. glabella has smooth, rounded leaves 1" - 2" long which, in the fall, often turn striking crimson shades. The flowers are a light yellow. Bunchgrass and Yellow Pine Zones.

FLOWERS (BLUE)

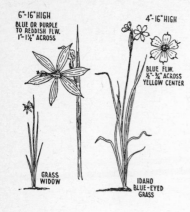

6"-16"HIGH
BLUE OR PURPLE
TO REDDISH FLW.
1"-1½" ACROSS

GRASS WIDOW

4"-16"HIGH

BLUE FLW.
½"-¾" ACROSS
YELLOW CENTER

IDAHO
BLUE-EYED
GRASS

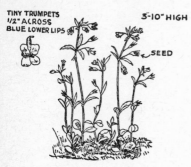

TINY TRUMPETS
½" ACROSS
BLUE LOWER LIPS

3"-10" HIGH

SEED

1'-2' HIGH

PURPLISH-BLUE
1"-1½" ACROSS

GRASS-LIKE
LEAVES

GRASS WIDOW
(Sisyrinchium inflatum)

This plant closely resembles satin flower but has sharp-pointed petals and grass-like leaves shorter than the main stem. Grass widow is a prolific bloomer and the large starry blooms beautify moist slopes. One sees a wide variety of colors, some almost a true blue, others shading to pinks and purples. Often white blooms add a touch of phantasy.

RANGE: Sagebrush Zone through the Bunchgrass Zone and into the Yellow Pine forests. Wilbur, Spokane, lower slopes of Blue Mountains.

IDAHO BLUE-EYED GRASS (S. idahoense) is a common spring flower of moist meadows in the Sagebrush and Bunchgrass Zones. Leaves are narrow and shorter than the flower stem. Three to nine short-lived dark blue flowers may blossom. Ellensburg, Pullman.

BLUE-EYED MARY
(Collinsia parviflora)

Innocence - Blue Lips

Blue-eyed Mary brings a picture of rocky openings and knolls green with fresh moss and bright with spring sunshine. Usually the dainty plant has a number of branched and spreading stems which produce a mat effect. The lower leaves are oblong to nearly round while the upper are almost stemless.

The fragile little flower, less than ½" long, is trumpet-like with two lower blue petals. Very often a single flower adorns the thin stem but in other plants a whorl of flowers rises from the leaf axils.

RANGE: Abundant April and May on dry exposed locations in the Coastal Forest Zone and across Washington in Sagebrush, Bunchgrass and Yellow Pine Zones.

CAMAS
(Camassia quamash)

Camas often is found with arbutus and garry oak which are typical trees of the Gulf Islands. The plant grows from a large, deep-seated bulb which once formed an important food item of the native Indians. The leaves are long and narrow and resemble coarse grass.

The flowers have three sepals and three petals, so similar in appearance that they are not ordinarily differentiated. The blue-purple flower is about 1" across and from 10 - 30 flowers and buds will be found on one stem. Occasionally a plant with white blooms will be seen.

RANGE: Dry places in Coastal Forest Zone but more abundant in wet meadows and Bunchgrass and Yellow Pine Zones. Ellensburg, Spokane and Blue Mountains.

C. leichtlinnii is a larger species that blooms a little later. The range is west of the Cascades.

(160)

BLUEBELL
(*Campanula rotundifolia*)
Harebell

This flower, the real "Bluebell of Scotland", is widely distributed throughout North America. The slender stems carry several beautiful blue bells near their tops. The stem leaves are thin and narrow but younger plants have rounded leaves at the base which usually disappear by the time the flowers are out.

RANGE: Spotty occurrence in sub-alpine elevations of Olympics and Cascades. Dry ground of Coastal Forests. Bunchgrass and Yellow Pine Zones. Spokane.

PIPERS HAREBELL (*C. piperii*) is only a few inches high. The small toothed leaves are less than 1" long and almost hidden by pale purple flowers about ½" across. Rocky places at high elevations of Olympics. Mt. Steele. Hurricane Ridge.

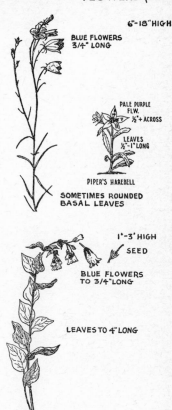

6"-18" HIGH

BLUE FLOWERS
3/4" LONG

PALE PURPLE
FLW.
½"+ ACROSS

LEAVES
½"-1" LONG

PIPER'S HAREBELL

SOMETIMES ROUNDED
BASAL LEAVES

WESTERN LUNGWORT
(*Mertensia platyphylla*)

Of the dozen or so lungworts in Washington about half the number reach 2' in height or over. All are fairly easily recognized by their clusters of blue bells. See page 174 for others. Most of the taller plants grow in humid situations or at mountain elevations. All are characterized by broad, alternate leaves and the seeds have a long appendage protruding from them.

This plant has the usual long-stemmed basal leaves and almost clasping upper leaves. The tightly packed clusters of buds gradually evolve into beautiful blue bells during early summer months.

RANGE: Moist places and rich soils of Coastal Forest Zone. Grays Harbour County and Puget Sound region.

1'-3' HIGH

SEED

BLUE FLOWERS
TO 3/4" LONG

LEAVES TO 4" LONG

BLUE SAILORS
(*Cichorium intybus*)
Chicory

Blue sailors is included as a wildflower although it could be more properly classed as an escape from cultivation. The bright blue flowers have taken their name from an old legend concerning a sailor's sweetheart who was deserted but nevertheless kept a faithful watch for him. The gods took pity on her and turned her into this plant which still haunts the roadsides from July to September.

The deep taproot has been used considerably in the past as a coffee substitute. The occurrence of blue sailors near the sites of early-day construction camps may be due to this use when coffee was extremely scarce. The tissuey blue flowers, from 1" - 1½" across, usually open in the morning but close in the afternoon.

RANGE: Sporadic occurrence along roadsides and in waste places. Coastal region and Bunchgrass Zone.

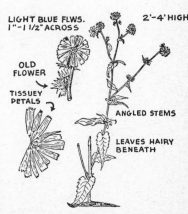

LIGHT BLUE FLWS.
1"-1 1/2" ACROSS

2'-4' HIGH

OLD
FLOWER

TISSUEY
PETALS

ANGLED STEMS

LEAVES HAIRY
BENEATH

FLOWERS (BLUE)

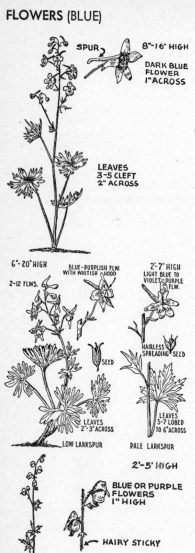

SPUR

8"-16" HIGH

DARK BLUE
FLOWER
1" ACROSS

LEAVES
3-5 CLEFT
2" ACROSS

6"-20" HIGH

2-12 FLWS.

BLUE-PURPLISH FLW.
WITH WHITISH HOOD

SEED

LEAVES
2"-3" ACROSS

LOW LARKSPUR

2'-7' HIGH
LIGHT BLUE TO
VIOLET-PURPLE
FLW.

HAIRLESS
SPREADING SEED

LEAVES
5-7 LOBED
TO 6" ACROSS

PALE LARKSPUR

2'-5' HIGH

BLUE OR PURPLE
FLOWERS
1" HIGH

HAIRY STICKY

LEAVES TO 4" WIDE
MOSTLY 5 LOBED

DELPHINIUM
Larkspur *(Delphinium menziesii)*

Delphiniums or larkspurs, as they are commonly called, range over most of North America and at least 6 species grow in the State. Although they may be from 6"-6' in height they are immediately recognized by the peculiar dark blue or purple flower with its long spur. The leaves too are featured by being deeply cleft into 3-5 main fingers and these usually cut again. A number of the delphiniums are considered very poisonous to grazing stock. This species is usually about 12" high.

RANGE: Dry places of Coastal forests and Cascades. Sagebrush, Bunchgrass and Yellow Pine Zones. Ellensburg, Yakima, Spokane.

LOW LARKSPUR
(Delphinium bicolor)

Generally low larkspur is about a foot high with many cleft alternate leaves to 3" across. The blue and white flowers on long stems form wide loose heads of bright hue. The complicated flower with its wings and spurs has several shades of blue or purples. Two small petals bent back into the spur are whitish or yellowish making recognition quite easy.

RANGE: Mostly sub-alpine slopes of Cascades and Olympics.

PALE LARKSPUR *(D. glaucum)* is an exceptionally tall larkspur of rich shady meadows often at higher elevations. Leaves and stems usually have a loose bluish or waxy bloom. Upper leaves may be few-cleft or entire. The flower head is narrow and extended. Flowers are short stemmed, about 1" long and range from pale blue to dark purple. Middle mountain to alpine elevations. Cascade, Olympic and Blue Mountains.

MONKSHOOD
(Aconitum columbianum)

Monkshood will be found as an individual or in a small patch and then not seen again in the entire vicinity. Moist open woods up to 4,500' elevation are preferred. Monkshood raises a stout stem 3'-5' in the air, and tipped with a long loose cluster of large dark blue flowers.

The palmately veined leaves are deeply lobed and grow alternately from the main stem. Lower leaves have long stems but these decrease in length the higher they are up. One petal forms a large "monkshood" which lends such distinction to each bloom. The flowers are about 1" long and either hang from the tip of the main stem or short side branches. The seeds and roots are poisonous. Monkshood is a late bloomer.

RANGE: Middle elevations of Cascades. Wet places of Yellow Pine Zone and upward in Wenatchee and northeastern mountains.

LUPINES
(Lupinus spp.)

Lupines are one of the more common widespread flowers in Wash. Over 20 species give a range from sea level to alpine heights and an adaptability to a wide variety of soils. They are a common roadside plant at the Coast, a range plant on better soils in the Interior, and particularly abundant above middle mountain elevations.

The leaflets radiate from the leaf stem like a number of thin fingers. Some species have 5 - 10 leaflets, others 10 - 17. The leaflets "sleep" at night by folding down like a closed umbrella. During the daytime the whole head rotates as the sun moves. The flowers, which cluster in long spikes, are generally from light blue to purple in color but several species are white to cream. Lyall's lupine is a dwarf plant only a few inches high with woolly leaves and occurs at high elevations.

RANGE: Widespread through Washington except in deep shade or most arid regions.

BLUE JACOB'S LADDER
(Polemonium humile)
(P. pulcherrimum)

Blue Skunkleaf, Polemonium

The name for this plant results from the ladder-like arrangement of the small leaves and their rather rank odor. Its tufted form with cheerful bright blue flowers looks like an escape from a rock garden. The flowers in clusters at the ends of the stem are in bloom during June and July.

RANGE: To 5,000' in open forests and sub-alpine slopes of Olympics and Cascades.

There are several different polemoniums in Washington. One has white flowers and another is from 1' - 2' high with erect, unbranched stems and showy blue flowers.

VERONICA
(Veronica alpina)

Alpine Speedwell

Although small in stature, the orderliness and brightness of this little flower draws one's attention to it. The small ovalish leaves are neatly arranged in several opposite pairs along the thin stem while the flowers and buds cluster at the very top. Often it will be found near blue Jacob's ladder and blooming at the same time.

The four blue symmetrical petals surround a round cream center. The flower is made quite distinctive by the anthers and style protruding beyond the petals.

RANGE: Sub-alpine and alpine slopes of Olympics and Cascades. Mt. Rainier, Mt. Stuart.

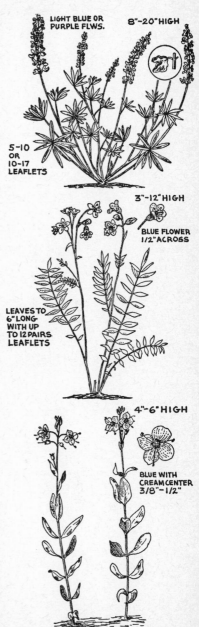

LIGHT BLUE OR PURPLE FLWS.

8"-20" HIGH

5-10 OR 10-17 LEAFLETS

3"-12" HIGH

BLUE FLOWER 1/2" ACROSS

LEAVES TO 6" LONG WITH UP TO 12 PAIRS LEAFLETS

4"-6" HIGH

BLUE WITH CREAM CENTER 3/8"-1/2"

BLUE-PURPLE FLWS. 1/2" LONG

3"-15" HIGH

SELF-HEAL
(*Prunella vulgaris*)

Heal-all

Self-heal may be found on dry soil along road edges or in moist shady places. The long heads of flowers vary in color from a light blue to a dark purple. Each flower is about ½" long and quite attractive if examined as an individual. Watch for self-heal in bloom during the entire summer. Here is another plant with square stems. Leaves are thin, alternate and from 1" - 2½" long.

RANGE: Across Washington in moist places at low to middle elevations. Seattle, Yakima, Pullman.

GENTIANS
(*Gentiana spp.*)

Gentians prefer shady glades or the most moist alplands for their shy appearance. There are a dozen or more species in Wash. all with opposite or whorled leaves and erect blue flowers balanced in an artistic symmetrical fashion.

FOUR-PARTED GENTIAN (*G. propinqua*) has several flowers rising from the leaf axils. It is often branched from near the base. Distinguished by flower being divided into four notches at tip. Spotty occurrence in Lincoln and Spokane Counties.

NORTHERN GENTIAN (*G. acuta*) or (*G. amarella*) has flowers in threes or more. The flower is divided into five notches at the tip. West of Cascades. Gulf Islands and along Coast. Spotty occurrence in swamps.

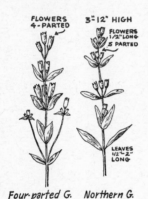

FLOWERS 4-PARTED

3"-12" HIGH

FLOWERS 1/2" LONG 5 PARTED

LEAVES 1/2"-2" LONG

Four-parted G.   Northern G.

BLUE VIOLET
(*Viola adunca*)

Violets, be they yellow, white or blue are recognized almost instantly by all. Unfortunately the wild violets do not have the fragrance of their cultivated relations. Being early bloomers of April and May they are discovered with the main display of spring flowers. In this species the long-stemmed leaves are roundish and heart shaped with shallow teeth. The color of the flowers ranges from pale to dark blue. Two of the petals which stick out from either side of the flower have fine hairs on them. See page 175 for other violets.

RANGE: Common throughout to sub-alpine slopes.

BLUE SWAMP VIOLET (*V. palustris*) is one of the half dozen native species with bluish flowers. The flowers range from blue to almost white. They have little or no stem. Wet places from Coastal forests to sub-alpine slopes of Cascades. Also on easterly side.

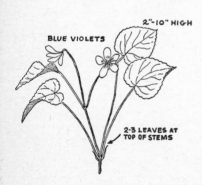

2"-10" HIGH

BLUE VIOLETS

2-3 LEAVES AT TOP OF STEMS

AMERICAN BROOKLIME
(*Veronica americana*)
Speedwell

The dainty blue garden forget-me-not is closely related to brooklime. A four-parted flower, about 1/4" across, with two spreading stamens will serve to distinguish the group of nearly a dozen species found in Washington. As the name suggests this straggling plant is found in wet places. The ribbed stem may vary from 4" - 30" high but usually carries 3 - 5 pairs of leaves. Those at the bottom are oval-shaped and scarcely toothed while the upper ones have distinct teeth and are more sharply pointed. Flowers are carried in airy clusters from May to July. The plant was once considered of high medicinal value in Europe.

RANGE: Wide range across North America in wet places. From Sagebrush Zone to fair altitudes.

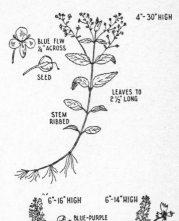

4"-30" HIGH

BLUE FLW 1/4" ACROSS

SEED

LEAVES TO 2 1/2" LONG

STEM RIBBED

COLUMBIA SYNTHYRIS
(*Synthyris stellata*)

There are four synthyris in Washington. In general they have broad, roundish basal leaves palmately veined. Flowers are small and blue to blue-purple. The calyx is 4 parted and the 2 stamens are protruding.

Fifty years ago Columbia synthyris was not known to occur in Washington. Its leaves are almost round and cut into a number of rounded lobes which are toothed. The flower stem exceeds the leaves and holds a mass of small blue purple flowers.

RANGE: April and May on slopes of the Cascade Mountains protruding into the Columbia River Gorge region.

FRINGED SYNTHYRIS (*S. schizantha*) has proportionally wider leaves than the above. Stems and leaf ribs are hairy. The flower head is a fuzzy mass of blue-purplish blooms each with its four fringed petals. June and July on moist banks and bluffs at middle mountain elevations of the Cascade and Olympic Mountains.

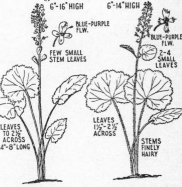

6"-16" HIGH   6"-14" HIGH

BLUE-PURPLE FLW.

FEW SMALL STEM LEAVES

BLUE-PURPLE FLW.

2-4 SMALL LEAVES

LEAVES TO 2 1/2 ACROSS 4"-8" LONG

LEAVES 1 1/2"-2 1/2" ACROSS

STEMS FINELY HAIRY

COLUMBIA SYNTHYRIS   FRINGED SYNTHYRIS

ROUND - LEAVED SYNTHYRIS
(*Synthyris reniformis*)
Snow-Queen

Snow-queen is a descriptive name for as soon as the snow is off the ground the shy little purple flowers make a welcome appearance. Often the plants are widespread over the forest floor—the only blooms to be seen.

The large dull green leaves reach as high as the flowers and almost overshadow them. Flowers appear to have 4 sepals, 4 petals, 2 purple protruding stamens and a long style. The whole flower is only 1/4" long. The blooming time is March to May. At the higher elevations this plant may be found as the first trilliums appear.

RANGE: Open, well drained coniferous woods west of the Cascades at lower elevations.

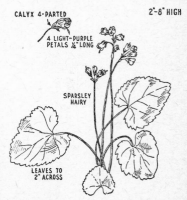

CALYX 4-PARTED

4 LIGHT-PURPLE PETALS 1/4" LONG

2"-8" HIGH

SPARSLEY HAIRY

LEAVES TO 2" ACROSS

(165)

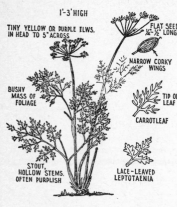

1'-3' HIGH

TINY YELLOW OR PURPLE FLWS.
IN HEAD TO 5" ACROSS

FLAT SEED
¼"-½" LONG

NARROW CORKY
WINGS

BUSHY
MASS OF
FOLIAGE

TIP OF
LEAF

CARROTLEAF

STOUT,
HOLLOW STEMS.
OFTEN PURPLISH

LACE-LEAVED
LEPTOTAENIA

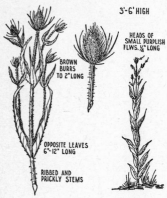

3'-6' HIGH

HEADS OF
SMALL PURPLISH
FLWS. ½" LONG

BROWN
BURRS
TO 2" LONG

OPPOSITE LEAVES
6"-12" LONG

RIBBED AND
PRICKLY STEMS

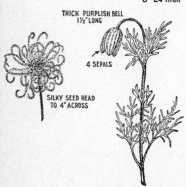

8"-24" HIGH

THICK PURPLISH BELL
1½" LONG

4 SEPALS

SILKY SEED HEAD
TO 4" ACROSS

CARROT LEAF
(Leptotaenia dissecta multifida)
(Lomatium dissecta multifida)

This common spring plant of rocky slopes is separated from the lomatiums on the basis of narrow thickened corky wings on the seed rather than thin wings. It blooms in April and May and the big tousled ball of fern-like leaves, usually slightly less than 2' high, is very decorative. Some plants have yellow flower heads—others purple. The heavy aromatic roots were once roasted and eaten by the Indians.

RANGE: Bunchgrass Zone. Chelan, Ellensburg, Wenatchee, Klickitat County. Pullman.

LACE-LEAVED LEPTOTAENIA (L. dissecta) ranges on both sides of the Cascades. It has slightly thicker leaf segments and slightly shorter seeds. Flowers generally purple, occasionally yellow. Westerly portion of Bunchgrass Zone.

TEASEL
(Dipsacus sylvestris)

This large coarse weed is especially noticeable in April and May when its tall prickly dead stem and great spiny burrs tower above the verdant spring greenery.

Its large opposite leaves often reach 12" in length. During summer months dense spikelike heads of pale purplish flowers are supported by an involucre with long bracts. Then brown burrs of imposing proportions form. When dry they are a perfect symmetry of long curving spines. So stiff and evenly spaced are the spines that the large burrs were used by the early pioneers to card or 'tease' wool—thus its introduction from Europe. The burrs, when dipped, make an attractive winter decoration.

RANGE: Mostly damp places in Bunchgrass Zone. Garfield, Pullman, Dayton, Prosser.

SUGAR BOWLS
(Clematis hirsutissima)

Leather Flower

Sugar bowls is different from most flowers in the bulk of the heavy dark purple nodding bell ornamented by rounded ridges padded with white woolly hair. It is somewhat leathery in texture and flares into 4 ragged-edged sepals. There are no petals. The stamens are grouped into a tight cluster giving a yellow throat. Like the other clematis it has a beautiful white feathery seed head to 4" across.

The leaves are generally hairy and vary from 2" - 5" in length and are deeply cut into a shred-like pattern. They have a strychine taste and an early explorer says one tribe of Indians spurred on their tired horses by rubbing the leaves in their nostrils.

RANGE: Blooming during late spring on grassy slopes of the Yellow Pine Zone throughout Eastern Washington. Spokane.

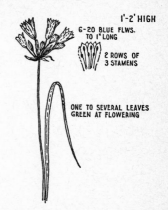

LARGE-FLOWERED BRODIAEA
(Brodiaea grandiflora)

Other generic names used for the *Brodiaea* are *Hookera, Triteleia,* and *Hesperscordum.* Two common names are cluster lily and wild hyacinth. All brodiaea grow from small bulbs and most are an excellent food. Unbranched stems are topped by a radiating cluster of trumpet-like flowers with a line down each petal. Leaves are one to several, grass-like, and often withered away by the time the plant is in bloom.

Large-flowered brodiaea grows to 2' high and has green leaves in June at the same time as the flowers. The bright blue trumpets to 1" long form a cluster of from 6 - 20 flowers. The stamens are in 2 rows. Many species only have three stamens with the other three being reduced to white sterile filaments resembling petals.

RANGE: Abundant in grassy slopes of Sagebrush, Bunchgrass and Yellow Pine Zones. Spokane, Pullman.

HARVEST BRODIAŁA
(Brodiaea coronaria)

This beautiful flower is an indescribable color with vivid tones of blue, purple, and violet. The open trumpet is 1" long. The graceful petals are curved back and they and the long buds are veined with a distinctive purple line down the center. The three sterile stamens resemble three small white petals.

Often this plant is under a foot high and the very narrow leaves have withered by the time the flowers appear. The small bulbs, deeply buried, are very nutritious and were dug by the Indians.

RANGE: On dry exposed situations in Coastal Forest Zone. Gulf Islands, Tacoma.

BICOLORED BRODIAEA
(Brodiaea bicolor)

This lovely cluster lily, with its often drooping blooms in delicate shades of blue and white, is relatively scarce. The dark blue tube is almost twice as long as the white or pale blue lobes. Flowers may reach an inch in length.

RANGE: Blooming May and June on dry slopes and plains of Sagebrush Zone. Chelan County and southward.

OOKOW *(B. pulchella)* has an exceptionally long stem sometimes to 4' in length. The tight cluster of dark purple flowers appear after the leaves have withered. Ookow is an Indian name for this plant whose bulb was once used for food. It blooms in dry places during June and July in the Coastal Forest Zone.

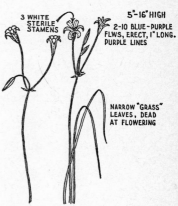

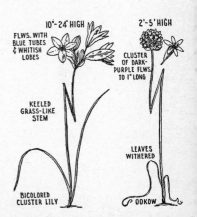

FLOWERS (BLUE)

1'-2' HIGH
6-20 BLUE FLWS. TO 1" LONG
2 ROWS OF 3 STAMENS
ONE TO SEVERAL LEAVES GREEN AT FLOWERING

3 WHITE STERILE STAMENS
5"-16" HIGH
2-10 BLUE-PURPLE FLWS, ERECT, 1" LONG. PURPLE LINES
NARROW "GRASS" LEAVES, DEAD AT FLOWERING

10"-24" HIGH
FLWS. WITH BLUE TUBES & WHITISH LOBES
KEELED GRASS-LIKE STEM
BICOLORED CLUSTER LILY

2'-5' HIGH
CLUSTER OF DARK-PURPLE FLWS. TO 1" LONG
LEAVES WITHERED
OOKOW

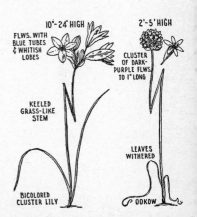

FLOWERS (BLUE)

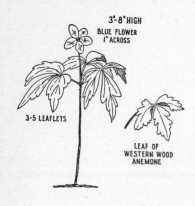

3"-8" HIGH

BLUE FLOWER
1" ACROSS

3-5 LEAFLETS

LEAF OF
WESTERN WOOD
ANEMONE

BLUE ANEMONE
(Anemone oregana)

Most anemones are white with a pale blue tinge but this fragile bloom of April and May is a soft sky blue color. Unfortunately the petal-like sepals are short-lived thus robbing this slender little plant of its main attraction. The three leaves form a whorl toward the top of the stem. Each of the 3 - 5 leaflets is coarsely toothed.

RANGE: Moist woods mostly east of the Cascades. Blue Mountains.

WESTERN WOOD ANEMONE *(A. quinquefolia)* is slightly larger than the above and has a white flower often tinged with purple. It ranges across Washington in moist mountain forests.

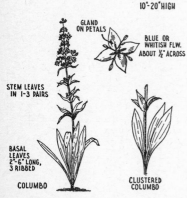

10"-20" HIGH

GLAND
ON PETALS

BLUE OR
WHITISH FLW.
ABOUT ½" ACROSS

STEM LEAVES
IN 1-3 PAIRS

BASAL
LEAVES
2"-6" LONG,
3 RIBBED

COLUMBO

CLUSTERED
COLUMBO

COLUMBO
(Frasera albicaulis)

Frasera

This member of the gentian family shows its relationship by having smooth opposite stem leaves. The flower has both pistils and stamens, the latter alternating with the pale blue or sometimes white petals. The Frasera group differ from the gentians in having a flat rather than a tubular flower and also a hairy gland on each petal.

The plant has one to several stout stems with a cluster of long-stemmed basal leaves. Its pretty head of symmetrical flowers is seen during May and June.

RANGE: Open slopes and swales of the Bunchgrass Zone and extending into the Sagebrush Zone.

CLUSTERED COLUMBO *(F. fastigiata)* has wider basal and stem leaves and a bunched flower head of from 1 - 5 clusters of pale blue flowers. It often reaches 4' in height. Blooming time is from May to July in the Yellow Pine Forest Zone and the Blue Mountains.

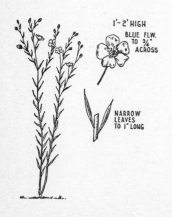

1'- 2' HIGH

BLUE FLW.
TO ¾"
ACROSS

NARROW
LEAVES
TO 1" LONG

WILD FLAX
(Linum lewisii)

A person may encounter this plant over a rather large range and never see it elsewhere.

Its saucer-like flowers of brightest blue are bound to arouse a desire to know more about it. These are carried on thin stems near the top of a single slender plant to 2' high or one branched near ground level. Each sky-blue bloom is about ¾" across and has its flower parts in fives... June to August is blooming time. Seed heads form brownish balls almost ¼" across.

The leaves are neatly staggered in alternate fashion and seldom are over 1" long. Linen thread has been made from the fibrous stems of the flax family since time immemorial.

RANGE: East of Cascades in Bunchgrass and Yellow Pine Zones.

NETTLELEAF HORSEMINT
(Agastache urticifolia)

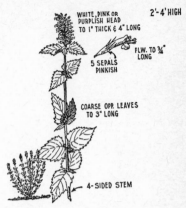

This plant, as the name suggests, looks much like a nettle or a mint and grows in similar bushy clumps on moist ground. From 2' - 4' high, it has coarsely toothed, alternating, opposite pairs of leaves to 3" long.

Dense flower heads are to 1" thick and 4" long. The general coloring effect may be white, pink, or purplish. Each long thin trumpet flower is about ¾" long and has a notched upper lip and a 3-lobed lower one. The 5 narrow sepals are often pinkish tinged. It will be seen in bloom from late April on.

RANGE: Sagebrush Zone. Ferry, Stevens, Spokane, Whitman, Columbia, and Walla Walla Counties.

MOUNTAIN MONARDELLA
(Monardella odoratissima)

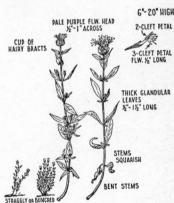

The plant is sometimes a straggly affair with several stems or may grow as a compact cluster to 20" high. This species shows a great variation in the shape of the leaves. Generally they are thickish and densely dotted with glands on the underside. Smaller leaves and branchlets often occur in the leaf axils. Crushed leaves emit a strong mint perfume.

Pale purple flowers are about ½" long and held in a greenish or purplish globe of fuzzy overlapping scales. Each thin flower has two lips, the upper being 2-cleft, the lower 3-cleft. Purple stamens on purple stalks are further ornamentations. It blooms during June and July.

RANGE: Sagebrush, Bunchgrass, and Yellow Pine Zones. Republic, Cle-elm, Yakima, Blue Mountains.

DRUMMOND'S ROCKCRESS
(Arabis drummondii)

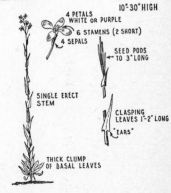

The 20 or more species of rockcress have small flowers in pastel shades of white, pink, or purple. They belong to the *Cruciferae*, referring to the cross-like arrangement of the petals. Other family characteristics are a single erect stem, 4 sepals, 4 petals, and 6 stamens of which 2 are short ones. Stem leaves are alternate and usually with clasping bases. Leaves have a distinctive bitter taste. Long narrow flattened seed pods split open lengthways. Rock cresses have a wide distribution from arid valley to alpine meadows.

RANGE: Sub-alpine Zone of Cascades and Olympics.

TOWER MUSTARD (*A. glabra*) is much coarser and leaves are to 2½" long and ½" wide while seed pods average between 3" - 4" long. The tiny white flowers form a dense cluster. Edge of Bunchgrass and Yellow Pine Zones.

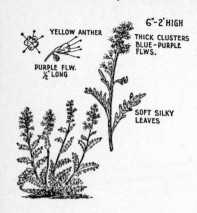

YELLOW ANTHER

PURPLE FLW.
½" LONG

6"-2' HIGH

THICK CLUSTERS
BLUE-PURPLE
FLWS.

SOFT SILKY
LEAVES

MOUNTAIN PHACELIA
(Phacelia sericea)

Silky Phacelia

Mountain phacelia with its beautiful spikes of fuzzy violet flowers is in sharp contrast to the pure bright colors of most alpine blooms. The fuzzy appearance comes from long protruding stamens with a yellow dot at their tip. The long stamens are a characteristic of the phacelias as is the disagreeable odor or absence of smell.

Mountain phacelia forms a profusion of flower stems. Its leaves are so silky with fine hair as to appear silvery on occasion. The blooming time is late summer.

RANGE: Dry rocky places above timberline in Olympics and Cascades. Hurricane Ridge.

ONE-FLOWERED CANCER ROOT
(Orobanche uniflora)

Naked Broom-rape

Plant parasitics have no green leaves for nourishment is obtained by feeding on the roots of other plants. Flowers range in color from yellowish-brown to purplish tints and scales on the lower stem are general.

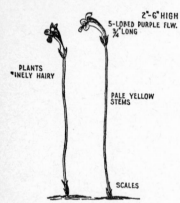

2"-6" HIGH
5-LOBED PURPLE FLW.
¾" LONG

PLANTS
FINELY HAIRY

PALE YELLOW
STEMS

SCALES

This oddity has thin stems, naked except for several scales, and a purplish flower resembling a penstemon with two upper flower lobes and three lower ones. The flower is about ¾" long and has a faint fragrance. On occasion the bloom may be yellowish. Watch for it in April and May in open forests at low elevations.

RANGE: Moist grassy places across Washington. Gulf Islands, Tacoma, Ellensburg, Pullman, Blue Mountains.

CLUSTERED BROOM-RAPE (*O. fasciculata*) is often parasitic on such dry land species as sagebrush and eriogonums. The short visible section of stem is very scaly as well as coarsely hairy and glandular. The typical flower from ½" - ¾" long has two broad upper lobes and is 3-lobed below. Although usually purple-tinged it may be yellowish in color. May and June are the months it blooms. Dry sandy soils mostly east of the Cascades. Olympic Mountains, Wenatchee, Coulee City, Spokane.

BUNCHED BROOM-RAPE (*O. comosa*) has a dense cluster of purple flowers each about ¾" long and with long, thin sepals. Blooming time is from June to September. Exposed bluffs along Coast and Bunchgrass Zone. Chelan, Grand Coulee.

GROUND-CONE (*Boschniakia strobiliacea*) is parasitic on salal. Flowers ½" - ¾" long poke out between the upper leaves. The upper lip is undivided but the lower is broken into three hairy lobes. Indians ate this plant. Lower elevations west of the Cascades.

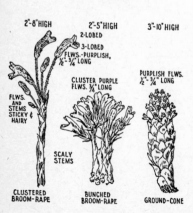

2"-8" HIGH

FLWS.
AND
STEMS
STICKY &
HAIRY

SCALY
STEMS

CLUSTERED
BROOM-RAPE

2"-5" HIGH
2-LOBED
3-LOBED
FLWS.-PURPLISH.
½"-¾" LONG

CLUSTER PURPLE
FLWS. ¾" LONG

BUNCHED
BROOM-RAPE

3"-10" HIGH

PURPLISH FLWS.
½"-¾" LONG

GROUND-CONE

FALSE LADY'S SLIPPER
(Calypso bulbosa)

Calypso - Lady's Slipper

Once the delicately tinted jewel has been found in the quiet seclusion of the mossy forest floor its beauty can hardly be forgotten for here is one of Nature's treasures in miniature. The little white bulb is deeply cradled in a protective layer of moss and needles. Only one shiny green leaf grows at the base of the reddish stem.

The colorful little orchid blooms during April to June.

RANGE: Throughout Washington in shady coniferous forests up to elevations of 4500'. Seattle, Olympia, Spokane, Blue Mountains.

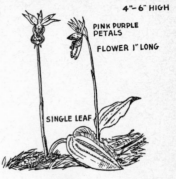

4"-6" HIGH

PINK PURPLE PETALS

FLOWER 1" LONG

SINGLE LEAF

CORAL ROOT
(Corallorhiza spp.)

Coral root is named from its mass of gnarled, knobby roots which resemble a piece of coral. The plant is parasitic and therefore can do without leaves except for small scales. There are several species in Washington all having single stout stems clustered with small orchid-like flowers. One has a white lip and others are colored either purple or brown. One has its blossoms handsomely striped while yet another produces pure yellow flowers.

Coral roots usually are found in fairly open and moist forests. They bloom during May and June but often the dead stalks are noticeable for months.

RANGE: Different species in various parts of Washington.

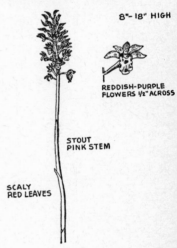

8"-18" HIGH

REDDISH-PURPLE FLOWERS ½" ACROSS

STOUT PINK STEM

SCALY RED LEAVES

PURPLE PEA
(Lathyrus nuttallii)

The peas and vetches (Vicia spp.) are similar in appearance and mixed with many introduced species. Both have thin weak stems which are held up by twining tendrils. The leaves are formed of from 3 - 5 pairs of opposite leaflets. The "sweet pea" flowers provide the most easily recognized feature. Most of the vetches have smaller flowers and leaves than the peas.

Purple pea is a common plant particularly in moist Coast forests. Its string of purple blossoms with their bluish keels are almost hidden in the salal or other supporting shrubs. They are in bloom May and June.

RANGE: Shady woods of Coastal regions. Olympics, Cascade Mountains and Yellow Pine Zone bordering the Cascades.

BEACH PEA (L. maritimus) is a coarse trailer or climber found along the sea shore. Leaflets 3 - 5 pairs. From 6 - 10 large purple flowers. Purplish pods to 3" long.

GRAY BEACH PEA (L. littoralis) is a low, short vine gray in color from long silky hairs. Leaflets 1 - 3 pairs. From 3 - 6 blue flowers. Sea beaches.

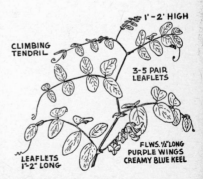

1'-2' HIGH

CLIMBING TENDRIL

3-5 PAIR LEAFLETS

FLWS. ½" LONG PURPLE WINGS CREAMY BLUE KEEL

LEAFLETS 1"-2" LONG

(171)

FLOWERS (PURPLE)

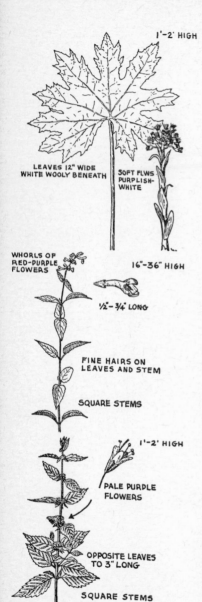

1'-2' HIGH

LEAVES 12" WIDE WHITE WOOLY BENEATH

SOFT FLWS PURPLISH-WHITE

WHORLS OF RED-PURPLE FLOWERS

16"-36" HIGH

½ - ¾" LONG

FINE HAIRS ON LEAVES AND STEM

SQUARE STEMS

1'-2' HIGH

PALE PURPLE FLOWERS

OPPOSITE LEAVES TO 3" LONG

SQUARE STEMS

COLTSFOOT
(*Petasites speciosa*)

Butterbur

Coltsfoot is among the earliest of the spring flowers and may be seen from March onwards. The first flowers are often in advance of the leaves thus leading to some confusion in linking the two at a later date. The purplish-white, sweet-scented flowers are in a soft loose head at the top of a thick stem 8" -16" high. These turn into seeds without visible change in color or shape.

The leaves are up to a foot across and white woolly beneath. Each leaf has from 7 - 9 toothed lobes which are often split again.

RANGE: Damp ground in Coastal Forest Zone with sporadic occurrence on east slopes of Cascades.

ALPINE COLTSFOOT (*P. frigida*) grows to 1' high and has kidney-shaped leaves to 4" long. Sub-alpine to alpine meadows. Olympics and Cascades.

HEDGE NETTLE
(*Stachys ciliata*)

This is a coarse weedy plant forming extensive masses of green until the red-purple flowers dress it in gay color. The flowers are trumpet-like with a protruding lower lip and form in whorls of about 6 at the top of the stems. During June hedge nettle is in bloom. The leaves suggest wild mint but they have a rank smell and are finely hairy. Main stems are square which may come as a shock to most people who believe all flower stems are round.

RANGE: At lower elevations in damp ground west of the Cascade Mountains. Spotty on east side.

S. palustris is less than 2' high and has light purple flowers. Wet ground east of the Cascade Mountains in Bunchgrass Zone. Sporadic in Coastal region. Spokane, Coulee City.

CANADA MINT
(*Mentha canadensis*)

Wild Mint

There is only one native mint in Washington but several escapes have established themselves. Mint will be found around the edges of damp places and might often pass unnoticed except for the clean, spicy smell when it is stepped on. The flowers are an unobtrusive purple to pink color and form in balls between the opposite leaves. They are in bloom from July to August. The leafy plant grows erect with stout squarish stems which may be quite hairy on the upper sections.

RANGE: Wet places of Coastal region. Also Sagebrush, Bunchgrass Zones. Seattle, North Yakima, Coulee City.

PENSTEMON
(Penstemon spp.)

Beard Tongue

At the Coast this beautiful plant chooses rocky bluffs and slides but in the higher mountains it is fairly common on gravel or sandy soils.

Of the dozen or more species in Wash. less than half that number are commonly recognized. Two forms, *P. scouleri* and *P. menziesii* often are classed as shrubs because of their woody stems and evergreen leaves. All have a 5-lobed calyx, a funnel-like flower with two lips, the upper having 2 lobes and the lower 3. There are 5 stamens but only 4 anthers leaving one sterile. In some species the throat or tongue is very hairy.

MENZIES PENSTEMON *(P. menziesii)* is a shrubby plant with thick, evergreen, ovalish leaves less than 1" in length. The throat or tongue of the flower is bristly with hairs. The range is alpine slopes in the high mountains of the Cascades and Olympics. The blooming period is during July and August.

SHRUBBY or **SCOULER'S PENSTEMON** *(P. scouleri)* *(P. fruticosus)* is very similar to the above except for its narrow, serrated leaves. The range is east of the Cascades at middle to subalpine elevations. Masses of bloom on rocky cliffs during May are likely to be this penstemon.

LITTLE FLOWER PENSTEMON *(P. procerus)* hasn't the mat-like effect of the above two species but grows upright to 12" high. The flowers are a dark blue and about ½" long. They grow in thick clusters from the topmost leaf axils and are out in early and mid-summer depending on the elevation. Olympics, Cascade Mountains, Ellensburg, Yakima, Spokane.

(P. tolmie) is often given for this species or one very similar. For other penstemons see page 105.

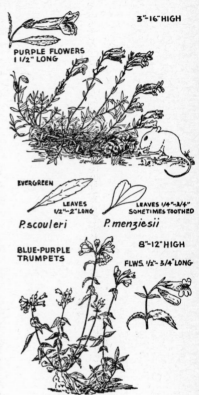

3"-16" HIGH

PURPLE FLOWERS 1½" LONG

EVERGREEN

LEAVES ½"-2" LONG
P.scouleri

LEAVES ¼"-¾" SOMETIMES TOOTHED
P. menziesii

BLUE-PURPLE TRUMPETS

8"-12" HIGH

FLWS. ½"-¾" LONG

SIMPSON'S CACTUS
(Pediocactus simpsonii)

Hedgehog Thistle, Pediocactus

The three cacti found in Washington are very easy to tell apart by their shapes and well separated ranges. Simpson's cactus is a single blunt cone, ranging from 2" - 5" in height and to several inches across. It is covered with a pattern of prominent bumps each carrying a cluster of needle-like spines from ¼" - ¾" long. Like most cacti the flowers are delicate and tissuey with several rows of petals. One or several of these 1" - 2" wide blooms may be perched on top of the bulbous pin cushion. They vary widely in color from purple to a weak yellow or rose. In bloom April and May when their habitat of rocky exposed soils is rich with spring wild flowers.

RANGE: Stoney ridges of Sagebrush Zone in Kittitas and Douglas Counties.

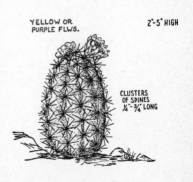

YELLOW OR PURPLE FLWS.

2"-5" HIGH

CLUSTERS OF SPINES ¼"-¾" LONG

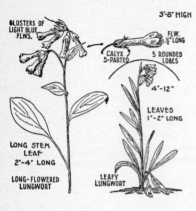

CLUSTERS OF LIGHT BLUE FLWS.

3"-8" HIGH

FLW. ½" LONG

CALYX 5-PARTED

5 ROUNDED LOBES

4"-12"

LEAVES 1"-2" LONG

LONG STEM LEAF 2"-4" LONG

LONG-FLOWERED LUNGWORT

LEAFY LUNGWORT

3"-10" HIGH

SEED POD 1"-3" LONG

PURPLE FLOWER ¼" ACROSS

OLIVE-GREEN LEAVES 1"-3" LONG THICK & VELVETY

3'-8' HIGH

PURPLE PETALS

YELLOW ANTHERS

LEAVES 3-LOBED TO 4" LONG

BERRIES GREEN THEN BRIGHT RED ¼" LONG

LONG - FLOWERED LUNGWORT
(Mertensia longiflora)
(Mertensia pulchella)

Anyone hiking in Central or Eastern Washington in the spring will likely find this flower. Its heads of blue with the odd pink-tinged bloom are so profuse they appear to almost overbalance the low stem. This has few leaves but the lower one or two are long-stemmed. It blooms from April to late June.
RANGE: Sagebrush and Bunchgrass Zones of Eastern Washington to the low mountains flanking the Cascades. Blue Mountains.

LEAFY LUNGWORT (M. oblongifolia) usually has a tuft of long-stemmed basal leaves while the higher leaves have no stem. Flowers are grouped in a massed cluster and are between ¼" - ½" long. Buds have a pinkish tinge which sometimes persists to the flower. Most common in Bunchgrass Zone. Elmira and westward. Ellensburg, Klickitat County.

DAGGER - POD
(Parrya cheiranthoides)
(Phoenicaulis cheiranthoides)

Common Phoenicaulis

One of the distinctive spring wildflowers, dagger-pod adds a gay note of color from April to June to dry exposed places east of the Cascades. Its tuft of olive-green leaves, thickish and velvety with hairs provides an attractive base for the flower-laden stalk. The small purple flowers about ¼" across are carried on long stems which stick abruptly out from the central stem. Elongated seed pods are shaped like a broad-based dagger. The two sides separate to release the several tiny seeds.
RANGE: Rocky exposed places at low elevations of the Sagebrush Zone. Ellensburg.

BITTERSWEET NIGHTSHADE
(Solanum dulcamara)

Climbing Nightshade

Of the several nightshades in Washington, this climber, often interwoven in dense shrubbery has highly decorative flowers or bright red berries.

The leaves with their two ear-like lobes will mark it immediately. Flowers closely resemble peacock or shooting star with deep purple to blue petals flaring back from a narrow yellow cone of stamens. Green berries about ¼" long may be seen on the same vine as the flowers which are in evidence from May to August. Ripened berries are a very bright red.

Climbing nightshade is a native of Europe and has escaped from cultivation in the west.
RANGE: Damp shady places at lower elevations on both sides of the Cascades.

SAGEBRUSH VIOLET
(Viola trinervata)

Three-Nerved Violet

You may not recognize this as a violet for it grows where sagebrush is the typical ground cover and its deeply cut leaves are quite different to most violets. The flower, blooming from March to May, is distinctly two-toned with the two upper petals being a deep purple and the remainder a mauve to white streaked with veins. Often there is a yellow spot in the throat. Some of the larger leaves have 3 very distinct veins, the outer ones following close to the edge of the leaf.

RANGE: Widespread in dry gravelly soils of the Bunchgrass Zone southward from Grand Coulee. Goldendale.

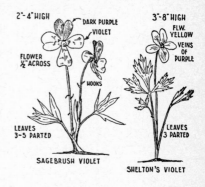

NARROW - LEAVED SKULLCAP
(Scutellaria angustifolia)

The skullcaps take their name from a curious little projection or crest on the calyx. They are plants of moist ground with long funnel-like flowers of a dull bluish color which easily escape the attention. Pairs of slender branches form in the leaf axils of the sturdier plants. This species has the largest flowers of the group and blooms from early to mid-summer.

RANGE: Moist places in the Bunchgrass and Yellow Pine Zones. Douglas, West Klickitat, Spokane and Whitman Counties.

MARSH SKULLCAP (S. galericulata) occurs in marshy ground and grows from 1' - 3' high. The flowers form in pairs and bloom from July and August. Range as above.

MAD-DOG SKULLCAP (S. laterifolia) has clusters of pairs of blue flowers so tiny as to easily pass notice. A late summer flower it is found in damp ground of the Coastal Forest Zone.

LONG - STEMMED TRILLIUM
(Trillium petiolatum)

This trillium or wake-robin is one of two species common in Washington. The three leaves branch from a short stem about an inch long which is attached to a creeping rootstalk rather than a bulb. Leaves are round and have stems almost as long as themselves. Cradled in the cup formed by the joining leaves is a delicate purple or maroon flower with 6 dark purple anthers. All the flower parts are in threes. The bloom averages about 2" across and is out in April and May doing its best to "wake the robins" and usher in spring.

RANGE: Shady and more moist places of Bunchgrass Zone in Eastern Washington. Spokane, Pullman.

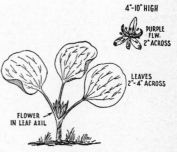

(175)

FLOWERS (PURPLE)

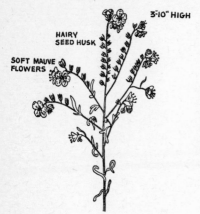

HAIRY SEED HUSK

SOFT MAUVE FLOWERS

3"-10" HIGH

PHACELIA
(*Phacelia linearis*)

This pretty little wildflower is fairly common in arid waste places such as road edges. Sometimes there is a single main stem but more often a few short branches. As the branchlets extend, new flowers grow at the tip and the seeds of former blooms stand as husks along the twigs. The soft mauve or lavender color is one not often duplicated. A few thin twisting leaves adorn the higher stems but 3-lobed leaves are general on the lower branches. The blooming period is from May 15 - June 15.

RANGE: Gulf Islands, Cascades. Most abundant in dry ground of Sagebrush, Bunchgrass and Yellow Pine Zones. Spokane, Yakima.

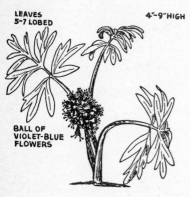

LEAVES 5-7 LOBED

4"-9" HIGH

BALL OF VIOLET-BLUE FLOWERS

BALLHEAD WATERLEAF
(*Hydrophyllum capitatum*)

Like other wild flowers such as peacocks, yellow bells and buttercups, it blooms in early spring while the ground is still moist. The leaves are divided into 5 - 7 lobes, each of which may be further lobed. When young, these succulent "waterleaves" make excellent greens. The flowers mass in an appealing ball of violet blue made misty by a large number of protruding stamens.

RANGE: Sagebrush, Bunchgrass, and Yellow Pine Zones. Wenatchee, Pullman.

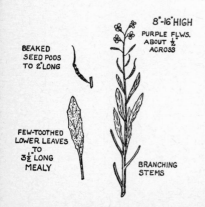

BEAKED SEED PODS TO 2"LONG

FEW-TOOTHED LOWER LEAVES TO 3½"LONG MEALY

8"-16"HIGH

PURPLE FLWS. ABOUT ½ ACROSS

BRANCHING STEMS

PURPLE CROSS FLOWER
(*Chorispora tenalla*)

Chorispora

This native of Asia is a relatively recent arrival in Washington. However it has found the drier regions so suitable that it has spread rapidly and threatens to become a serious weed nuisance.

The much-branched plants carry loose clusters of 4 - petalled purple flowers. Petals reduce to a narrow base. The curved seed pods stand out abruptly from the stem with a thin tip in the form of a long beak.

Lower leaves have stems and wavy margins from scattered teeth. Upper leaves tend to be stemless and without teeth.

RANGE: Blooming in early spring in Bunchgrass Zone with intrusions into Sagebrush and Yellow Pine Zones. Spokane, Pullman.

MEADOW RUE
(*Thalictrum occidentale*)

The very delicacy of meadow rue will catch the attention for in shape it is a graceful airy mass of small, 3-lobed leaves each with a thread-like stem. Look closely and you may see tiny upright purple flowers on one plant and drooping green and purple filmy clusters on another. This results from there being female and male flowers on different plants. The male flowers are particularly delicate and attractive with their tassel of silky purple stamens.

Almost everywhere one finds Indian paintbrush growing there will be meadow rue. Shady, fairly moist places at middle elevations are preferred.

RANGE: Throughout Washington. Wet places in Yellow Pine Zone. Pullman, Blue Mountains.

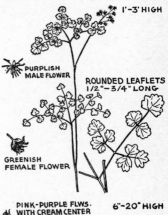

1'-3' HIGH

PURPLISH MALE FLOWER

ROUNDED LEAFLETS 1/2"-3/4" LONG

GREENISH FEMALE FLOWER

LONG-PLUMED PURPLE AVENS
(*Geum ciliatum*)

Although not a particularly common wildflower, the long-plumed purple avens is distinctive enough to command attention. It is a plant of open slopes at low and middle elevations where it may be found with such companions as lupine and sticky geranium.

The purplish stems bear three peculiar flowers. These appear purple from the long conspicuous sepals which flank the cream-colored petals. After blooming in late May or June the flower turns into a white-plumed seed head very like that of the western anemone and pasque flower.

The leaves grow in a tuft from the base of the stem and are deeply and finely lobed.

RANGE: Common east of Cascades in Bunch-grass and Yellow Pine Zones. Spotty occurrence in Coast region and Gulf Islands.

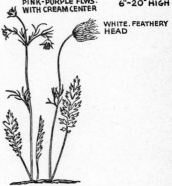

PINK-PURPLE FLWS. WITH CREAM CENTER

6"-20" HIGH

WHITE, FEATHERY HEAD

ELEPHANT HEAD
(*Pedicularis groenlandica surrecta*)

This plant will be recognized as one of the louseworts or *Pedicularis spp.* which have tightly packed flowers clustered on a spike and a curved bill to each flower. See page 154.

It grows in moist mountain meadows where it may reach 2' in height. The little elephant head flowers with upthrown trunk won't be forgotten once seen or mistaken for anything else. Their color is purple to red and, like most mountain flowers, they will be in bloom during July or August. The fringed leaves mostly occur near the base of the plant.

RANGE: Moist places near timberline in Olympics and Cascades. Mt. Rainier, Stevens Pass.

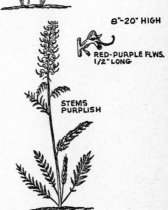

8"-20" HIGH

RED-PURPLE FLWS. 1/2" LONG

STEMS PURPLISH

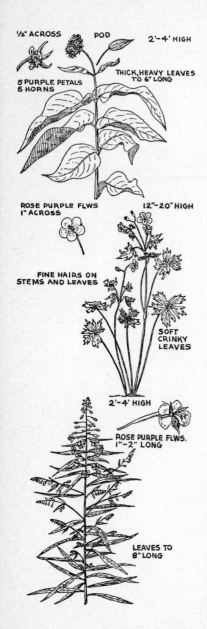

½" ACROSS   POD   2'-4' HIGH

5 PURPLE PETALS
5 HORNS

THICK, HEAVY LEAVES
TO 6" LONG

ROSE PURPLE FLWS
1" ACROSS

12"-20" HIGH

FINE HAIRS ON
STEMS AND LEAVES

SOFT
CRINKY
LEAVES

2'-4' HIGH

ROSE PURPLE FLWS.
1"-2" LONG

LEAVES TO
8" LONG

MILKWEED
(*Asclepias speciosa*)

These heavy looking plants form stout clusters 2'-4' high along roadsides and fields. The thick fleshy leaves may be to 6" long. The smallest nick in the finely hairy leaves or stem releases a thick milky fluid which protects the nectar of the flowers from climbing insects with sharp claws.

The purplish flowers bunch together in a knobby head several inches across. Each flower is a complicated structure with 5 purple petals and 5 curved horns protruding from the central stamen tube. July and August are the usual blooming months. In the fall, long seed pods split open to release thousands of silky parachutes.

RANGE: East of Cascades in Sagebrush and Bunchgrass Zones. Wenatchee, Ellensburg, Pullman.

STICKY GERANIUM
(*Geranium viscosissimum*)

Cranesbill

Sticky geranium's coarse appearance comes from a branching of stout stems and lobed leaves all covered with sticky hairs. The most attractive feature is the rose-purple flowers from 1"-1½" across. Each petal is finely veined. The blooming period is from late May to July.

RANGE: East of Cascades in open forests and aspen glades and in Bunchgrass Zone. Pullman, Spokane, Blue Mountains.

FIREWEED
(*Epilobium angustifolium*)

Its usual height, of from 3'-5' raises it above most of the ground vegetation. The long, lance-shaped leaves are up to 8" long. Large, pink-purple flowers are strewn abundantly along the slight branchlets and keep fireweed in the picture for several summer months. The flowers develop seed pods which split open and disgorge hundreds of fluffy, white seeds. Fireweed is especially abundant on old burns and clearings as pioneer growth. Fireweed honey rates high with bee keepers.

RANGE: Sporadic occurrence across Washington.

ALPINE FIREWEED (*E. alpinum*) is a low shrubby plant to 16" high growing along mountain streams. The flowers are a beautiful mauve color. Subalpine and alpine slopes of Olympics, Cascades and Blue Mountains.

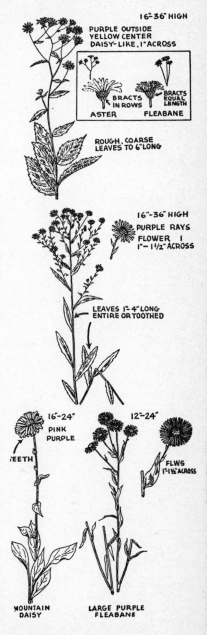

LARGE PURPLE ASTER
(Aster conspicuus)

This aster is only one of about 30 in Wash. which, as a group, may be confused with fleabanes. Very widespread from valley bottom to middle mountain elevations. It grows to 2' high on gravelly soils in fairly open forests. Often it is quite ragged in shape. The flowers in the wide-spreading head are exceptionally colorful with their golden centers and purple petals. Since spring and early summer flowers are over by July, this plant captures its share of attention for the remainder of the summer.

RANGE: East of Cascade Mountains in Bunchgrass and Yellow Pine Zones. Lake Chelan, Spokane, Blue Mountains.

OLYMPIC ASTER: Has white petals. See page 118.

DOUGLAS ASTER
(Aster douglasii)

There are over two dozen species of asters in the State and few people will profess to tell many apart. The Douglas aster is representative of several widespread species on the Coast and in the Interior which have showy heads of many bright purple flowers. Usually the stout stems are branched a number of times leading to a rounded outline. The coarse leaves haven't stems and may or may not be toothed. This aster or similar species grows on a well drained soil such as found under open fir forests or along roadsides. It blooms during August and September.

RANGE: Coastal forests and lower east slopes of Cascades. Chelan.

LARGE PURPLE FLEABANE
(Erigeron speciosus)

The difference between fleabanes and asters is shown above. The unusual name fleabane comes about from the belief that these plants would repel fleas.

During the summer months this showy "Michaelmas daisy" often reaches 2' in height and is rather bushy from long thin leaves reaching almost to the top. Lower leaves have stems but the upper have not. The flowers are massed in loose clusters with each yellow center surrounded by nearly a hundred thin purple ray-petals. Under favourable conditions the flower may be 2" across but more often it is slightly over 1". The blooming season is rather prolonged from late May to September.

RANGE: Common east of Cascades. Spotty at Coast.

MOUNTAIN DAISY (E. salsuginosus) is a handsome plant common in high mountains and alpine meadows. Its pink-purple petals are wide like an aster and are toothed at the tip. Generally one flower to the stem. Olympics, Cascades, Blue and other mountain systems at sub-alpine to alpine elevations.

(179)

FLOWERS (PURPLE)

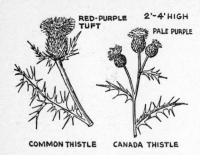

RED-PURPLE TUFT

2'-4' HIGH

PALE PURPLE

COMMON THISTLE   **CANADA THISTLE**

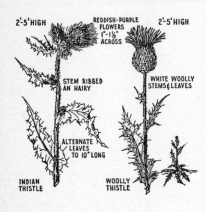

2'-5' HIGH

REDDISH-PURPLE FLOWERS 1'-1½' ACROSS

2'-5' HIGH

STEM RIBBED AN HAIRY

WHITE WOOLLY STEMS & LEAVES

ALTERNATE LEAVES TO 10" LONG

INDIAN THISTLE

WOOLLY THISTLE

BRISTLY PURPLISH FLW.

3'-5' HIGH

BROWN BURR

COMMON THISTLE
(*Cirsium lanceolatum*)

Pasture Thistle - Bull Thistle

There are over a half-dozen species, about half of them being introduced from Europe. Most have reddish or purplish flowers except the white thistle (*C. hookerianum*). The single purple blossoms on their bristly green bur may be 2" across. Blooming time is July and August.

RANGE: Common thistle particularly abundant in Bunchgrass and Yellow Pine Zones of Eastern Washington.

CANADA THISTLE (*C. arvensis*) doesn't have the stiff spiny leaves of the above nor as bright a flower. The pale purple flowers grow in flat-topped clusters. This is an introduced plant with the same general range as the above.

INDIAN THISTLE
(*Cirsium edule*)

Edible Thistle

The "ball" part of the flowers is a white woolly mass with many spines thus forming attractive pedestals for the several rose-purple blooms.

The thick stem 2' - 5' high carries leaves to 10" long. These are very ragged and often those near the top are twice-lobed. Thin spines provide armament. The plump roots are about 1' long and can be boiled and eaten. The blooming period is from late spring to late summer.

RANGE: Low to high elevation mostly west of the Cascades. An attractive plant of alpine meadows. Seattle, Mt. Rainier, Ellensburg, Blue Mountains.

WOOLLY THISTLE (*C. undulatum*) has an overall silvery white color of leaves and stems and a beautiful display of rose to lavender flower heads. Older plants branch freely and carry single flowers at the tip of each branch. Leaves are to 8" long, deeply cut, and protected by long yellowish spines. Poor dry soils east of Sagebrush Zone. Yakima, Wenatchee, Spokane.

COMMON BURDOCK
(*Arctium minus*)

Dock

Its exceptionally large leaves and spiny burs arouse one's curiosity. The thick stem is much branched and the leaves are about the size of rhubarb but woolly on the underside. Purplish-tinged flowers are covered with rough, hooked bristles. By fall the sturdy plant is well covered near its top by hard round burs which cling tenaciously to clothing or animal hair.

Common burdock (*A. minus*) is an abundant roadside weed.

RANGE: Lower elevations throughout Washington.

CUSHION FLEABANE
(*Erigeron poliospermus*)
Cushion Erigeron

Cushion fleabane, although limited in range, is a good example of a group of low fleabanes. Like many plants of dry regions its leaves and stems are a dull green from being finely hairy. The leaves are thin and vary from ½" - 1½" in length.

The single flowers are very attractive being a soft purple or violet shade. From 25 - 30 ray petals enclose a yellowish-green center. Blooms about 1" across are seen in April and May. Dwarf Mountain Fleabane, page 120, may have purple flowers and should be checked.

RANGE: Widely distributed in Sagebrush Zone. Spokane, Walla Walla, Wenatchee.

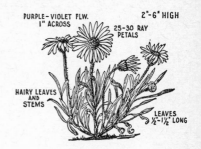

PURPLE-VIOLET FLW. 1" ACROSS — 2"-6" HIGH — 25-30 RAY PETALS — HAIRY LEAVES AND STEMS — LEAVES ½"-1½" LONG

MOUNTAIN DENTARIA
(*Dentaria macrocarpa*)
Mountain Toothwort

Leaves of the shy little purple flowers nodding on thick succulent stems appear scattered in a variety of shapes and with no apparent connection to the flower. This is caused by creeping rootstalks. The smaller stem leaves are 3 - 7 parted but most often 3 - lobed.

Flowers are pink purple with pink veins on the petals which help direct an insect to the important flower parts. The cross-like arrangement of the 4 petals indicates it belongs to the mustard or *Cruciferae* family. Seeds form in upright narrow pods 1" - 1½" long. Mountain dentaria may be seen from late March to the end of May.

RANGE: Mostly in shady woods of Klickitat and Yakima Counties.

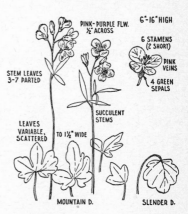

PINK-PURPLE FLW. ½" ACROSS — 6"-16" HIGH — 6 STAMENS (2 SHORT) — PINK VEINS — 4 GREEN SEPALS — STEM LEAVES 3-7 PARTED — SUCCULENT STEMS — LEAVES VARIABLE, SCATTERED — TO 1½" WIDE — MOUNTAIN D. — SLENDER D.

WESTERN IRIS
(*Iris missouriensis*)
Rocky Mountain Iris

No native iris grows in British Columbia but there are two species in Washington, and about eight in Oregon. Stout, round stems may reach 3′ high and usually carry 2 consecutive blooms during May to July. These are very showy being a purplish-blue with darker veins on sepals and petals. There is a good deal of similarity between the sepals, petals, and styles. The stout leaves to ½" wide are similar to garden varieties.

RANGE: Very limited west of Cascades. Haynes, Sequim, Whidby Island. Covering wet bottomlands east of Cascades in Sagebrush and Bunchgrass Zones. Pullman, Yakima, Ellensburg.

OREGON IRIS (*I. tenax*) has a single bloom and leaves climbing high on the stem. The flower is light to dark purple but occasionally white. Indians used fibres from the leaves to make twine. May to July on dry exposed situations west of the Cascades.

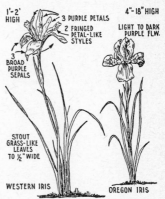

1′-2′ HIGH — 3 PURPLE PETALS — 2 FRINGED PETAL-LIKE STYLES — 4"-18" HIGH — LIGHT TO DARK PURPLE FLW. — 3 BROAD PURPLE SEPALS — STOUT GRASS-LIKE LEAVES TO ½" WIDE — WESTERN IRIS — OREGON IRIS

FLOWERS (PURPLE)

2"- 6" HIGH

PURPLE, VIOLET-LIKE FLW. TO ¾" LONG

FLESHY, STICKY LEAVES TO 1" LONG

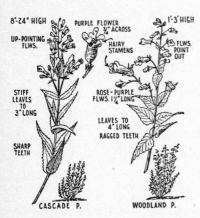

8"-24" HIGH
UP-POINTING FLWS.

PURPLE FLOWER ¾" ACROSS
HAIRY STAMENS

1'-3' HIGH
FLWS. POINT OUT

STIFF LEAVES TO 3" LONG

ROSE-PURPLE FLWS. 1¼" LONG

SHARP TEETH

LEAVES TO 4" LONG RAGGED TEETH

CASCADE P.

WOODLAND P.

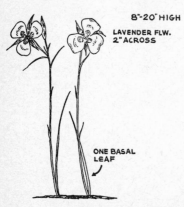

8"-20" HIGH
LAVENDER FLW. 2" ACROSS

ONE BASAL LEAF

COMMON BUTTERWORT
(Pinguicula vulgaris)

This charming little flower 2" - 6" high might pass for a violet by reason of its single rich purple, violet-like flower. The leaves to 1" long are yellowish green and form a low rosette around the stem. They are fleshy and sticky and flies caught on them are digested to help feed this most unusual plant. Like another insect-feeding flower, the sundew, the edges of bogs or wet rocky places are preferred.

The pretty bloom is strongly 2-lipped, the 3-lobed lower one much exceeding the 2-lobed upper. A bold spur provides suitable balance.
RANGE: Sub-alpine and alpine elevations in Olympics and Cascades. Mt. Rainier, Stevens Pass.

CASCADE PENSTEMON
(Penstemon serrulatus)
(Penstemon diffusus)
Spreading Penstemon

This is a showy plant with its bright head of purplish-blue trumpets. Often it forms a cluster of erect stems but sometimes it is branching and almost mat-like. The leaves are stiff, sharp-toothed, and quite attractive.

The typical penstemon flower with its 2-lobed upper lip and 3-lobed lower, is a lovely purplish-blue and over an inch long. It is particularly full-throated giving a wide face and blooms all summer.
RANGE: Cascade and Olympic Mountains from low to sub-alpine elevations.

WOODLAND PENSTEMON *(P. nemorosus)* has one or several erect stems. Leaves are large and coarsely toothed. Flowers are ridged and rose-purple with hairy stamens. Blooms June to August. Range as above.

GREEN-BANDED MARIPOSA LILY
(Calochortus macrocarpus)

This species ranges from the most arid regions to near timberline but all are quite characteristic in form.

The simplicity of this beautiful flower imparts an air of rarity that is further enhanced by its random appearance in drab range land. The stout stem carries one or more pale purple or lavender blooms often 2" across. The three large petals are marked on the inside with dark blotches near their base and a green band down their centre. One thin leaf grows from the base of the stem. The mariposa lily is seldom found in any quantity and often escapes notice because of its delicate shading. It will be found in bloom during late May and into June.
RANGE: Dry slopes of the Sagebrush and Bunchgrass Zones. Steamboat Rock, Ellensburg, Pullman.

YOUTH-ON-AGE
(Tolmiea menziesii)

Despite the intriguing name most persons pass up this plant because of its inconspicuous flowers. But examine the leaves in the late summer and you will see that the reason for the odd name is because small leaves are growing from the base of the old leaf blades. As the old leaves wither they slowly drop to the ground, giving the new leaves a chance to root.

Youth-on-age may reach 2′ in height and from April to June carry a flower stem adorned by small yet odd-looking flowers. These are greenish streaked with purple and with petals reduced to 4 thread-like projections. Leaves are lobed and round-toothed with a fine covering of white hairs.

RANGE: Common plant of Douglas fir forests west of Cascades. Clallam County. Seattle.

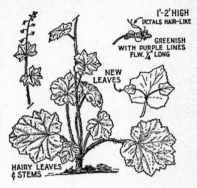

FLOWERS (BROWN-GREEN)

1′-2″ HIGH
PETALS HAIR-LIKE

GREENISH WITH PURPLE LINES
FLW. ¼″ LONG

NEW LEAVES

HAIRY LEAVES & STEMS

WESTERN STENANTHIUM
(Stenanthium occidentale)

Bronze Bells

Fortunately this shy plant is easily distinguished in the lush growth along shady mountain creeks. Its lily family characteristics are shown by a root bulb and the grass-like leaves. These arise from near the stem and are up to 10″ long.

The drooping flowers are aptly called bronze bells for they take their unusual color from a greenish background streaked through with purple. Notice that the flower parts are in sixes and how the stamens form a cluster of tiny golden dots in the throat. The flowers have an elusive tangy perfume. The blooming time is from April to August depending on exposure and elevation.

RANGE: Middle mountain to alpine heights. Olympic and Cascade Mountains.

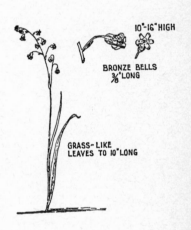

10″-16″ HIGH

BRONZE BELLS
⅜″ LONG

GRASS-LIKE LEAVES TO 10″ LONG

WILD GINGER
(Asarum caudatum)

Because this plant has very inconspicuous flowers and low leaves, the beginner seldom notices it.

The large heart-shaped leaves generally occur in extensive patches from the creeping habit. Two leaves arise from every node and may be to 6″ long and 3″ across. Fine hairs cover the stem and veins and lower margin of the leaf.

The curious flower, purplish-brown, and growing singly, hugs the ground closely and remains unseen unless searched out. It is bell-like with 3 wide-spreading lobes. The whole plant has a faint ginger smell most pronounced when a root is crushed.

RANGE: In Coastal regions from rich bottom-lands to 3,500′ elevation. Eastward it is found in damp places and beside creeks from the Yellow Pine Zone to the Mountain Forest Zone.

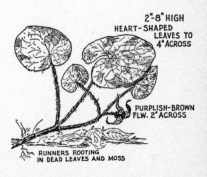

2″-8″ HIGH
HEART-SHAPED LEAVES TO 4″ ACROSS

PURPLISH-BROWN FLW. 2″ ACROSS

RUNNERS ROOTING IN DEAD LEAVES AND MOSS

(183)

2'- 4' HIGH

FLOWERS
OLIVE-GREEN
TO BROWN
⅛" LONG

ALTERNATE LEAVES
DULL GREEN
¾"- 4' LONG

DRAGON SAGEWORT
(*Artemisia dracunculoides*)

False Tarragon

This coarse weedy plant has a wide occurrence in certain parts of the Interior.

Dry gravelly banks or road slopes are favored localities. A dozen or so thick woody stems form a 3' high spray of narrow dull-green leaves. These are alternate and up to 3" long. Occasionally some of the lower leaves are deeply 3-lobed.

The tiny olive-green or brownish flowers are less than ⅛" long and carried during late summer months on thin stems near the top.

RANGE: Common in Sagebrush and Bunchgrass Zones. Yakima, Spokane, Wawawai.

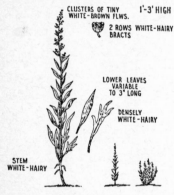

CLUSTERS OF TINY
WHITE-BROWN FLWS.   1'-3' HIGH

2 ROWS WHITE-HAIRY
BRACTS

LOWER LEAVES
VARIABLE
TO 3" LONG

DENSELY
WHITE-HAIRY

STEM
WHITE-HAIRY

CUDWEED SAGEWORT
(*Artemisia gnaphalodes*)

Mugwort

Two characteristics of this range plant warrant its inclusion. One is the slight resemblance to sagebrush through the shape of the leaves and their aromatic sage smell and the other is the overall silvery color. Cudweed sagewort is found on dry soils usually fully exposed to the sun.

Unlike sagebrush with its twisted stems, this plant grows erect from 1' - 3' high. Often it consists of one stem but on occasion it branches freely.

Leaves are up to 3" long and have a silvery sheen from a dense mat of soft white hairs on both sides. Most are entire but lower ones may be lobed. Flowers form in August in dense clusters.

RANGE: Dry regions east of Cascade Mountains. Wenatchee, Chelan, Spokane, Blue Mountains.

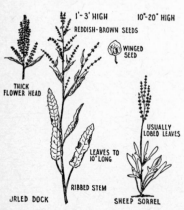

1'- 3' HIGH   10"-20" HIGH

REDDISH-BROWN SEEDS

WINGED
SEED

THICK
FLOWER HEAD

USUALLY
LOBED LEAVES

LEAVES TO
10" LONG

RIBBED STEM

CURLED DOCK

SHEEP SORREL

CURLED DOCK
(*Rumex crispus*)

The numerous docks or sorrels have a weedy appearance and are recognized by their coarse-ribbed stems, and particularly by the spaced clusters of small russet flowers or winged seeds, which in some species measure ¼" across. Foliage and seeds have a sharp acid taste.

Curled or yellow dock grows to 3' high and is named from the tendency of the leaves to curl along the edges. Some leaves are without teeth and others have a finely waved margin. The flower head may be open or in a dense cluster. Blooming time is from June to August.

RANGE: Sporadic at Coast. More common in Sagebrush and Bunchgrass Zones.

SHEEP SORREL (*R. acetosella*) usually less than a foot high, carries very small reddish flowers and seeds. Long-stemmed leaves to 3" long may be entire or lobed. Poor, exposed soils across the State.

STINGING NETTLE
(Urtica lyallii)

The chances are that a person will first discover stinging nettle the hard way for there is little to tell of its presence in the thickets. After a few encounters one watches for the rather ragged opposite leaves and the inconspicuous drooping clusters of greenish or whitish flowers. The coarsely toothed leaves are covered with fine stinging hairs which cause a severe irritation lasting for several days. Often great masses of it grow together making it almost impossible to pass through. Young nettle makes excellent greens and Indians used it in weaving cord. Some European species produce an excellent fibre equal to the best linen.
RANGE: Across the State in damp, shady places. Seattle, Spokane.

FLOWERS (BROWN-GREEN)

2'-4' HIGH

SMALL GREENISH FLOWERS

LEAVES TO 4" LONG

RIBBED STEMS WITH FINE SPINES

NORTHWESTERN TWAYBLADE
(Ophrys caurina)
(Listera caurina)

There are only three twayblades in Western North America and all occur in Washington. There is no difficulty in recognizing them by the two leaves near the center of the stem and the tiny greenish-purple flowers. They are inconspicuous forest plants found from sea level to heights of 6,000'. May, June, and July will see them in bloom.
RANGE: From Coastal forests to middle mountain elevations across Washington. Mt. Baker, Olympics.

HEART-LEAVED T. (*O. cordata*) and BROAD-LIPPED TWAYBLADE (*O. convallarioides*) have a wide range also but are confined mostly to mountain forests.

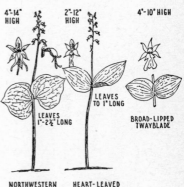

4"-14" HIGH

2"-12" HIGH

4"-10" HIGH

LEAVES 1"-2½" LONG

LEAVES TO 1" LONG

BROAD-LIPPED TWAYBLADE

NORTHWESTERN TWAYBLADE

HEART-LEAVED TWAYBLADE

CHOCOLATE LILY
(Fritillaria lanceolata)

Rice Root

This peculiar dark brown and green flower hardly seems real when compared with the usual bright-colored flowers of springtime. Because of its dull tones it can be missed among the grass or low brush where it grows. The cup-like flower, about 1" across, hangs down and has 6 mottled petals. The narrow-pointed leaves form whorls about the stem. The alternate name rice root comes from the appearance of the large white bulb covered with nodules resembling rice. The bulbs are edible and taste somewhat like rice when cooked.
RANGE: Coastal forests and open woods of Yellow Pine Zone.

F. kamtchatcensis is a sturdier species with broader leaves than the above. The flower is not so mottled and a cluster of them is not common. Its range is west of the Cascade Mountains.

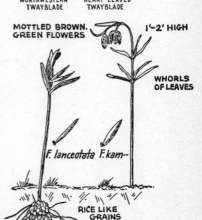

MOTTLED BROWN, GREEN FLOWERS

1'-2' HIGH

WHORLS OF LEAVES

F. lanceolata *F. kam---*

RICE LIKE GRAINS

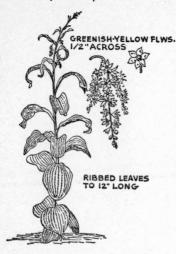

GREENISH-YELLOW FLWS.
1/2" ACROSS

RIBBED LEAVES
TO 12" LONG

INDIAN HELLEBORE
(Veratrum eschocholtzii)
(Veratrum viride)

Green Hellebore - False Hellebore

This is a tall rank plant with large plaited and heavily ribbed leaves. The exotic appearance would be more in place in the tropics than the mountain swales and meadows it prefers. The large size of from 3' - 5' brings it to attention sooner or later. Having a wide tolerance, Indian hellebore is found in shady moist forests near sea level and from there up to alpine meadows. This gives it a blooming period from May to August.

The flowers are an unusual inconspicuous color. They form in thin branching spikes and are small and yellowish-green, a color that gives little or no contrast with their surroundings.

The roots contain a powerful poison which is used in medicine as well as for an insect poison.
RANGE: Moist mountains throughout Washington.

MANY
WHITE FLOWERS
IN DENSE
END CLUSTERS

3'-8' HIGH

DULL WHITE FLOWER
1/2"- 3/4" ACROSS
6 STAMENS

YELLOW-GREEN
LEAVES TO 12" LONG
RIBBED

STOUT WOOLLY STEM
UNBRANCHED

WHITE FALSE - HELLEBORE
(Veratrum californicum)

California False Hellebore

The false-hellebores, the largest of mountain meadow plants and sometimes reaching 8' in height, are among the first to be noticed by visitors. Usually it forms a clump of several stems and often extensive patches. The big boat-shaped leaves, prominently ribbed, and to 1' long are unmistakable. The magnificent plumed flower head dominates its neighboring flowers by sheer spectacle during July and August. The single small flower is a gem of symmetry ornamented by a Y-shaped green gland near the base of each petal-like part. The thick roots and young shoots are considered poisonous.
RANGE: Generally above 4,500', wet meadows.
TAILED FALSE HELLEBORE *(V. caudatum)* is very similar but the flower clusters tend to droop and the terminal stalk is elongated. The Y-shaped green petal gland is absent. Montesana, Chehalis River. Infrequent in Coastal region.

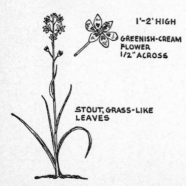

1'-2' HIGH

GREENISH-CREAM
FLOWER
1/2" ACROSS

STOUT, GRASS-LIKE
LEAVES

GREEN LILY
(Zigadenus elegans)

Mountain Deathcamas - Wand Lily

The green lily produces such fascinating greenish-white flowers that it may be sure of receiving notice. These are carried on a spike and present a charming sight with their symmetrical arrangement of 6 waxy petals each decorated with a green or yellow spot near its base.

The plant grows from large bulbs and puts up a cluster of heavy grassy leaves. Most leaves spring from the base but a few small ones may be found on the stem. There is a suspicion that the plant is poisonous. Blooming late June to August.
RANGE: Fairly abundant at higher elevations in Olympics and Wenatchee Mountains.

CAT-TAIL
(Typha latifolia)

Bulrush - Tule

Cat-tail because of its wide distribution throughout North America and characteristic form is known to almost everyone. There is only the one species. The spongy dark brown spikes, 4" - 8" long and one inch thick, contain the pollen grains. Leaves are long, flat and about an inch wide. Indians in the Interior used the thin leaves to weave mats for use inside their summer shelters and also to make the walls of the shelter.

Cat-tails are always found in mud or shallow water where they form a dense jungle beloved by red-wing blackbirds and muskrats.

RANGE: Throughout Washington but most plentiful around ponds and swamps. Usually at low and middle elevations.

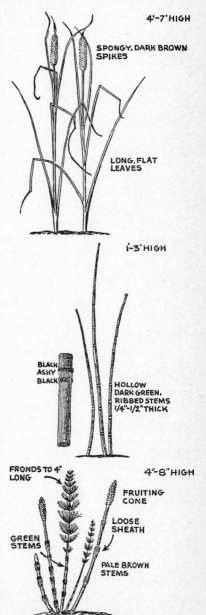

4'-7' HIGH

SPONGY, DARK BROWN SPIKES

LONG, FLAT LEAVES

1-3' HIGH

BLACK ASHY BLACK

HOLLOW DARK GREEN, RIBBED STEMS 1/4"-1/2" THICK

FRONDS TO 4" LONG

4"-8" HIGH

FRUITING CONE

LOOSE SHEATH

GREEN STEMS

PALE BROWN STEMS

SCOURING RUSH
(Equisetum hyemale)

The scouring rush is recognized easily by its ridged green stem marked into definite sections by narrow ash-colored and black bands.

The hollow stems will pull apart into short sections. The finely ridged stems are gritty to the touch thus leading to the name. Several species with various slight differences to the above are to be found in certain localities.

RANGE: Common along the edge of Interior lakes and ponds east of the Cascades.

COMMON HORSETAIL
(Equisetum arvense)

The name horsetail comes from the sterile green stems with their whorls of wire-like branches. These are the stems most commonly seen for they last all summer whereas the pale unbranched stalks occur early in the season. Horsetails have hollow jointed stems and no leaves as they are commonly thought of but the fringed scales around the stem joints actually are reduced leaves. The green sterile stems help out by performing the function of leaves. The pale brown stems bear a small cone at their tips which holds the spores or seeds. Small particles of silica give them their scouring quality.

Horsetail usually grows in a mass rather than as a stray individual. Moist sandy soils as often found in wet places along road edges are chosen. There are a half dozen or more species, but all will be recognized as horsetails.

RANGE: Damp sandy places throughout Washington at low and middle elevations.

APPENDIX

COMMON FERNS
NATURE'S CALENDAR
EDIBLE PLANTS
GLOSSARY

COMMON FERNS

WOODSIA *(Woodsia spp.)* is found on dry rocky places. *W. oregana* in quite abundant in the Bunchgrass Zone where it is the common fern on rocky places. Its bunchy tuft of fronds are from 4" - 12" high. The fronds are smooth beneath. Coulee City, Pullman.

RANGE: *W. scopulina* has sticky, hairy fronds. Range much as above, Wenatchee River, Spokane and into low foothills of Cascades.

PARSLEY FERN - ROCK BRAKE *(Cryptogramma acrostichoides):* A densely tufted little fern 6" - 12" high growing in rocky places at higher elevations. There are two distinct types of frond, the fertile being the taller and having its margins rolled under to enclose the spores. Mostly sub-alpine Zone of Olympics and Cascades. Mt. Rainier, Steven's Pass, Lake Chelan.

POLYPODY - LICORICE FERN *(Polypody spp.):* The thickish roots have a licorice flavor which accounts for one common name. Often found on mossy cliffs, logs or tree trunks. A sparse fern with fronds to 12" long and 1" - 3" wide. Spores are large and round. Frond leaves are lobed to the midrib—a partial identifying feature. Species differ in the shape of the pinnae (small frond leaves). The Coastal Forest Zone species tends to be sharp pointed while *P. hesperium* with rounded pinnae is mostly in the Sub-alpine Zone of the Olympics and Cascades.

LADY FERN *(Athyrium filex-femina):* A large graceful fern, common in damp shady woods to 4,000'. Fronds to 4' long and 10" wide arch outward. They are widest below their centre and taper in both directions. Coast and mountain forests of Olympics and Cascades. Alpine Lady Fern *(A. alpestre americanum)* is more stiffish in appearance with fronds rarely over 2' long and 3" wide. Ranges on rocky places at sub-alpine and alpine elevations throughout.

MAIDENHAIR *(Adiantum pedatum aleuticum)* is the most delicate of our ferns with each tiny leaf frond fringed along the upper edge. Shiny black stems are not usually over 2' high. Often massed in damp, shady places.

RANGE: Coastal Forest Zone to elevations of 5,000'. Also occurs on east slopes of southern Cascades.

DEER FERN *(Struthiopteris spicant):* A common fern in shady Coastal forests. Easily recognized from its two distinct types of fronds. The fertile or spore-bearing fronds shooting from the centre of the plant are often 3' high. Non-fertile or vegetative fronds are evergreen and form a low rosette. They taper toward both ends and have pinnules or leaves almost to the base. A favored food of elk in the Olympic National Park.

RANGE: Coastal Forest Zone.

SWORD FERN *(Polystichum munitum)* forms dark green, symmetrical sprays of fronds to 3' long. Pinnules or side leaves are sharp-pointed and sharp-toothed. The underside is almost orange in color from twin rows of spore cases. Fronds are shipped east in large quantities for florists' decorations.

RANGE: Coastal Forest Zone.

BRACKEN *(Pteridium aquilinum pubescens)* is a widepread and luxuriant fern. Coarse in growth and often to 6' high. Stems do not cluster from a compact base as with most ferns. A line of spore cases follows around the margins of the leaves. Found at lower elevations in coniferous forests west of the Cascades and also in shady places from the Bunchgrass Zone to mountain elevations. Blue Mountains.

COMMON FERNS

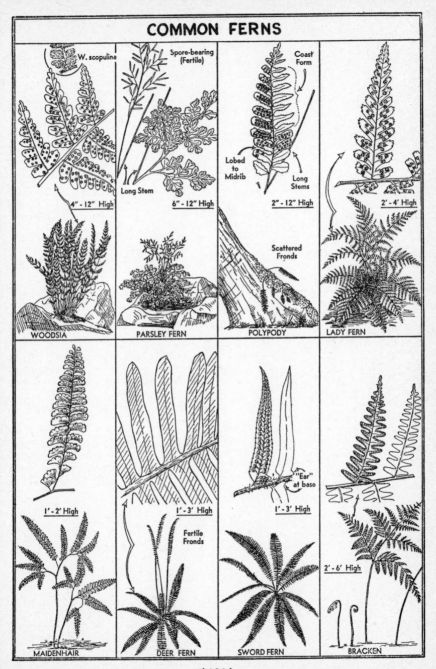

W. scopulina

4" – 12" High

WOODSIA

Spore-bearing (Fertile)

Long Stem

6" – 12" High

PARSLEY FERN

Coast Form

Lobed to Midrib

Long Stems

2" – 12" High

Scattered Fronds

POLYPODY

2' – 4' High

LADY FERN

1' – 2' High

MAIDENHAIR

1' – 3' High

Fertile Fronds

DEER FERN

"Ear" at base

1' – 3' High

SWORD FERN

2' – 6' High

BRACKEN

NATURE'S CALENDAR
FOR SOME
TREES AND SHRUBS

Legend: IN BLOOM ▇ IN FRUIT ▢

ADD ONE WEEK FOR EVERY 1000 FT. OF ELEVATION.

TREES	MARCH	APRIL	MAY	JUNE	JULY	AUG.	SEPT.	OCT.	REMARKS
ARBUTUS									RED BERRIES
BLACK HAWTHORN									NO SMELL TO FLOWERS
BITTER CHERRY									RED BERRIES
W. CHOKE CHERRY									PURPLISH-BLACK BERRIES
BROADLEAF MAPLE									
DOGWOOD									MAY BLOOM TWICE A YEAR
PACIFIC CRABAPPLE									APPLE BLOSSOM FRAGRANCE

SHRUBS

SHRUBS	MARCH	APRIL	MAY	JUNE	JULY	AUG.	SEPT.	OCT.	REMARKS
BLACKBERRY, TRAILING									
BLACK TWINBERRY									
BROOM									
CLEMATIS, WHITE									WHITE FLOWERS AND SEEDS
CURRANT, RED-FLOWER									
DEVIL'S CLUB									BRIGHT RED BERRIES
ELDER, BLUE-BERRY									
ELDER, RED-BERRY									
GOAT'S BEARD									
HARDHACK									
HAZEL									YELLOW CATKINS
HONEYSUCKLE, ORANGE									
INDIAN-PLUM									
KINNIKINNICK									SHINY RED BERRIES
LABRADOR TEA									
MAHONIA, TALL									
MOCK ORANGE									
NINEBARK									
OCEAN SPRAY									
RED-OSIER DOGWOOD									WHITE BERRIES
SALAL									
SALMONBERRY									
SASKATOON BERRY									
SILVERBERRY									
SNOWBRUSH									
SOOPOLALLIE									
THIMBLEBERRY									
TWINBERRY, RED									
TWIN-FLOWER									SWEET PERFUME
WAXBERRY									WHITE BERRIES TO MIDWINTER
WILD ROSE									HIPS LAST ALL WINTER

NATURE'S CALENDAR
FOR SOME
COASTAL FLOWERS

* ALSO FOUND EAST OF CASCADES (Coast Range) ADD ONE WEEK FOR EVERY 1000 FT. OF ELEVATION

ALL BLOOMING PERIODS ▬▬ SOLID LINES

FLOWERS	MARCH	APRIL	MAY	JUNE	JULY	AUGUST	SEPT.	REMARKS
* ALUMROOT								SEVERAL SPECIES
* ASTER, DOUGLAS								
AVENS, LARGE-LEAVED								
* BLEEDING HEART								MINOR OCCURRENCE IN INTERIOR
* BLUEBELLS								MOST COMMON IN INTERIOR
* BLUE-EYED GRASS								
* BLUE-EYED MARY								
* BLUE SAILORS								MAY BLOOM AGAIN IN LATE SUMMER
* BUNCHBERRY								
* BUTTERCUP								TWO SPECIES
CAMAS								
* CAMAS, DEATH								
* CANADA MINT								
* CHOCOLATE LILY								
* COLTS FOOT								DRY, EXPOSED PLACES
* COLUMBINE								MANY DIFFERENT SPECIES
* CORAL ROOT								FLUFFY COTTON BALL
* COTTON GRASS								
* COW PARSNIP								
* DELPHINIUM								SIMILAR SPECIES FOUND IN INTERIOR
EASTER LILY								
FAIRY BELLS, OREGON								FOLLOWED BY RED BERRIES
* FALSE LADY'S SLIPPER								
FALSE BUGBANE								
* FALSE SOLOMON'S SEAL								
FIELD CHAMOMILE								
* FIELD CHICKWEED								
* FIREWEED								
* FOAM FLOWER								
* FRINGE CUPS								
* GOLDENROD								
GROUNDSEL, COMMON								
* GUMWEED								
* HEDGE NETTLE								
* HELLEBORE, INDIAN								
* INDIAN PAINTBRUSH								SPECIES FOUND AT LOWER LEVELS
INDIAN PIPE								
* LUPINE								
* MINER'S LETTUCE								

(193)

FLOWERS	MARCH	APRIL	MAY	JUNE	JULY	AUGUST	SEPT.	REMARKS
*MINER'S LETTUCE, SIBERIAN		▓						
*MONKEY FLOWER, RED				▓				HIGH MOUNTAINS
*MONKEY FLOWER, YELLOW			▓	▓	▓			GREAT ALTITUDINAL RANGE
*MONTIA		▓	▓					
*NETTLE, STINGING			▓	▓				
*ONION, HOOKER'S				▓				
*OXEYE DAISY			▓	▓				LIMITED EAST OF CASCADES
*PEACOCK		▓	▓					
*PEARLY EVERLASTING					▓	▓		
*PIPSISSEWA				▓	▓			
*PURPLE PEA		▓	▓					
*PUSSY TOES, ROSY & WHITE			▓	▓				
*PYROLA				▓	▓	▓		MANY PLANTS DON'T BLOOM
*RATTLESNAKE PLANTAIN					▓			
SATIN FLOWER		▓						
*SAXIFRAGE		▓	▓					
*SKUNK CABBAGE	▓	▓						
SEA BLUSH			▓	▓				SOME SPECIES IN INTERIOR
*SELF HEAL				▓	▓			
*SILVER-GREEN			▓	▓				
*SILVERWEED				▓				FLOWERS INCONSPICUOUS
*SPRING GOLD		▓	▓					
*STAR FLOWER			▓	▓				
*STAR-FLOWERED SOL. SEAL			▓	▓				
*STONECROP				▓	▓			
*TANSY					▓	▓		
*THISTLE, COMMON					▓	▓		SEA COAST PLANT
THRIFT			▓	▓				
*WILD TIGER LILY				▓	▓			
*TRILLIUM, WESTERN		▓	▓					
*TWISTED STALK			▓					
*WATER PARSNIP					▓			
*WILD LILY-OF-THE-VALLEY			▓	▓				RUBY BERRIES AFTER FLOWERS
WOOLY SUNFLOWER		▓	▓					
*VANILLA LEAF		▓	▓					
*VIOLET, BLUE		▓	▓					
*VIOLET, YELLOW		▓	▓					
*YARROW				▓	▓			
*QUEEN'S CUP				▓				BLUE BERRY AFTER FLOWER

NATURE'S CALENDAR
FOR
INTERIOR FLOWERS

FLOWERS	MARCH	APRIL	MAY	JUNE	JULY	AUGUST	SEPT.	REMARKS
ALUMROOT, OVAL-LEAF				▓	▓			
ARNICA, HEART-LEAF			▓	▓	▓			
ASTER, LARGE PURPLE					▓	▓		
AVENS, LONG-PLUMED, PURPLE			▓	▓				COMMON ROADSIDE FLOWER
BEARD TONGUE, SCOULER'S				▓				
BEARD TONGUE, LITTLE FLW.				▓	▓			
BITTERROOT			▓					VERY DRY PLACES
BROWN-EYED SUSAN				▓	▓			
CACTUS				▓				
CINQUE FOILS				▓	▓			
ERIOGONUM, TALL WHITE				▓	▓			OTHER SIMILAR SPECIES
FLEABANE, LARGE PURPLE			▓	▓	▓	▓	▓	
FLEABANE, WHITE				▓	▓			
GERANIUM, STICKY			▓	▓	▓			FROM LOW TO HIGH ELEVATIONS
JACOB'S LADDER, BLUE			▓	▓				
LADIES TRESSES					▓	▓		SEVERAL SPECIES
LEPTOTANAENA (Carrot Leaf)		▓	▓					PALE PURPLE FLOWER
LILY, MARIPOSA				▓				
LEMONWEED			▓	▓				
LILY, SNOW			▓					YELLOW
ONION, NODDING				▓	▓			
MEADOW RUE			▓	▓				DEPENDING ON ELEVATION
MILKWEED					▓	▓		
MOCCASIN FLOWER				▓				
MONKSHOOD				▓	▓	▓	▓	IN MOIST MOUNTAINS
OYSTER PLANT				▓				
PEPPER POD		▓	▓	▓				
PHACELIA				▓				
PHLOX				▓				
PHLOX, DOUGLAS			▓	▓				
RAGWORT, GIANT				▓				
SCARLET GILIA				▓	▓	▓		RED TRUMPETS
SPRING SUNFLOWERS		▓	▓	▓				
VERONICA				▓				
WATER KNOTWEED					▓	▓		
WATERLEAF, BALLHEAD		▓	▓					PINK CONES
WATER PLANTAIN					▓	▓		LOW TO HIGH ELEVATIONS
YELLOW BELL		▓						SWAMPY PLACES
YELLOW POND LILY				▓	▓			

(195)

EDIBLE PLANTS

Other than well known berries.

NAME	EDIBLE PARTS	PREPARATION	SEASON
Bitterroot	Thick roots	Peeled and boiled	May
Bracken	Young shoots and roots	Shoots boiled—roots roasted	April - August
Bunchberry	Red berry	Eaten raw	August - September
Camas	Bulb	Boiled or roasted	April - May
Cow Parsnip	Young flower stems	Peel and use raw in salad or cook as greens	May - June
Fireweed	Stem centers	Split stalk and eat raw	June - August
Kinnikinnick	Red berry	Eaten raw	September - December
Mahonia (Oregon Grape)	Blue berries	Raw after first frosts	September - November
Milkweed	Young leaves or seed pods	Boiled	June or August
Miner's Lettuce	Leaves and stems	Raw in salads	April - May
Mountain Lily	Bulb	Boiled	June-July
Rice Root	Bulb	Boiled	April - May
Oyster Plant	Root or young shoots	Boiled	Spring or Fall
Salmonberry	Young stem shoots	Eaten raw	April - May
Siberian Miner's Lettuce	Leaves and stems	Raw in salads	April - May
Spring Sunflower	Root or seeds	Root boiled—seeds raw	May
Thimbleberry	Young stem shoots	Eaten raw	April - May
Wild Onions	Bulb	Boiled	May - July
Wild Roses	Outer part of fruit or hips	Eaten raw	September - December
Wild Tiger Lily	Bulb	Boiled	May - July

NOTE — When leaves or stems are boiled one or two waters should be thrown away to eliminate any bitterness.

The berries of the following plants are edible although not generally favored: crowberry, salal, silverberry, blue- and black-berry elder, soopolallie, wild cherries, gooseberries, currants, cloudberry, teaberry, Pacific crab-apple, hawthorne, Indian plum, thimble-berry, salmonberry, mountain ash.

GLOSSARY

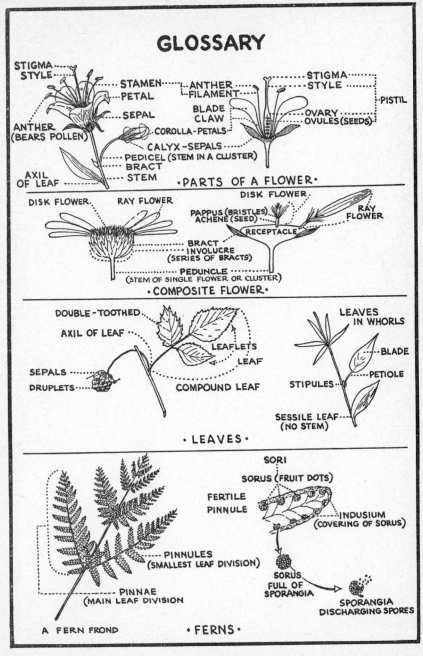

PARTS OF A FLOWER

STIGMA
STYLE
STAMEN
PETAL
SEPAL
ANTHER
(BEARS POLLEN)
AXIL
OF LEAF
CALYX—SEPALS
PEDICEL (STEM IN A CLUSTER)
BRACT
STEM
COROLLA—PETALS

ANTHER
FILAMENT
BLADE
CLAW
STIGMA
STYLE
PISTIL
OVARY
OVULES (SEEDS)

COMPOSITE FLOWER

DISK FLOWER
RAY FLOWER
DISK FLOWER
PAPPUS (BRISTLES)
ACHENE (SEED)
RECEPTACLE
RAY FLOWER
BRACT
INVOLUCRE
(SERIES OF BRACTS)
PEDUNCLE
(STEM OF SINGLE FLOWER OR CLUSTER)

LEAVES

DOUBLE-TOOTHED
AXIL OF LEAF
LEAFLETS
LEAF
SEPALS
DRUPLETS
COMPOUND LEAF

LEAVES
IN WHORLS
BLADE
PETIOLE
STIPULES
SESSILE LEAF
(NO STEM)

FERNS

SORI
SORUS (FRUIT DOTS)
FERTILE
PINNULE
INDUSIUM
(COVERING OF SORUS)
PINNULES
(SMALLEST LEAF DIVISION)
PINNAE
(MAIN LEAF DIVISION
SORUS
FULL OF
SPORANGIA
SPORANGIA
DISCHARGING SPORES
A FERN FROND

(197)

INDEX

(199)

INDEX—Continued

INDEX—Continued

KEY TO EVERGREEN TREES

NEEDLE OR SCALELIKE

NEEDLE LEAVES   SCALE LEAVES

BUNDLE LEAF   SINGLE LEAF   WITH BERRIES   WITH CONES

LEAVES RESINOUS

WESTERN JUNIPER

ROCKY MTN. JUNIPER

PRICKLY   SMOOTH

2.3 & 5 NEEDLES
PINES

MANY

=2's LODGEPOLE

LARCHES (2)

YELLOW CEDAR   *RED CEDAR*

=3's PONDEROSA

4-SIDED & STALKED
SPRUCES

FLAT NEEDLES

=5's WHITE

DOUGLAS FIR

SITKA

HEMLOCK (2)

=5's WHITEBARK

ENGELMANN

DWARF JUNIPER (Shrublike)

YEW

TRUE FIRS
(Round leaf scars)

NOBLE   *ALPINE*   *AMABILIS*   *GRAND*

Groove   Bracts

BRUSHED UP   POINTING AHEAD   TWO-RANKED